D1626224

Hymns for the People

FULL MUSIC EDITION

Edited by
David Peacock

with
Roger Mayor, Christopher Norton
and
Michael Perry (Words Editor)

Marshall Pickering
An Imprint of HarperCollins*Publishers*
JUBILATE 2000
Jubilate 2000 is an imprint of Jubilate Hymns

Marshall Pickering is an imprint of
HarperCollins*Religious*
Part of HarperCollins*Publishers*
77–85 Fulham Palace Road,
Hammersmith, London W6 8JB

This edition first published in Great Britain in 1993 by Marshall Pickering

Reprinted: 95 94 93
Impression number: 10 9 8 7 6 5 4 3 2 1

The compilers assert the moral right to be identified as the compilers of this work

ISBN 0 551 02510 7

Words only edition ISBN 0 551 02511 5

Music and text set by Barnes Music Engraving Ltd, East Sussex, England
Printed and bound in Great Britain by HarperCollins Manufacturing, Glasgow

A catalogue record for this book is available from the British Library

Also edited by the Jubilate group:

Hymns for Today's Church
Church Family Worship
Carols for Today
Carol Praise*
Play Carol Praise*
Let's Praise!*
Come Rejoice!*
The Wedding Book*
Lollipops for organ*
The Dramatised Bible*
Prayers for the People*
Psalms for Today
Songs from the Psalms
World Praise*

* *Available from HarperCollins*

Preface

Why another hymn book?

Recent years have seen in some churches a radical reduction in the number of 'hymns' within their worship repertoire. Many established texts have been in the danger of being lost to numerous worshipping communities.

There are several reasons for this. Firstly, the musical style that has accompanied hymn-texts in the past is out of keeping with the prevailing musical vocabulary of some congregations. The organ is very rarely used, if at all, and the music group is the main accompaniment. The majority of the congregation has an affinity with a more contemporary style. Secondly, the hymn texts that are used offer outmoded phrases and expressions. Established hymns have been regarded by some as being out of step with the current textual vocabulary of the rest of the church's worshipping language.

The value of hymns

For the purposes of this book, we have defined a hymn as a text that develops a theme in logical sequence. We have deliberately avoided defining a hymn by its musical characteristics. We believe that, as such, hymns are an essential part of our worship diet because of their intrinsic nourishment value. They are complimentary to worship songs. *Hymns for the People* is an attempt to make hymns more accessible to churches who have largely dispensed with them.

The words

The careful revision of texts has been the product of many years of research by Jubilate editorial teams. Accordingly, a group of writers within Jubilate has ensured that the selection of texts for *Hymns for the People* is both relevant and appropriate to contemporary worship. We have also tried to include a number of texts produced by hymn writers within the last ten years. We have attempted to provide items that cover a breadth of themes and a range of uses within community worship. However, it should be noted that some of the credal hymns do not completely represent the creed on which they are based.

Some of the hymns include indications for dividing the congregation into two groups to sing either particular verses or sections of the hymn. We have avoided using *men* and *women*, since this may be inappropriate in some congregations.

The music

The music for *Hymns for the People* gives the book its own unique contribution. Every hymn-tune has been extensively re-arranged for music-group, with introductions and links between the verses. All the items have guitar chords with the bass guitar line 'shadowed' in many of the keyboard parts. A drum pattern indication (1) is included in nearly all the items to give the correct feel to the hymn. These rhythmic patterns are listed in the section *Drum Kit Patterns* at the end of the book. Metronome markings are important, since, in order for the arrangements to work well, the tempo may be different from the usually accepted speed for a particular tune. We would urge players to generally veer towards a more restrained tempo for many of the hymns.

Some of the recent texts have been given new settings in the style of current worship songs. There are also a number of traditional texts with new settings. We believe it is now possible to use established hymns creatively within flows of praise and worship; for songs and hymns to be used alongside each other with stylistic credibility.

Finding your way around

The hymns are arranged alphabetically, but an extensive thematic index at the back of the book provides an invaluable help to the worship planner. The biblical index covers nearly three thousand references. The musician will find both metrical and alphabetical indexes to the tunes included in the book.

Hymns for the People is an attempt to rescue hymn-texts from being put on the shelf. We hope that church communities who have genuinely found it difficult to incorporate many hymns within their worship will now be able to broaden their repertoire and that congregations will be enabled to use material that provides in-depth vocabulary for praise, thanksgiving, heart worship and response to God in both lifestyle and service.

A full set of acknowledgements appears on the next page, but I would especially like to thank Michael Perry, whose original vision it was to produce such a book, and Roger Mayor and Christopher Norton for their talented and stimulating assistance. Together, we dedicate this hymnbook to the service of worshipping communities and to the glory of God.

David Peacock (Editor)

Legal Information
and Acknowledgements

Reprinting
Those seeking to reprint material in this book which is the property of
Jubilate Hymns or associated authors and composers (attributed
'/Jubilate Hymns') may write to the Copyright Manager, Jubilate
Hymns Ltd, 61 Chessel Avenue, Southampton SO2 4DY. In the
United States of America these copyrights and those of Timothy
Dudley-Smith are administered by Hope Publishing Company, Carol
Stream, Illinois 60188.

Items by authors and composers administered by Jubilate, together with
those held by some major copyright holders (Thankyou Music,
CopyCare, Make Way Music etc.) are covered by the licence scheme
operated by the Christian Copyright Licensing Ltd, 26 Gildredge Road,
Eastbourne, East Sussex BN21 4SA (0323 417711).

Recording and Broadcasting
Jubilate Hymns and associated authors and composers, and Word &
Music are members of the Mechanical Copyright Protection and
Performing Right Societies.

Acknowledgements
We are grateful to all those who contributed to the compilation of
Hymns for the People. We owe our thanks most particularly to those
authors and composers who readily created or adapted their work to
meet the needs of the book. We mention especially Roger Mayor and
Christopher Norton for their expertise, help and support; Christopher
Idle, Michael Saward, Jane Sinclair and Geoff Twigg for their help
with the texts; Angela Griffiths, Clifford Roseweir, Jane Peacock,
Valerie Parker and Ann Jenner for getting the material ready for
publication.

For the major task of copyright clearance and assistance in preparing the
work we are deeply grateful to Bunty Grundy of Jubilate Hymns.

David Peacock (Editor)
Michael Perry (Words Editor)

1 A child is born for us today

WE'LL CALL HIM JESUS   8 6 8 6 6 5 5

Words: from Isaiah 9
Pearl Beasley
Music: Brian Hoare
arranged David Peacock

child_ is born for us__ to-day, a son to us__ is
(2) comes to be the 'Prince of peace', to all the world a
(3) those who walk the dark - est way has dawned a shin - ing

given;_____ the sav - iour comes to guide our way and
friend;_____ his migh - ty love will ne - ver cease, his
light_____ far brigh - ter than the brigh - test day, a

2

A purple robe

A PURPLE ROBE   8 6 8 6 Triple

Words: Timothy Dudley-Smith
Music: David Wilson
arranged Roger Mayor

6

Sensitively ♩. = 60

1 A pur - ple robe, a crown of thorn, a reed in his_ right
(4) hangs, by whom the world was made, be - neath the dark-ened

hand;_____ be - fore the sol - diers' spite and scorn I
sky;_____ the ev - er-last - ing ran - som paid, I

see my sav - iour stand. 2 He bears be - tween the
see my sav - iour die. 5 He shares on high__ his

3

Abide with me

EVENTIDE   10 10 10 10

Words: Henry Francis Lyte
Music: William Monk
arranged Roger Mayor

11

Slow ♩ = 76

1 A - bide with me, fast falls the e - ven -
2 Swift to its close ebbs out life's lit - tle
3 I need your pre - sence ev - ery pass - ing

- tide; the dark-ness deep - ens: Lord, with me a -
day; earth's joys grow dim, its glo - ries pass a -
hour: what but your grace can foil the temp-ter's

4 I have no fear with you at hand to bless;
  ills have no weight and tears no bitterness.
  Where is death's sting? Where, grave, your victory?
  I triumph still if you abide with me.

5 Hold now your cross before my closing eyes;
  shine through the gloom and point me to the skies!
  Heaven's morning breaks and earth's vain shadows flee:
  in life, in death, O Lord, abide with me!

4

All creation join to say
(Love's redeeming work)

WÜRTTEMBERG 7 7 7 7 4

Words: Charles Wesley
in this version Jubilate Hymns
Music: from 'Hundert Arien'
arranged David Peacock

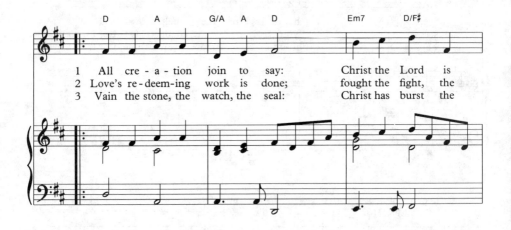

1 All cre-a-tion join to say: Christ the Lord is
2 Love's re-deem-ing work is done; fought the fight, the
3 Vain the stone, the watch, the seal: Christ has burst the

risen to - day! raise your joys and tri - umphs high;
bat - tle won: see, our Sun's ec - lipse has passed;
gates of hell; death in vain for - bids his rise –

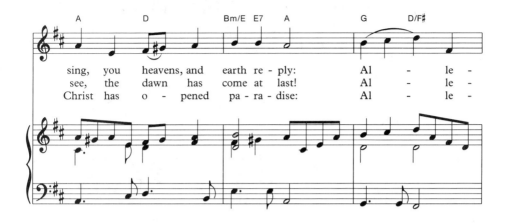

sing, you heavens, and earth re - ply: Al - le -
see, the dawn has come at last! Al - le -
Christ has o - pened pa - ra - dise: Al - le -

Fine

- lu - ia!
- lu - ia!
- lu - ia!

4 Now he lives, our glorious king;
  now, O death, where is your sting?
  Once he died, our souls to save –
  where's your victory, boasting grave?
   Alleluia!

5 So we rise where Christ has led,
  following our exalted head;
  made like him, like him we rise –
  ours the cross, the grave, the skies:
   Alleluia!

6 Hail the Lord of earth and heaven!
  praise to you by both be given;
  every knee to you shall bow,
  risen Christ, triumphant now:
   Alleluia!

5 All creatures of our God and King
(First tune)

EASTER SONG   8 8 4 4 8 8 with Alleluias

Words: after Francis of Assisi
William Draper
in this version Jubilate Hymns
Music: Geistliche Kirchengesang
arranged David Peacock

1 All crea-tures of our God and King,
2 Swift rush-ing wind so wild and strong,
3 Cool flow-ing wa-ter, pure and clear,

lift up your voice and with us sing:
white clouds that sail in heaven a-long,
make mus-ic for your Lord to hear:

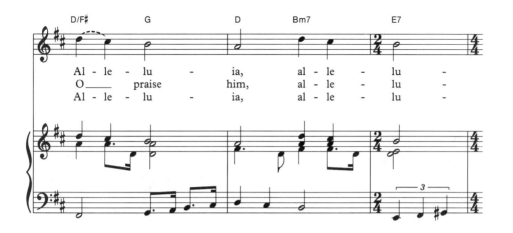

Al - le - lu - ia, al - le - lu -
O___ praise him, al - le - lu -
Al - le - lu - ia, al - le - lu -

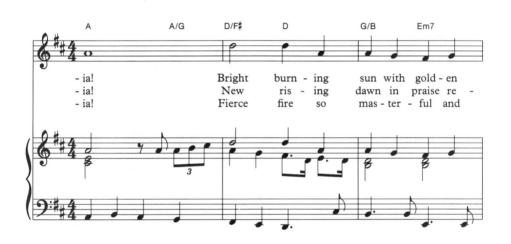

- ia! Bright burn - ing sun with gold - en
- ia! New ris - ing dawn in praise re -
- ia! Fierce fire so mas - ter - ful and

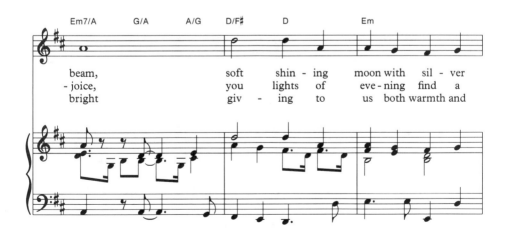

beam, soft shin - ing moon with sil - ver
- joice, you lights of eve - ning find a
bright giv - ing to us both warmth and

Chorus

gleam,
voice;
light,

O___ praise him, O___

praise him, Al - le - lu - ia, al - le -

- lu - ia, al - le - lu -

4   Earth ever fertile, day by day
     bring forth your blessings on our way,
       O praise him, alleluia!
     All fruit and crops that richly grow,
     all trees and flowers God's glory show;
       O praise him . . .

5   People and nations, take your part,
     love and forgive with all your heart.
       Alleluia, alleluia!
     All who long pain and sorrow bear,
     trust God and cast on him your care;
       O praise him . . .

6   Death, once the ancient enemy,
     hear now our Easter melody,
       O praise him, alleluia!
     You are the pathway home to God,
     our door to life through Christ our Lord:
       O praise him . . .

7   Let all things their Creator bless
     and worship him in lowliness:
       Alleluia, alleluia!
     Praise, praise the Father, praise the Son,
     and praise the Spirit, Three-in-One,
       O praise him . . .

5 All creatures of our God and King
(Second tune)

LITTLEMORE   8 8 4 4 8 8 and Alleluias

Words: after Francis of Assisi
William Draper
in this version Jubilate Hymns
Music: Martin Cox
arranged David Peacock

1 All crea-tures of   our
2 Swift rush-ing wind   so
3 Cool flow-ing wa -   ter,

God   and   King,   lift   up your voice   and
wild and   strong,   white clouds that sail   in
pure and   clear,_   make mu - sic for   your

Chorus

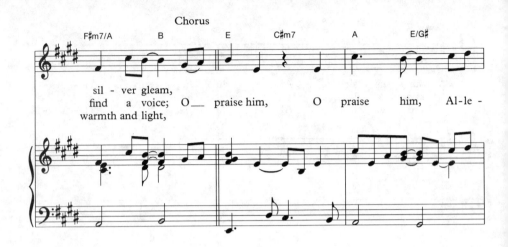

sil - ver gleam,
find a voice; O__ praise him, O praise him, Al-le -
warmth and light,

- lu - ia, al - le - lu - ia,__ al - le - lu -

- ia!

4 Earth ever fertile, day by day
  bring forth your blessings on our way,
      O praise him, alleluia!
  All fruit and crops that richly grow,
  all trees and flowers God's glory show;
      O praise him . . .

5 People and nations, take your part,
  love and forgive with all your heart.
      Alleluia, alleluia!
  All who long pain and sorrow bear,
  trust God and cast on him your care;
      O praise him . . .

6 Death, once the ancient enemy,
  hear now our Easter melody,
      O praise him, alleluia!
  You are the pathway home to God,
  our door to life through Christ our Lord:
      O praise him . . .

7 Let all things their Creator bless
  and worship him in lowliness:
      Alleluia, alleluia!
  Praise, praise the Father, praise the Son,
  and praise the Spirit, Three-in-One,
      O praise him . . .

Instrumental obligato

6 All glory, praise and honour

ST THEODULPH   7 6 7 6 D

Words: after Theodulph
John Neale
in this version Jubilate Hymns
Music: Melchior Teschner
arranged Christopher Norton

All glory, praise and honour, to you, redeemer, king, to whom the lips of children made sweet hosannas ring.

Verse

1 You are the king of Is - rael, great Da-vid's great - er
2 The com - pa - ny of an - gels are prais - ing you on
3 The peo - ple of the He - brews with palms be - fore you

son; you ride in low - ly tri - umph, the Lord's a - noint - ed
high, and we with all cre - a - tion to - ge-ther make re -
went; our praise and prayer and an - thems be - fore you we pre -

one!
- ply: All
- sent.

CODA

sweet ho - san-nas ring.

4 To you before your passion
   they sang their hymns of praise;
   to you, now high exalted,
   our melody we raise:
      All glory, praise . . .

5 As you received their praises,
   accept the prayers we bring:
   for you delight in goodness,
   O good and gracious king!
      All glory, praise . . .

Verses *2* and *4* may be omitted

7   All hail the power of Jesus' name

MILES LANE   8 6 8 6 (CM) extended

12

Words: after Edward Perronet and John Rippon
in this version Jubilate Hymns
Music: Later form of melody by William Shrubsole
as in the Australian Hymn Book 1977
arranged Roger Mayor

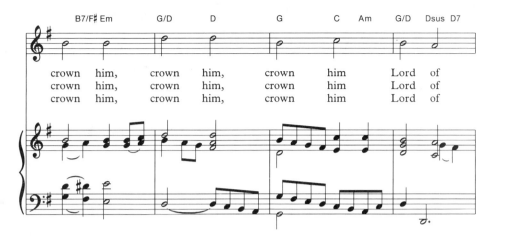

crown him, crown him, crown him Lord of
crown him, crown him, crown him Lord of
crown him, crown him, crown him Lord of

all.
all.
all.

2 Come, all.
3 Crown
4 Let

4 Let all who trust in Christ exclaim
   in wonder, to recall
   the one who bore our sin and shame,
   and crown him Lord of all.

5 Then in that final judgement hour
   when all rebellions fall,
   we'll rise in his triumphant power
   and crown him Lord of all.

8 All my heart this night rejoices

ALL MY HEART   8 3 3 6 D

Words: after Paul Gerhardt
Catherine Winkworth
in this version Word & Music
Music: David Peacock

2

heart   this night re - joic - es, as I hear,   far and
(2) from   a hum-ble man - ger comes the call,   'One and
(3) then,   from ev - ery na - tion; here let all,   great and
(4) Lord,   with love I'll che - rish, live to you,   and with

near,   sweet-est an - gel__ voi - ces. 'Christ is
all,   run from sin___ and__ dan - ger! Christ-ians
small,   kneel in a - dor - a - tion; love him
you   dy - ing, shall___ not__ pe - rish, but shall

9 All people that on earth do dwell
(First tune)

OLD 100TH   8 8 8 8 (LM)

14

Words: from Psalm 100
William Kethe
in this version Jubilate Hymns
Music: melody from the Genevan Psalter
arranged Christopher Norton

1 All peo-ple that on earth do dwell,
2 Know that the Lord is God in - deed,
3 O en - ter then his gates with praise,

sing to the Lord with cheer - ful voice;
he formed us all with - out our aid;
and in his courts his love pro - claim;

4 For God our mighty Lord is good,
his mercy is for ever sure;
his truth at all times firmly stood,
and shall from age to age endure.

5 Praise God the Father, God the Son,
and God the Spirit evermore;
all praise to God the Three-in-One –
let heaven rejoice and earth adore!

9   All people that on earth do dwell
(Second tune)

ALL PEOPLE   8 8 8 8 (LM)

8

Words: from Psalm 100
William Kethe
in this version Jubilate Hymns
Music: Roger Jones
arranged Roger Mayor

Latin feel ♩ = 116

1 All   peo-ple that on earth do dwell,   sing   to the Lord with
3 O   en-ter then his gates with praise,   and   in his courts his

cheer-ful   voice;   serve   him with joy, his prai-ses tell, come now be-
love pro-claim;   give   thanks and bless him all   your days: let ev-ery

Verse 5 is omitted in this setting

10

All shall be well

Song 46 10 10

Words: Timothy Dudley-Smith
Music: Orlando Gibbons
arranged David Peacock

1 All shall be well! for on our Eas-ter skies see Christ the Sun of
2 All shall be well! the sac-ri-fice is made; the sin-ner freed, the
3 All shall be well! the cross and pas-sion past; dark night is done, bright

4 All shall be well!
  Lift every voice on high,
  'Death has no more dominion, but shall die.'

5 Jesus alive!
  rejoice and sing again,
  'All shall be well for evermore, Amen!
  All shall be well for evermore, Amen!'

11   All things bright and beautiful

ALL THINGS BRIGHT AND BEAUTIFUL
7 6 7 6 and refrain

Words: Cecil Alexander
Music: William Monk
arranged Christopher Norton

All things bright and beau - ti - ful, all crea - tures great and small, all things wise and won - der - ful — the Lord God made them

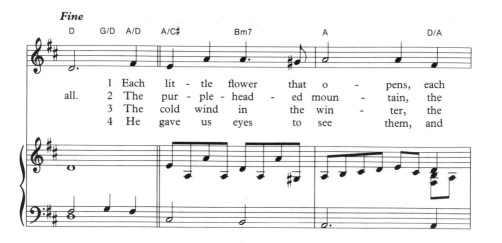

Fine

D G/D A/D A/C♯ Bm7 A D/A

all.
1 Each lit - tle flower that o - pens, each
2 The pur - ple - head - ed moun - tain, the
3 The cold wind in the win - ter, the
4 He gave us eyes to see them, and

A/C♯ Bm7 E7 A F♯7 Bm

lit - tle bird that sings — he made their glow - ing
ri - ver run - ning by, the sun - set, and the
pleas - ant sum - mer sun, the ripe fruits in the
lips that we might tell how great is God al -

D.S. al Fine

E A D A/E E7 G/A A7

col - ours, he made their ti - ny wings.
morn - ing that brigh - tens up the sky:
gar - den — he made them ev - ery one.
- migh - ty, who has made all things well!

12   Alleluia! Raise the anthem

UNSER HERRSCHER   8 7 8 7 8 7

Words: Job Hupton and John Neale
in this version Jubilee Hymns
Music: Joachim Neander
arranged Christopher Norton

1 Al - le - lu - ia! Raise the an - them,
2 Long be - fore he formed the moun - tains,
3 There for us and our re - demp - tion
4 Praise and hon - our to the Fa - ther,

let the___ skies re - sound with praise;
spread the___ seas or made the sky,
see him___ all his life - blood pour:
praise and___ hon - our to the Son,

13   Alleluia, sing to Jesus

HYFRYDOL   8 7 8 7 D

Words: William Dix
Music: Rowland Prichard
arranged David Peacock

Rock style ♩ = 112

1&4 Al - le - lu - ia, sing to
2 Al - le - lu - ia! – not as
3 Al - le - lu - ia! – bread of

Je - sus! his the scep - tre, his the throne:
or - phans are we left in sor - row now:
hea - ven, here on earth our food, our stay:

Al - le - lu - ia! – his the tri - umph, his the vic - to -
Al - le - lu - ia! – he is near us; faith be - lieves, nor
Al - le - lu - ia! – here the sin - ful come to you from

14   Almighty God

ALMIGHTY GOD, OUR HEAVENLY FATHER
Irregular

Words: from *The Alternative Service Book 1980*
adapted Christopher Rolinson
Music: Christopher Rolinson
arranged David Peacock

11

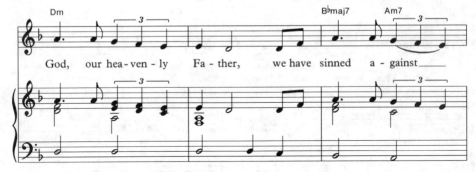

The congregation may divide at Ⓐ and Ⓑ

15   Almighty God, we thank you

ALMIGHTY GOD, WE THANK YOU
Irregular

Words: from *The Alternative Service Book 1980*
Music: Christopher Rolinson
arranged David Peacock

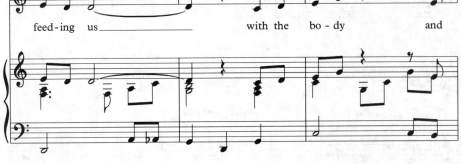

Al-migh-ty God, we thank you for
feed-ing us with the bo-dy and
blood of your Son,

16   Amazing grace

AMAZING GRACE   8 6 8 6 (CM)

Words: John Newton
in this version Jubilate Hymns
Music: traditional
arranged Roger Mayor

13

Gospel feel ♩. = 72

Capo 3(D)

- maz - ing grace – how sweet the
(2) grace first taught my heart to
(3) ev - ery dan - ger, trial and

sound – that saved a wretch like me!
fear, his grace my fears re - lieved:
snare I have al - rea - dy come;

4   The Lord has promised good to me,
     his word my hope secures;
     my shield and stronghold he shall be
     as long as life endures.

5   And when this earthly life is past,
     and mortal cares shall cease,
     I shall possess with Christ at last
     eternal joy and peace.

17 And it can be

SAGINA   8 8 8 8 8 8 extended

10

Words: Charles Wesley
in this version Jubilate Hymns
Music: Thomas Campbell's *Bouquet*
arranged Christopher Norton

1 And can it be that
2 What mys-tery here! – the
3 He left his Fa - ther's

I___ should gain   an in - terest in the___ Sav-iour's blood?
Im - mor-tal dies; who can___ ex - plore his___ strange de - sign?
throne a - bove – so free,_ so___ in - fi - nite his grace –

Died he for me,_ who caused his pain; for me,____ who him____ to
In vain the first - born se - raph tries to sound___ the depths___ of
emp - tied him-self___ of all but love, and bled___ for A - dam's

The traditional version of this text is found in the words edition

Music arrangement: © 1993 HarperCollins*Religious*

Words: © in this version Jubilate Hymns

4 Long my imprisoned spirit lay,
   fast bound in sin and nature's night:
   your sunrise turned that night to day;
   I woke – the dungeon flamed with light.
   My chains fell off, my heart was free;
   I rose, went out to liberty!

5 No condemnation now I dread;
   Jesus, and all in him, is mine!
   Alive in him, my living head,
   and clothed in righteousness divine,
   bold I approach the eternal throne
   and claim the crown through Christ my own.

18   Angel voices ever singing

ANGEL VOICES   8 5 8 5 8 7

3

Words: Francis Pott
in this version Jubilate Hymns
Music: Edwin Monk
arranged Christopher Norton

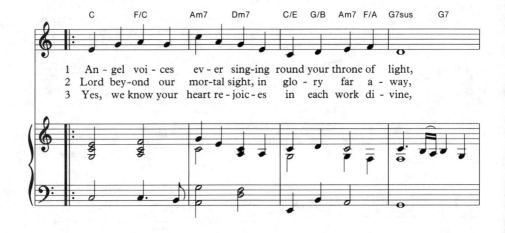

1 An - gel voi - ces   ev - er sing-ing round your throne of   light,
2 Lord bey-ond our   mor-tal sight, in   glo - ry   far a - way,
3 Yes, we know your heart re - joic - es   in   each work di - vine,

an-gels' mu - sic   ev - er ring-ing rests not   day or   night:
can it   be that   you de-light in   sin-ners' songs to - day;
us - ing minds and   hands and voic-es   in your great de - sign;

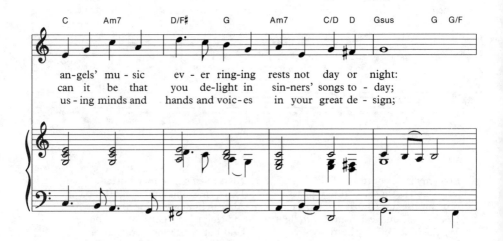

Chords: Em A Dm G C F

thou - sands on - ly   live to bless you   and con - fess you
may   we know that   you are near us   and will hear us?
crafts - man's art and mu - sic's mea-sure   for your plea-sure

Chords: G7sus G7 C F/C G/C F/C C

Lord   of might.
Yes,   we may!
all   com - bine.

4 Here to you, great God, we offer
     praise in harmony,
   and for your acceptance proffer
     all unworthily
   hearts and minds and hands and voices
     in our choicest psalmody.

5 Honour, glory, might and merit
     for your works and ways,
   Father, Son and Holy Spirit,
     God through endless days;
   with the best that you have given
     earth and heaven render praise.

19 Angels from the realms of glory

IRIS   8 7 8 7 and refrain

Words: James Montgomery
in this version Jubilate Hymns
Music: French traditional melody
arranged David Peacock

1 An-gels from the_ realms of glo-ry, wing your flight through
2 Shep-herds in the_ fields a-bid-ing, watch-ing_ by your
3 Wise men, leave your con - tem-pla-tions! Bright-er_ vis - ions_
4 Though an in-fant_ now we view him, he will share his_

all the earth; her-alds of cre - a - tion's sto - ry,
flocks at night: God with us is_ now re - sid-ing –
shine a - far: seek in him the_ hope of na-tions,
Fa - ther's throne, ga-ther all the_ na - tions to him;

20
As water to the thirsty

OASIS   7 6 7 6 6 6 4 4 6

Words: Timothy Dudley-Smith
Music: T Brian Coleman
arranged Roger Mayor

1 As wa - ter to the thir - sty, as beau - ty to the
2 Like calm in place of clam - our, like peace that fol-lows
3 As sleep that fol-lows fe - ver, as gold in-stead of

eyes, as strength that fol-lows weak - ness, as
pain, like meet - ing af - ter part - ing, like
grey, as free - dom af - ter bond - age, as

21 As with gladness

Dix   7 7 7 7 7 7

Words: William Dix
in this version Jubilate Hymns
Music: Conrad Kocher
arranged Christopher Norton

Brightly ♩ = 132

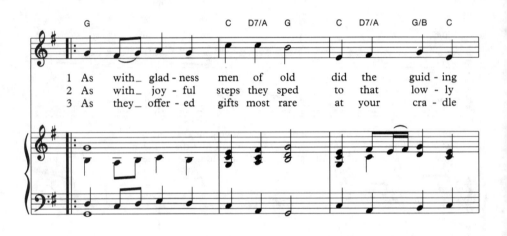

1 As with gladness men of old did the guid-ing
2 As with joy-ful steps they sped to that low-ly
3 As they offer-ed gifts most rare at your cra-dle

star be-hold, as with joy they hailed its light,
man-ger bed, there to bend the knee be-fore
plain and bare, so may we with ho-ly joy

4 Holy Jesus, every day
  keep us in the narrow way,
  and when earthly things are past,
  bring our ransomed souls at last:
  where they need no star to guide,
  where no clouds your glory hide.

5 In the heavenly country bright
  none shall need created light –
  you, its light, its joy, its crown,
  you its sun which goes not down;
  there for ever shall we sing
  alleluias to our king.

22   At the name of Jesus

CAMBERWELL   6 5 6 5 D

Words: Caroline Noel
in this version Jubilate Hymns
Music: Michael Brierley
arranged Roger Mayor

1 At the name of Je - sus   ev - ery knee shall bow,
2 At his voice cre - a - tion   sprang at once to sight,
3 Humb-led for a sea-son,   to re-ceive a name

ev - ery tongue con - fess him   king of glo - ry_ now;
all the an - gel fa-ces,   all the hosts_ of_ light;
from the lips of sin-ners   un - to whom he_ came;

Music: © 1960 Josef Weinberger Ltd
12–14, Mortimer Street, London W1N 7RD.
Reproduced by permission of the copyright holders

this the Fath-er's plea-sure, that we call him Lord,
thrones and dom-in - a - tions, stars up - on their way,
faith - ful - ly he bore it spot-less to the last,

who from the be - gin - ning was the migh - ty Word.
all the heaven-ly or - ders, in their great ar - ray.
brought it back vic - tor - ious when from death he passed:

4 Bore it up triumphant
  with its human light,
 through all ranks of creatures
  to the central height;
 to the eternal Godhead,
  to the Father's throne,
 filled it with the glory
  of his triumph won.

5 Name him, Christians, name him,
  with love strong as death,
 but with awe and wonder,
  and with bated breath;
 he is God the saviour,
  he is Christ the Lord,
 ever to be worshipped,
  trusted and adored.

6 In your hearts enthrone him;
  there let him subdue
 all that is not holy,
  all that is not true;
 crown him as your captain
  in temptation's hour,
 let his will enfold you
  in its light and power.

7 With his Father's glory
  Jesus comes again,
 angel hosts attend him
  and announce his reign;
 for all wreaths of empire
  meet upon his brow,
 and our hearts confess him
  king of glory now.

Verses 2 and 6 may be omitted

23   At your feet we fall

AT YOUR FEET WE FALL   Irregular

From Revelation 1
Words and music: Dave Fellingham
Music arranged David Peacock

3

With steady strength ♩ = 116

1 At your feet we fall,_____ migh-ty
2 There we see you stand,_____ migh-ty
3 Like the shin-ing sun_____ in its

ri - sen Lord,_____ as we come be - fore your throne to wor - ship
ri - sen Lord,_____ clothed in gar-ments pure and ho - ly, shin - ing
noon-day strength,__ we now see the glo - ry of your wond-rous

you!_____ By your Spi - rit's power_____ you now
bright;_____ eyes of flash-ing fire,_____ feet like
face:_____ once that face was marred,____ but now

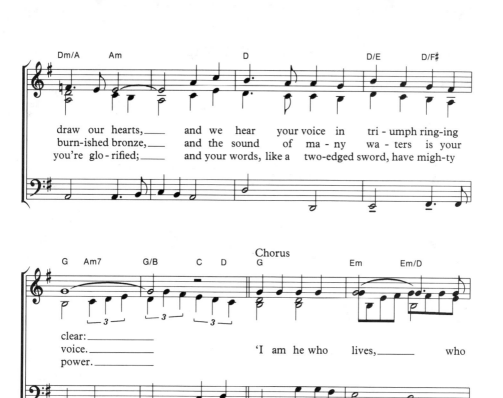

draw our hearts,_____ and we hear your voice in tri - umph ring-ing
burn-ished bronze,_____ and the sound of ma - ny wa - ters is your
you're glo - rified;_____ and your words, like a two-edged sword, have migh-ty

Chorus

clear:
voice._____
power._____

'I am he who lives,_____ who

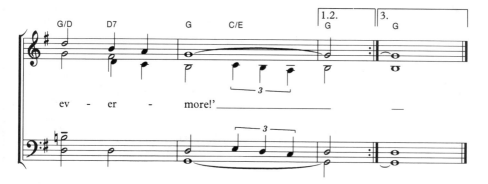

lives and was dead: be - hold I am a - live - for

ev - er - more!'_____

24 Away in a manger

CRADLE SONG   11 11 11 11

Words: verses 1, 2 unknown
verse 3 John MacFarland
Music: William Kirkpatrick
arranged David Peacock

1 A-
- way in a___ man - ger, no___ crib for a bed, the_
(2) cat - tle are_ low - ing, the_ ba - by a - wakes, but_
(3) near me, Lord Je - sus; I___ ask you to stay close

lit - tle Lord Je - sus laid_ down his sweet head; the
lit - tle Lord Je - sus no___ cry - ing he makes: I
by me for ev - er and_ love me, I pray; bless

25

Baptised in water

BAPTISED IN WATER   5 5 8 D

Words: Michael Saward
Music: Alistair Goudie

1 Bap - tised in wa - ter, sealed by the Spi - rit,
2 Bap - tised in wa - ter, sealed by the Spi - rit,
3 Bap - tised in wa - ter, sealed by the Spi - rit,

cleansed by the blood— of Christ our king;
dead in the tomb— with Christ our king;
marked with the sign— of Christ our king;

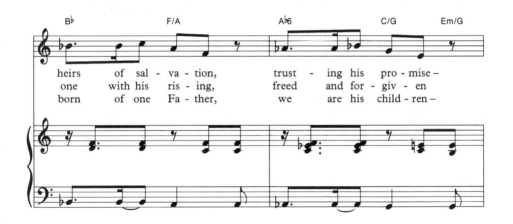

heirs of sal - va - tion, trust - ing his pro - mise –
one with his ris - ing, freed and for - giv - en
born of one Fa - ther, we are his child - ren –

faith - ful - ly now_____ God's praise we sing.
thank - ful - ly now_____ God's praise we sing.
joy - ful - ly now_____ God's praise we

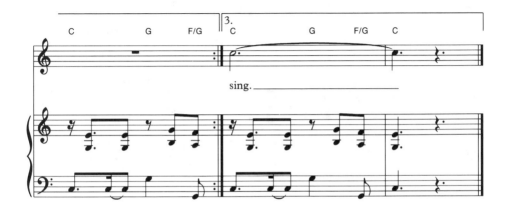

sing._____

26   Be still, for the presence of the Lord

BE STILL   9 6 6 6 6 6 9 6

Words and music: David Evans
Music arranged Christopher Norton

10

1 Be still, for the pre-sence of the Lord, the ho - ly One, is here;
2 Be still, for the glo - ry of the Lord is shin-ing all a - round;
3 Be still, for the pow - er of the Lord is mov-ing in this place:

come bow be - fore him now with him now with
he burns with ho - ly fire, with
he comes to cleanse and heal, to

re - ver-ence and fear: in him no sin is found –
splen-dour he is crowned: how awe-some is the sight –
mi - ni-ster his grace – no work too hard for him.

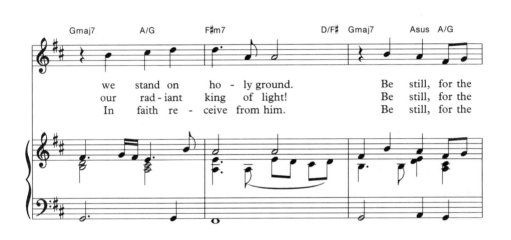

we stand on ho - ly ground. Be still, for the
our rad - iant king of light! Be still, for the
In faith re - ceive from him. Be still, for the

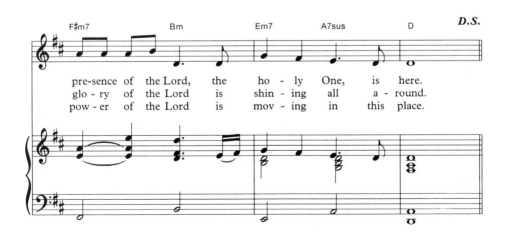

D.S.

pre-sence of the Lord, the ho - ly One, is here.
glo - ry of the Lord is shin - ing all a - round.
pow - er of the Lord is mov - ing in this place.

27   Because the Lord is my shepherd

BECAUSE THE LORD   Irregular

From Psalm 23
Words and music: Christopher Walker

Words and music: © 1985 Christopher Walker,
published by Oregon Catholic Press, 5536 N E Hassalo,
Portland, Oregon 97213, USA

28   Bless the Lord

CREATED THINGS   7 7 7 6

Words: Judy Davies
Music: Christopher Norton

11

Unhurried ♩ = 104

1 Bless the Lord, cre - a - ted things,
2 Sun and moon and stars of heaven,
3 Scorch-ing wind and bit - ter cold,

high-est_ hea-vens, an - gel host;   bless the Fa - ther, Spi - rit, Son:
show-ery_ wa - ters, rain and dew,   stor-my gale and fie - ry heat:
i - cy_ bliz-zard, morn-ing mist,   light and dark-ness, nights and days:

wor-ship, all cre - a - tion.

4   Frosty air and falling snow,
clouds and lightnings, dales and hills,
all that grows upon the earth:
worship, all creation.

5   Springs and rivers, ocean deeps,
whales and fishes of the sea,
prowling beasts and soaring birds:
worship, all creation.

6   All on earth who serve our God,
priestly people of the Lord,
upright, holy, humble hearts:
worship, all creation.

29 Before the heaven and earth

HEAVEN AND EARTH   6 6 8 6 (SM)

Words: from Philippians 2
Brian Black and Word & Music
Music: Christopher Norton

Calmly, but strong ♩ = 76

1 Be - fore the heaven and earth were made by God's de -
(2) in the form of God and rich be - yond com -
(3) heights of heaven he came to this world full of

- cree, the Son of God all - glo - rious
- pare, he did not think to grasp his
sin, to meet with hun - ger, ha - tred,

dwelt in God's e - ter - ni - ty. 2 Though Lord.
prize; nor did he lin - ger___ there. 3 From
hell—our life, our love to___ win. 4 The

4 The Son became true Man
   and took a servant's role;
   in lowliness and selfless love
   he came, to make us whole.

5 Obedient to his death –
   that death upon a cross,
   no son had ever shown such love,
   nor father known such loss.

6 To him enthroned on high,
   by angel hosts adored,
   all knees shall bow, and tongues confess
   that Jesus Christ is Lord.

Instrumental obligato

Melody part for B♭ instruments

30 Blessed are the pure in heart

PURE IN HEART 6 6 8 6 (SM)

Words: John Keble and William Hall
Music: Christopher Norton

12

Flowing ♩ = 92

1 Blessed are the pure in
2 The Lord, who left the
3 Still to the low - ly
4 Lord, we your pre - sence

heart,
heavens
soul
seek:

for they shall see our
our life and peace to
him - self he will im -
our in - ner life re -

God;_____ the se - cret of the
bring;_____ to dwell in low - li -
- part;_____ and for his dwell - ing
- new;_____ give us a pure and

Lord is_____ theirs, their soul is Christ's a -
- ness with___ us, our pat - tern and our
and his___ throne choo - ses the pure in
low - ly___ heart, a temp - le fit for

- bode.
king:
heart.
you.

Instrumental obligato

31 Blow upon the trumpet

JUBILANT   12 11 12 11

Words: from Psalm 98, Joel 2 etc.
Michael Perry
Music: Roger Mayor

10

The congregation repeats each line after the worship leader

God gives us the vic-to-ry through Christ our Lord!

32

Born in song

CHATSWORTH   393699

Words and music: Brian Hoare
Music arranged Roger Mayor

18

1 Born in
song! God's peo-ple have al-ways been sing - ing.
(2) king! he left all the glo-ry of hea - ven.
(3) song! God's Spi-rit is poured out a-mong us.

Born in song! hearts and voi-ces raised. So to-
Christ is king! born to share in our pain; cru-ci-
Sing the song! God has made us a-new; ev-ery

- day ... we wor-ship to - ge - ther: God a -
- fied, ... for sin - ners a - ton - ing; ri-sen, ex -
mem - ber part of the Bo - dy, gi-ven his

- lone ... is ... wor - thy to____ be praised.
- al - ted, ... soon to come_ a - gain.
power, ... his ... will to seek__ and do.

Fine

2 Christ is
3 Sing the
4 Tell the

4 Tell the world!
   all power to Jesus is given.
   Tell the world!
   he is with us always.
   Spread the word,
       that all may receive him;
   every tongue confess
       and sing his praise.

5 Then the end!
   Christ Jesus shall reign in his glory.
   Then the end
   of all earthly days.
   Yet above,
       the song will continue;
   all his people still
       shall sing his praise!

33 Born of the water

EVERGLADE 5 5 7 D

Words: Michael Perry
Music: Christopher Norton

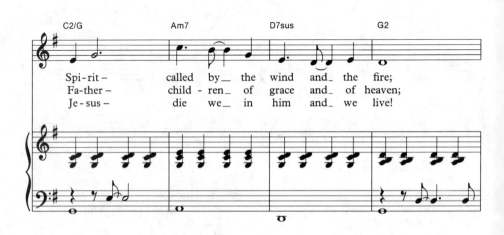

1 Born of the wa - ter, born of the Spi - rit – called by the wind and the fire;

2 One through re - demp-tion, one with the Fa - ther – child - ren of grace and of heaven;

3 Glo - ry, all glo - ry, glo - ry to Je - sus – die we in him and we live!

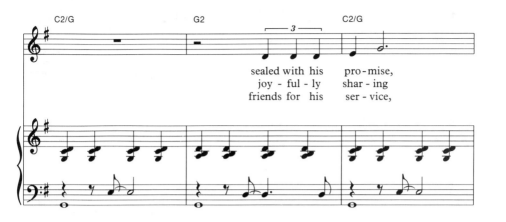

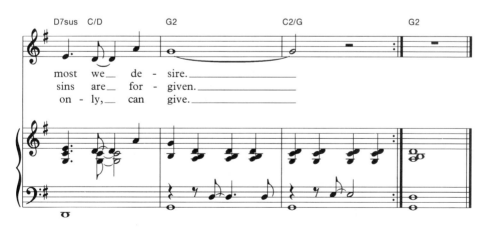

34   Bread of the world

SPIRITUS VITAE   9 8 9 8

Words: Reginald Heber
Music: Mary Hammond
arranged Christopher Norton

11

Moderato ♩ = 100

1 Bread of the world in mer - cy
2 Look on the heart by sor - row

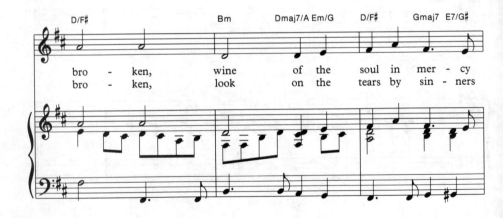

bro - ken, wine of the soul in mer - cy
bro - ken, look on the tears by sin - ners

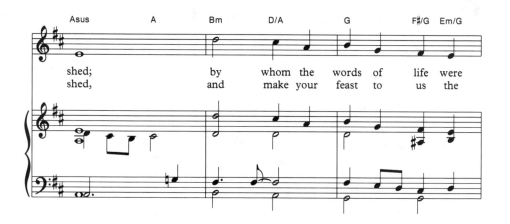

shed;   by   whom the   words   of   life   were
shed,   and   make your   feast   to   us   the

spo - ken   and   in whose   death our   sins   are
to - ken   that   by your   grace our   souls   are

dead: fed.

35   Break now the bread of life

LATHBURY   6 4 6 4 D

Words: Mary Lathbury
and Alexander Groves
in this version Word & Music
Music: William Sherwin
arranged David Peacock

1 Break now the bread of life,   dear Lord, to me
2 You are the bread of life,   O Lord, to me;
3 Now send your Spi-rit, Lord, to strength-en me,
4 Bless now the bread of life to me, to me,

as you once broke the bread be - side the
your ho - ly word, your truth, is food for
so let him touch my eyes that I may
as you once blessed the loaves by Ga - li -

36 Breathe on me, breath of God

TRENTHAM   6 6 8 6 (SM)

Words: Edwin Hatch
in this version Jubilate Hymns
Music: Robert Jackson
arranged Roger Mayor

1 Breathe on me, breath of God;
fill me with life a - new,

2 Breathe on me, breath of God,
un - til my heart is pure,

3 Breathe on me, breath of God;
ful - fil my heart's de - sire,

4 Breathe on me, breath of God:
so shall I ne - ver die,

37 Bring to the Lord a glad new song

JERUSALEM   8 8 8 8 D (DLM)

Words: from Psalms 149 and 150
Michael Perry
Music: C Hubert Parry
arranged Christopher Norton

Lyrics:

1 Bring to the Lord a glad new song, child-ren of grace ex-tol your king: your love and praise to God be-long to in-stru-ments of mu-sic, sing! Let those be

(2) -in these hal-lowed walls, wor-ship be--neath the dome of heaven; by cym-bals' sounds and trum-pets' calls let prai-ses fit for God be given: with strings and

38 Broken for me

BROKEN FOR ME   Irregular

Words and music: Janet Lunt
Music arranged Christopher Norton

12

Gently ♩ = 96

Chorus

Bro-ken for me,_____ bro-ken for

last time **to Coda** ⊕

you, the bo-dy of Je - sus_____

Verse

bro-ken for you.

1 He of-fered his
2 Come to my
3 This is my
4 This is my

39 Child in the manger

BUNESSAN 10 8 10 8

19

Words: after Mary MacDonald
Lachlan Macbean
Music: Gaelic melody
arranged Christopher Norton

1 Child in the man - ger, in - fant of
2 Once the most ho - ly child of sal -
3 Pro - phets fore - told him, in - fant of

Ma - ry, out - cast and stran - ger,
- va - tion gen - tle and low - ly
won - der; an - gels be - hold him

40 Christ in majesty ascending

REGENT SQUARE   8 7 8 7 8 7

3

Words: David Mowbray
Music: Henry Smart
arranged Roger Mayor

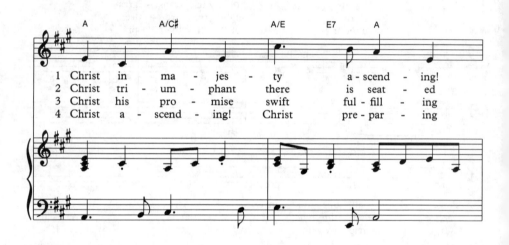

1 Christ in ma - jes - ty a - scend - ing!
2 Christ tri - um - phant there is seat - ed
3 Christ his pro - mise swift ful - fill - ing
4 Christ a - scend - ing! Christ pre - par - ing

Christ in splen - dour reigns on high;
and the race of faith is run;
sends his Spi - rit for the task;
an e - ter - nal dwell - ing - place;

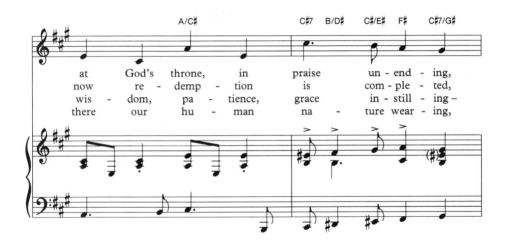

at God's throne, in praise un - end - ing,
now re - demp - tion is com - ple - ted,
wis - dom, pa - tience, grace in - still - ing –
there our hu - man na - ture wear - ing,

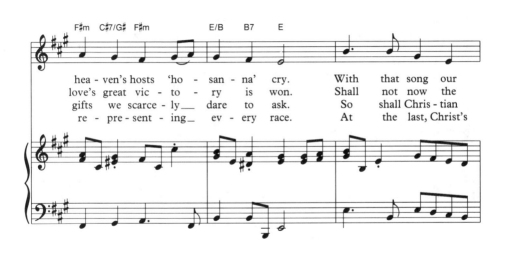

hea - ven's hosts 'ho - san - na' cry. With that song our
love's great vic - to - ry is won. Shall not now the
gifts we scarce - ly __ dare to ask. So shall Chris - tian
re - pre - sent - ing __ ev - ery race. At the last, Christ's

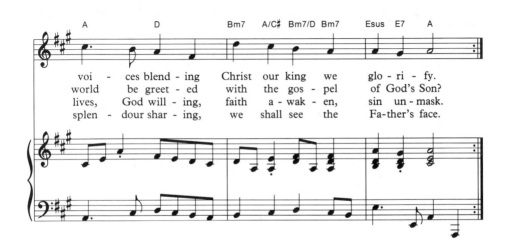

voi - ces blend - ing Christ our king we glo - ri - fy.
world be greet - ed with the gos - pel of God's Son?
lives, God will - ing, faith a - wak - en, sin un - mask.
splen - dour shar - ing, we shall see the Fa - ther's face.

41   Christ is alive

Christ Is Alive   8 8 8 8 (LM)

Words: Brian Wren
Music: Christopher Norton

12

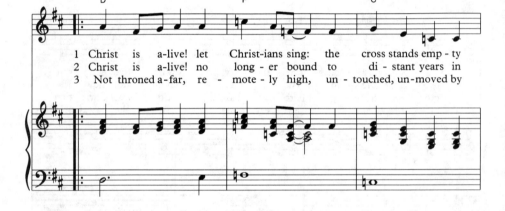

1 Christ is a-live! let Christ-ians sing: the cross stands emp - ty
2 Christ is a-live! no long - er bound to di - stant years in
3 Not throned a-far, re - mote - ly high, un - touched, un-moved by

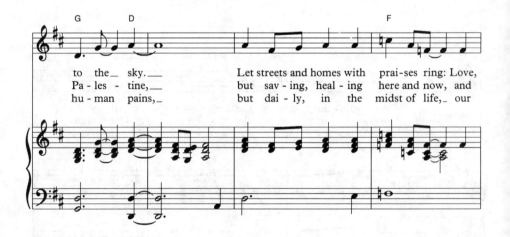

to the_ sky._   Let streets and homes with prai - ses ring: Love,
Pa - les - tine,_   but sav - ing, heal - ing here and now, and
hu - man pains,_   but dai - ly, in the midst of life,_ our

drowned in death, shall ne - ver die.____
touch - ing ev - ery place and_ time.____
Sav - iour in_ the God - head reigns._

4 In every insult, rift and war,
   where colour, scorn or wealth divide,
   Christ suffers still, yet loves the more,
   and lives where even hope has died.

5 Christ is alive, and comes to bring
   good news to this and every age,
   till earth and sky and ocean ring
   with joy, with justice, love, and praise.

Instrumental obligato

Christ is ascending

MACCABAEUS   10 11 11 11 and refrain

Words: David Mowbray
Music: adapted from George F Handel
arranged Christopher Norton

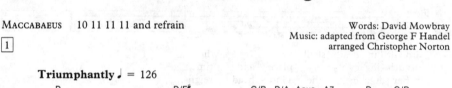

Triumphantly ♩ = 126

1 Christ is a - scend-ing! let__ cre - a - tion sing:
2 Watch the out-pour - ing from our Lord a - bove,
3 Come, Ho - ly Spi - rit, streng-then us to - day:

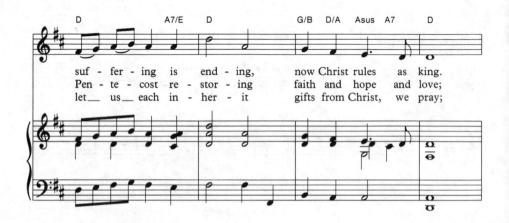

suf - fer - ing is end - ing, now Christ rules as king.
Pen - te - cost re - stor - ing faith and hope and love;
let__ us__ each in - her - it gifts from Christ, we pray;

Friends who stand dis - heart - ened soon are helped to know
bro - thers shall see vi - sions, sis - ters pro - phe - sy,
not_ for_ praise by oth - ers, but that they may give

Christ shall come in glo - ry, as they see him go.
sun_ and_ stars be dark - ened, won - ders fill the sky!
glo - ry_ to the Fa - ther by whose power we live!

Chorus

Christ is a - scend - ing, let_ cre - a - tion sing:

suf - fer - ing is end - ing, now Christ rules as king. king.

43   Christ is going to the Father

RUSSIAN AIR   8 7 8 7 D

12

Words: from John 16
Christopher Idle
Music: Russian traditional melody
arranged David Peacock

1 Christ is go - ing to the Fa - ther: heaven and hell and earth, at - tend! Marked by blood, in death made per - fect,

2 Christ is go - ing to the Fa - ther: from the world he came to save, bring - ing life to those who lis - ten,

3 Christ is go - ing to the Fa - ther: hear a new-born na - tion cry – earth re - newed by hea - ven's mus - ic,

44   Christy is made the sure foundation

WESTMINSTER ABBEY   8 7 8 7 8 7

Words: John Neale
in this version Jubilate Hymns
Music: Henry Purcell
arranged David Peacock

20

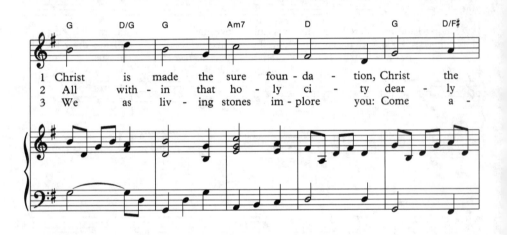

1 Christ   is   made   the   sure   foun - da - tion, Christ   the
2 All   with - in   that   ho - ly   ci - ty   dear - ly
3 We   as   liv - ing stones   im - plore   you: Come   a -

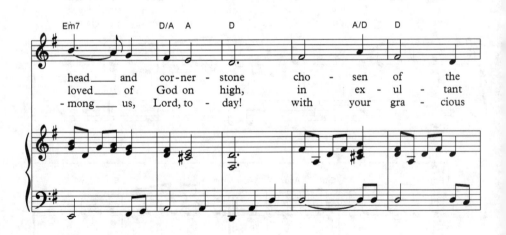

head___ and   cor - ner - stone   cho - sen   of   the
loved___ of   God on   high,   in   ex - ul - tant
- mong___ us, Lord, to - day!   with   your   gra - cious

4 Here entrust to all your servants
   what we long from you to gain –
   that on earth and in the heavens
   we one people shall remain,
   till united in your glory
   evermore with you we reign.

5 Praise and honour to the Father,
   praise and honour to the Son,
   praise and honour to the Spirit,
   ever Three and ever One:
   one in power and one in glory
   while eternal ages run.

45   Christ is risen

CHRIST IS RISEN   Irregular   Words and music: Christopher Rolinson

6

Joyfully ♩. = 76

Chorus

Christ is ri - sen! Al - le - lu - ia,

al - le - lu - ia! Christ is ri - sen!

Ri - sen in - deed, al - le - lu - ia!

Fine

Verse

1 Love's work is done, the bat-tle is won. Where now, O death, is your
2 Lord o-ver sin,___ Lord o-ver death, at his feet Sa-tan must
3 Tell it a-broad,___ 'Je-sus is Lord!' Shout it and let your praise

sting?   He rose a-gain to rule and to reign,
fall!   Ev-ery knee, bow!   All will con-fess
ring!   Glad-ly we raise   our songs of praise –

D.C. al Fine

Je-sus our con-quer-ing king.___
Je-sus is Lord o-ver all!___
wor-ship is our of-fer-ing.___

46   Christ is surely coming

LAND OF HOPE AND GLORY   11 11 11 11 11

Words: from Revelation 22
Christopher Idle
Music: Edward Elgar
arranged Roger Mayor

47   Christ is the king

LIEGE   8 8 8 4

Words: George Bell
Music: Roger Mayor

1 Christ is the king! O friends re - joice; bro-thers and sis - ters, with one voice let the world
2 O mag-ni - fy the Lord, and raise an-thems of joy and ho - ly praise for Christ's brave
3 They with a faith for ev - er new fol-lowed the king, and round him drew thou-sands of

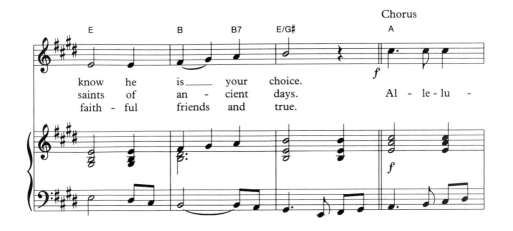

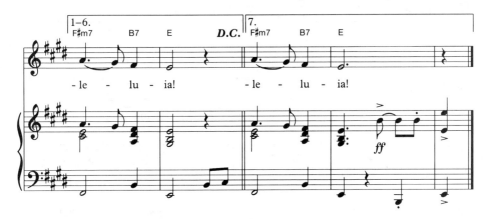

4 O Christian women, Christian men,
  all the world over, seek again
  the way disciples followed then.
      Alleluia . . .

5 Christ through all ages is the same:
  place the same hope in his great name;
  with the same faith his word proclaim.
      Alleluia . . .

6 Let Love's unconquerable might
  your scattered companies unite
  in service to the Lord of light.
      Alleluia . . .

7 So shall God's will on earth be done,
  new lamps be lit, new tasks begun,
  and the whole church at last be one.
      Alleluia . . .

48   Christ is the world's Light

WORLD'S LIGHT   10 11 11 6

Words: Frederick Pratt Green
Music: Christopher Norton

10

The congregation divides at A and B

Music: © 1993 HarperCollinsReligious

Words: © Stainer & Bell Ltd,
PO Box 110, Victoria House,
23, Gruneisen Road, London N3 1DZ

ALL if we have seen him, we have seen the Fa-ther:

Glo - ry to God on high! high!

2 Christ is the world's Peace, he and none other;
   no one can serve him;
      and despise another –
   who else unites us, one in God the Father?
      Glory to God on high!

3 Christ is the world's Life, he and none other;
   sold once for silver, murdered here,
      our Brother –
   he, who redeems us, reigns with the Father:
      Glory to God on high!

4 Give God the glory, God and none other;
   give God the glory, Spirit, Son and Father;
   give God the glory, God in Man my brother:
      Glory to God on high!

49　Christ the Lord is risen again

WÜRTTEMBERG　7 7 7 7 4

Words: after Michael Weisse
Catherine Winkworth
Music: from 'Hundert Arien'
arranged David Peacock

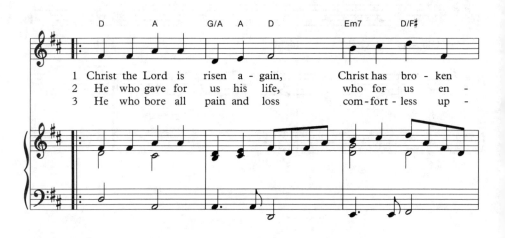

1 Christ the Lord is　risen a - gain,　　Christ has bro - ken
2 He who gave for　us his　life,　　who for　us en -
3 He who bore all　pain and loss　　com - fort - less up -

ev - ery　chain;　　hear the　an - gel　voic - es　cry,
- dured the　strife,　　is our　pas - chal　lamb to - day;
- on the　cross　　lives in　glo - ry　now on　high,

sing - ing ev - er - more on high: Al - le -
we too sing_ for joy and say: Al - le -
pleads for us_ and hears our cry: Al - le -

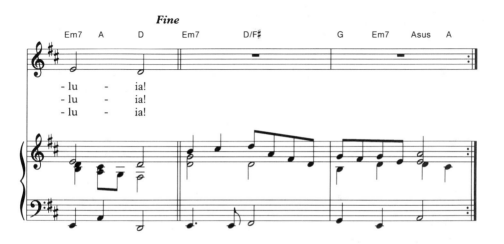

Fine

- lu - ia!
- lu - ia!
- lu - ia!

4 He who slumbered in the grave
   is exalted now to save;
   through the universe it rings
   that the lamb is King of kings:
      Alleluia!

5 Now he bids us tell abroad
   how the lost may be restored,
   how the penitent forgiven,
   how we too may enter heaven:
      Alleluia!

6 Christ, our paschal lamb indeed,
   all your ransomed people feed!
   Take our sins and guilt away;
   let us sing by night and day:
      Alleluia!

50 Christ triumphant, ever reigning

CHRIST TRIUMPHANT   8 5 8 5 7 9

Words: Michael Saward
Music: Michael Baughen
arranged Roger Mayor

1 Christ tri-umph-ant, ev - er reign-ing, Sav-iour, Mas - ter, King! Lord of heaven, our lives sus-tain - ing, hear us as we

2 Word in - carn - ate, truth re - veal - ing, Son of Man on earth! power and ma - jes - ty con-ceal - ing by your hum - ble

3 Suffer-ing ser - vant, scorned, ill - treat-ed, vic - tim cru - ci - fied! death is through the cross de-feat - ed, sin - ners jus - ti -

4 Priestly king, enthroned for ever
high in heaven above!
sin and death and hell shall never
stifle hymns of love:
    Yours the glory . . .

5 So, our hearts and voices raising
through the ages long,
ceaselessly upon you gazing,
this shall be our song:
    Yours the glory . . .

51   Christ whose glory fills the skies

RATISBON   7 7 7 7 7 7

Words: Charles Wesley
Music: from Johann Werner's *Choralbuch*
arranged David Peacock

7

Disco feel ♩ = 132

1 Christ whose glo - ry fills the skies, Christ the true, the on - ly light;
2 Dark and cheer - less is the dawn till your mer - cy's beams I see;
3 Vis - it then this soul of mine, pierce the gloom of sin and grief;

Sun of right - eous - ness, a - rise,
joy - less is the day's re - turn
fill me, ra - dian - cy div - ine,

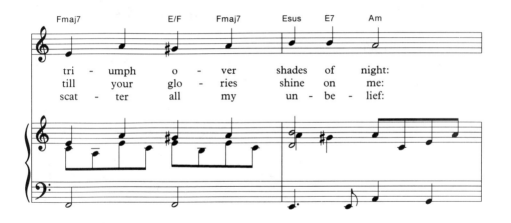

tri - umph o - ver shades of night:
till your glo - ries shine on me:
scat - ter all my un - be - lief:

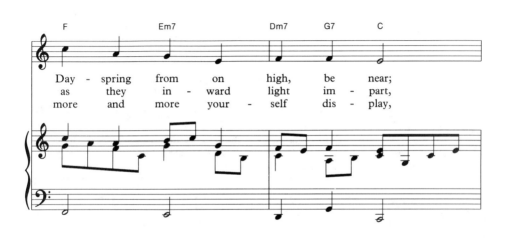

Day - spring from on high, be near;
as they in - ward light im - part,
more and more your - self dis - play,

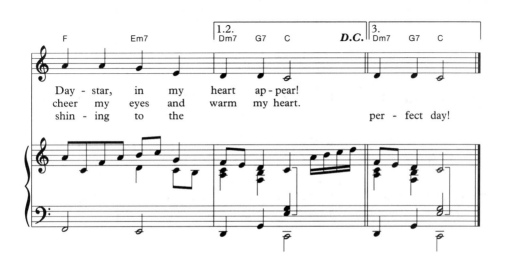

Day - star, in my heart ap - pear!
cheer my eyes and warm my heart.
shin - ing to the per - fect day!

52   Christ upon the mountain peak

GLORY   7 8 7 8 and Alleluia

Words: Brian Wren
Music: Christopher Norton

1

1 Christ up-on the moun-tain peak stands a-lone in glo-ry blaz-ing;
2 Trem-bling at his feet we saw Mo-ses and E - li-jah speak-ing:
3 Swift the cloud of glo-ry came, God pro-claim-ing in its thun-der
4 This is God's be - lov - èd Son! law and pro-phets fade be-fore him,

let us, if we dare to speak, with the saints and an-gels praise him —
all the pro-phets and the law shout through them their joy-ful greet-ing —
Je - sus as his Son by name! na - tions, cry a-loud in_ won-der —
First and Last, and on-ly One: let cre - a-tion now a - dore him —

Al-le-lu - ia! Al-le-lu - ia!

53   Christians, awake

YORKSHIRE   10 10 10 10 10 10

Words: John Byrom
in this version Jubilate Hymns
Music: John Wainwright
arranged Christopher Norton

12

Strongly ♩ = 126

1 Christ - ians, a - wake,   sal - ute the hap - py
2 First, to the watch - ful shep-herds it was
3 To Beth - le - hem these ea - ger shep-herds
4 Let us, like those good shep-herds, now em -

morn   on which the sav - iour of the
told,   who heard the her - ald an - gel's
ran   to see the won - der of our
- ploy   our grate - ful voic - es to de -

world was born; rise to a -
voice: 'Be - hold, I bring good
God made man; they found, with
- clare the joy: Christ, who was

- dore the my - ste - ry of love
news of your Mes - si - ah's birth
Jo - seph and the ho - ly maid,
born on this most hap - py day,

which hosts of an - gels chan - ted from a -
to you and all the na - tions here on
her son, the sav - iour, in a man - ger
round all the earth his glo - ry shall dis -

54 Church of God

Lux Eoi 8 7 8 7 D

12

Words: from 1 Peter 2
James Seddon
Music: Arthur Sullivan
arranged David Peacock

1 Church of God, e - lect and glo-rious,
2 God has called you out of dark-ness
3 Once you were an al - ien peo - ple,
4 Church of God, e - lect and ho - ly,

ho - ly na - tion, cho - sen race; called as God's own
in - to his most mar - vellous light; brought his truth to
stran - gers to God's heart of love; but he brought you
be the peo - ple he in - tends; strong in faith and

spe - cial peo - ple, roy - al priests and heirs of grace:
life with - in you, turned your blind - ness in - to sight.
home in mer - cy, ci - ti - zens of heaven a - bove.
swift to ans - wer each com - mand your mas - ter sends:

know the pur-pose of your call-ing, show to all his migh-ty deeds;
Let your light so shine a-round you that God's name is glo - ri - fied;
Let his love flow out to oth-ers, let them feel a Fa-ther's care;
roy - al priests, ful - fil your call-ing through your sac-ri - fice and prayer;

tell of love which knows no lim-its, grace which meets all
and all find fresh hope and pur-pose in Christ Je - sus
that they too may know his wel-come and his count - less
give your lives in joy-ful ser-vice – sing his praise, his

hu - man needs.
cru - ci - fied.
bless-ings share.
love de - clare.

55   Clothed in kingly majesty

BALMORAL   7 5 5

Words: from Psalm 93
Michael Saward
Music: Roger Mayor

12

Thoughtfully ♩ = 100

Capo 3(D)   N.C.

1 Clothed in king - ly ma - jes - ty, __
2 Lord of all, se - cure and strong,
3 Great - er than the ri - ver's roar __
4 Change-less as his law's de - crees,

robed in re - gal __ power,
throned bey - ond all __ time,
and the surg - ing __ sea,
crowned our ho - ly __ king,

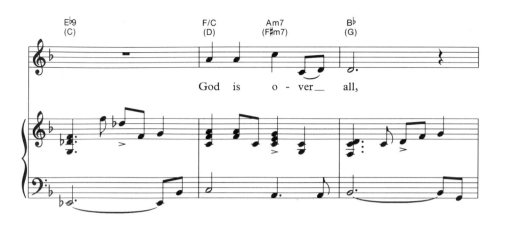

God is o - ver — all,

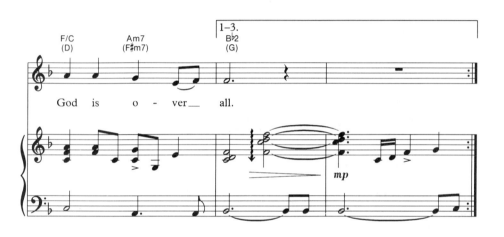

God is o - ver — all.

all.

56 Come and hear the joyful singing

Nos Galan   8 7 8 7 D

Words: Michael Perry
Music: Welsh traditional melody
arranged David Peacock

1 Come and hear the joy - ful sing - ing, set the bells of hea - ven ring - ing:
2 An - gels of his birth are tell - ing, Al - le - lu - ia, glo - ri - a, prince of peace all powers ex - cel - ling;
3 Choir and peo - ple, shout in won - der, al - le - lu - ia, let the mer - ry or - gan thun - der;

57   Come, O long-expected Jesus

CROSS OF JESUS   8 7 8 7

Words: Charles Wesley
in this version Jubilate Hymns
Music: John Stainer
arranged Christopher Norton

Medium tempo ♩ = 104

1 Come, O   long - ex - pect-ed Je-sus,
2   Is - rael's strength and   con-so - la-tion,
3   Born your   peo - ple   to de - li-ver,
4   By your   own   e - ter-nal Spi-rit

born to set_ your peo-ple free!_ From our fears and sins re - lease us:
born sal - va - tion to im - part;_ dear de - sire of ev - ery na-tion,
born a child and yet a king; born to reign in us for ev - er,
rule in all_ our hearts a - lone; by your all-suf - fi-cient me-rit

Christ in whom our rest shall be.
joy of ev - ery long - ing heart:
now your gra - cious king-dom bring:
raise us to_ your glo-rious throne!

58 Come and see

COME AND SEE   13 11 13 11 and refrain

Words and music: Graham Kendrick
Music arranged Christopher Norton

11

Worshipfully ♩ = 90

1 Come and
see,   come and see,   come and see the King of love;   see the
(2) weep,   come and mourn   for your sin that pierced him there;   so much
(3) heaven,   born to earth   to re-store us   to your heaven,   here we

pur-ple robe and   crown of thorns he   wears. _____   Sol-diers
deep-er than the   wounds of   thorn and   nail. _____   All our
bow in awe be-neath your search-ing   eyes. _____   From your

59 Come and see the shining hope

MARCHING THROUGH GEORGIA
13 13 13 8 10 10 13 8

10

Words: from Revelation 4, 5
Christopher Idle
Music: American traditional melody
arranged David Peacock

Strongly ♩ = 120

1 Come and see the shin-ing hope that
2 All the gifts you send us, Lord, are
3 Po - wer and sal - va - tion all be -

Christ's a - pos - tle saw; on the earth, con - fu - sion, but in
faith - ful, good and true; ho - li - ness and right - eous-ness are
- long to God on high! So the migh - ty mul - ti - tudes of

heaven an o - pen door, where the liv - ing crea - tures praise the
shown in all you do: who can see your great - est Gift and
hea - ven make their cry, sing - ing Hal - le - lu - jah where the

60 Come and sing the Christmas story

ALL THROUGH THE NIGHT   8 4 8 4 8 8 8 4

Words: Michael Perry
Music: Welsh traditional melody
arranged David Peacock

12

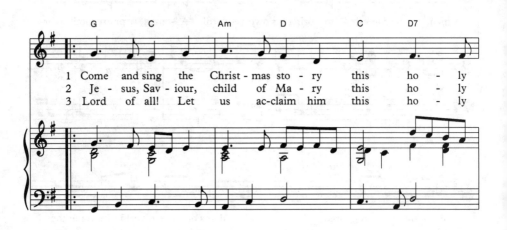

1 Come and sing the Christ - mas sto - ry   this   ho - ly
2 Je - sus, Sav - iour,   child   of Ma - ry   this   ho - ly
3 Lord   of all! Let   us   ac - claim him   this   ho - ly

night!   Christ is born: the   hope   of glo - ry   dawns   on   our
night,   in   a world con - fused and wea - ry   you   are   our
night;   king of our sal - va - tion name him, throned   in   the

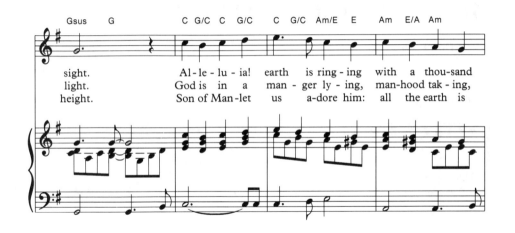

sight.
light.
height.

Al-le-lu-ia! earth is ring-ing with a thou-sand
God is in a man-ger ly-ing, man-hood tak-ing,
Son of Man-let us a-dore him: all the earth is

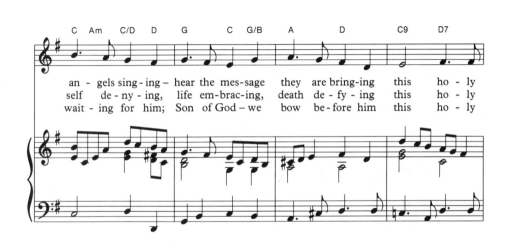

an-gels sing-ing – hear the mes-sage they are bring-ing this ho-ly
self de-ny-ing, life em-brac-ing, death de-fy-ing this ho-ly
wait-ing for him; Son of God – we bow be-fore him this ho-ly

night.
night.

night.

61 Come down, O Love divine

COME DOWN   6 6 11 D

Words: after Bianco da Siena
Richard Littledale
in this version Jubilate Hymns
Music: Roger Mayor

1 Come down, O Love di-vine! Seek out this soul of mine_____ and vis-it it with your own ar-dour glow-ing; O Com-fort-

2 O let it free-ly burn till earth-ly pas-sions turn_____ to dust and ash - es in its heat con- - sum-ing; and let your

3 Let ho-ly cha-ri-ty my out-ward ves-ture be,_____ and low-li-ness be-come my in-ner cloth-ing; true low-li-

4 And so the yearn-ing strong with which the soul will long_____ shall far sur-pass the power of hu-man tell-ing; for none can

62 Come let us join our cheerful songs

NATIVITY   8 6 8 6 (CM)

Words: Isaac Watts
Music: Henry Lahee
arranged Roger Mayor

3

1 Come let us join our cheer-ful songs with an-gels round the throne:___ ten thou-sand thou-sand are their tongues, but

2 Wor-thy the Lamb who died, they cry, to be ex-alt-ed thus!___ Wor-thy the Lamb, our lips re-ply, for

3 Je-sus is wor-thy to re-ceive all praise and power di--vine;___ and all the bless-ings we can give with

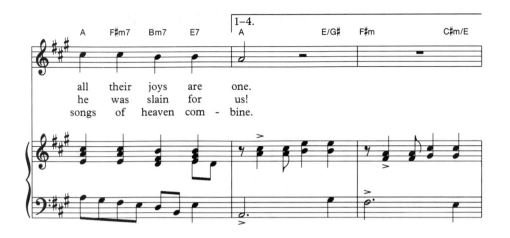

all their joys are one.
he was slain for us!
songs of heaven com - bine.

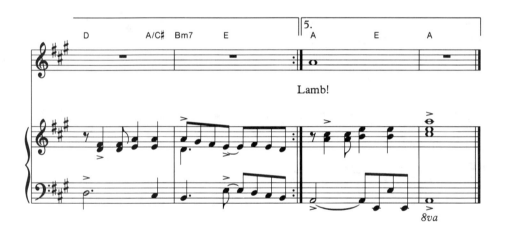

Lamb!

4 Let all who live beyond the sky,
the air and earth and seas
unite to lift his glory high
and sing his endless praise!

5 Let all creation join in one
to bless the sacred name
of him who reigns upon the throne,
and to adore the Lamb!

63   Come, let us worship Christ

I Am The Bread Of Life   Irregular

Words: after Suzanne Toolan
Michael Baughen
Music: Suzanne Toolan
arranged Roger Mayor

1 Come, let us wor - ship_ Christ   to the glo - ry of God the
2 'I am the bread of___ life;   he who comes to me shall not
3 'I am the door to___ life;   he who en - ters by me is

Fa - ther,___ for he is wor - thy of all our love;   he
hun - ger:___ and all who trust in me shall not thirst' –
saved,_____ a - bun - dant life he will then re - ceive' –

died and_ rose for us! praise him as Lord and sav-iour.
this is what Je - sus said: praise him as Lord and sav-iour. And when the
this is what Je - sus said: praise him as Lord and sav-iour.

Chorus

trum - pet shall sound and Je-sus comes in great power, then he will

raise us to be with him for ev - er - more! - more!

4 'I am the light of the world;
   if you follow me, darkness ceases,
   and in its place comes the light of life' –
   this is what Jesus said:
   praise him as Lord and saviour.
      And when the trumpet . . .

5 Lord, we are one with you;
   we rejoice in your new creation:
   our hearts are fired by your saving love –
   take up our lives, O Lord,
   and use us for your glory.
      And when the trumpet . . .

64   Come, light of the world

INVOCATIONS   10 9 6 6 10

Words and music: Paul Inwood

4 Come, hope of the world,
   comfort your people;
   come, hope of the world,
   comfort our hearts.
   Come heal all our sorrow
   with love and compassion;
   come, hope of the world
   bring peace to us all.

5 Come, Spirit of God,
   be with us now, Lord;
   come, Spirit of God,
   fill us with truth.
   Enlighten our lives, Lord,
   with radiance and power;
   come, Spirit of God,
   inspire all we do.

65 Come, you thankful people

ST GEORGE'S, WINDSOR 7 7 7 7 D

Words: Henry Alford
in this version Jubilate Hymns
Music: George Elvey
arranged David Peacock

1 Come, you thank-ful peo-ple, come, raise the song of har - vest home! fruit and crops are ga - thered in
2 All the world is God's own field, har - vests for his praise to yield; wheat and weeds to - ge - ther sown
3 For the Lord our God shall come and shall bring his har - vest home; he him-self on that great day,
4 Ev - en so, Lord, quick - ly come — bring your fi - nal har - vest home! ga - ther all your peo - ple in

May also be sung to the tune for 'Praise our God with shouts of joy' (238)

66   Comes Mary to the grave

EASTER MORNING   6 7 7 11

Words: from John 20
Michael Perry
Music: Norman Warren
arranged David Peacock

11

1 Comes

Ma - ry to the grave: no sing - ing bird has
(2) Je - sus at her side, no lon - ger Je - sus
(3) Ma - ry on this day we join our voi - ces

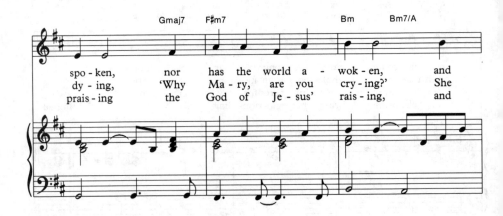

spo - ken, nor has the world a - wok - en, and
dy - ing, 'Why Ma - ry, are you cry - ing?' She
prais - ing the God of Je - sus' rais - ing, and

in her grief all love lies lost and bro - ken.
turns, with joy, 'My Lord! my love!' re -
sing the tri - umph of his love a -

2 Says - ply - ing

3 With - maz - ing.

67   Creator of the earth and skies

IMMORTAL PRAISE   8 8 8 8 (LM)

Words: Donald Hughes
Music: Christopher Norton

1 Cre-a-tor of the earth and skies, to whom all truth and power be-long:_ grant us your truth to make us wise,_ grant us your power to make us_ strong.

2 We have not known you: to the skies_ our mo-nu-ments of fol-ly soar; and all our self-wrought mi-ser-ies_ have made us trust our-selves the_ more._

4 We long to end this world-wide strife:_ how shall we fol-low in your way?_ Speak to us all your words of life_ un-til our dark-ness turns to_ day!_

Words: © Methodist Publishing House,
20 Ivatt Way, Westwood, Peterborough PE3 7PG

Fine

Bb/F (G)　Bb6/F (G)　F (D)　　　Bb/F (G)　Gm/C (Em)　F (D)

Db/Eb (Bb)　　　Eb (C)　　　Db/Eb (Bb)

3 We have not loved you: far and wide_ the wreck-age of our

Eb (C)　　　F (D)　　　Db/Eb (Bb)　　　Eb (C)

hat - red_ spreads; and e-vils wrought by hu-man pride re -

Db/Eb (Bb)　　　Eb (C)　　　F (D)　　　Bb/C (G)　Gm/C (Em)　Bb/C (G)

-coil on un - re - pent - ant_ heads. _

68 Creator Spirit, come, inspire

O RIGHTEOUS LORD   8 8 8 8 (LM)

Words: after Rabanus Maurus
and John Cosin
in this version Jubilate Hymns
Music: Christopher Norton

1 Cre - a - tor Spi - rit, come, in - spire
2 Your pure a - noint - ing from a - bove
3 A - noint and cheer our sad - dened face
4 Teach us to know the Fa - ther, Son,

our lives with light and heaven - ly fire;
is com - fort, life, and fire of love:
with all the ful - ness of your grace;
and you with them the Three - in - One;

now make us will - ing to re - ceive
so heal with your e - ter - nal light
re - move our fears, give peace at home —
whose praise through all the a - ges long

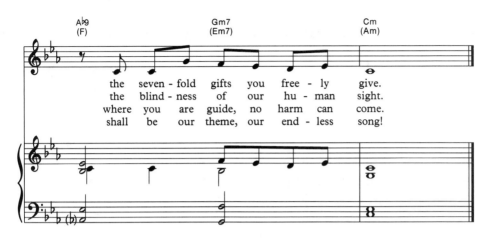

the seven - fold gifts you free - ly give.
the blind - ness of our hu - man sight.
where you are guide, no harm can come.
shall be our theme, our end - less song!

Optional instrumental part
Verses 1 and 3   Verse 2

p

D.C.

Verse 4

cresc.

dim.

69 Crown him with many crowns

DIADEMATA   6 6 8 6 D (DSM)

3

Words: Matthew Bridges and
Godfrey Thring
in this version Jubilate Hymns
Music: George Elvey
arranged Roger Mayor

With strength ♩ = 120

1 Crown him with ma - ny crowns, the Lamb up - on his throne, while heaven's e - ter - nal an - them drowns all mu - sic but its
2 Crown him the Lord of life tri - umph - ant from the grave, who rose vic - to - rious from the strife for those he came to
3 Crown him the Lord of love, who shows his hands and side – those wounds yet vi - si - ble a - bove in beau - ty glo - ri -

4 Crown him the Lord of peace –
his kingdom is at hand;
from pole to pole let warfare cease
and Christ rule every land!
A city stands on high,
his glory it displays,
and there the nations 'Holy' cry
in joyful hymns of praise.

5 Crown him the Lord of years,
the potentate of time,
creator of the rolling spheres
in majesty sublime:
all hail, Redeemer, hail,
for you have died for me;
your praise shall never, never fail
through all eternity!

Verse 4 may be omitted

70   Darkness like a shroud

ARISE SHINE   Irregular

Words and music: Graham Kendrick
arranged Christopher Norton

1 Dark - ness   like a shroud   co - vers the
2 Child - ren   of the light,   be clean and
3 Here a - mong us now,   Christ___ the
4 Like a   ci - ty bright,   so let us

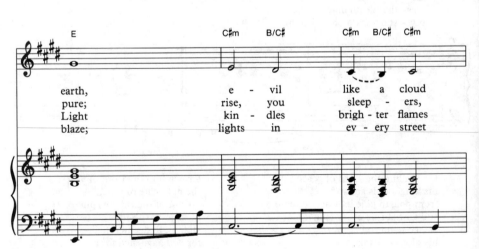

earth,   e - vil   like a cloud
pure;   rise, you   sleep - ers,
Light   kin - dles   brigh - ter flames
blaze;   lights in   ev - ery street

Words and music: © 1985 Thankyou Music,
PO Box 75, Eastbourne, East Sussex BN23 6NW.
Used by permission

Chorus

- rise, shine, your light has come, the glo-ry of the Lord has risen on you; a -

- rise, shine, your light has come _____ Je-sus the

1–3.
light of the world has come. _____

4.
light of the world, Je - sus the light of the

The congregation may divide at A and B

71

Dear Lord and Father

REPTON   8 6 8 8 6 extended

Words: John Whittier
in this version Jubilate Hymns
Music: C Hubert Parry
arranged David Peacock

12

1 Dear Lord and Fa-ther_ of man-kind, for-
(2) sim-ple trust like_ theirs who heard, be-
(3) sab-bath rest_ by_ Ga-li-lee! O

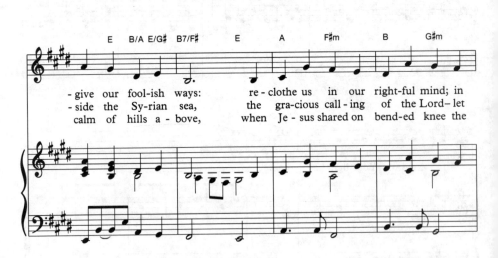

-give our fool-ish ways: re-clothe us in our right-ful mind; in
-side the Sy-rian sea,   the gra-cious call-ing of the Lord— let
calm of hills a-bove,   when Je-sus shared on bend-ed knee the

Chord symbols:
C#m — A — B/D# — B — E/G# — Bsus/F#B7/F# Fdim7

purer lives your service find, in deeper reverence praise, in
us, like them, obey his word: 'Rise up and follow me, rise
silence of eternity interpreted by love, in-

F#m — A/B — [1–5.] E — F#m7/E — [6.] E

deeper reverence praise. 2 In calm!
up and follow me!' 3 O
interpreted by love! 4 With

F#m7/E — E — F#m7/E — E

4 With that deep hush subduing all
   our words and works that drown
   the tender whisper of your call,
   as noiseless let your blessing fall
     as fell your manna down,
     as fell your manna down.

5 Drop your still dews of quietness,
   till all our strivings cease;
   take from our souls the strain and stress,
   and let our ordered lives confess
     the beauty of your peace,
     the beauty of your peace.

6 Breathe through the heats of our desire
   your coolness and your balm;
   let sense be dumb, let flesh retire,
   speak through the earthquake, wind, and fire,
     O still small voice of calm,
     O still small voice of calm!

72 Eternal light, shine in my heart

Seven Seas   8 8 8 8 (LM)

Words: after Alcuin
Christopher Idle
Music: David Peacock

-ter-nal power,_____ be my sup-port,_____ e -
-ter-nal Spi - rit, give me breath,_____ e -
last I come_____ be - fore your face_____ to

-ter - nal wis-dom, make me wise.
-ter - nal Sav-iour, come to_ me:
know you, my e - ter-nal God.

Instrumental obligato

73

Father God in heaven

KUM BA YAH   8 8 8 5

2

Words: from *The Lord's Prayer*
James Seddon
Music: traditional melody
arranged David Peacock

4 Lead us in your way, make us strong;
  when temptations come make us strong;
  save us from all sin, keep us strong –
    O Lord, hear our prayer.

5 All things come from you, all are yours –
  kingdom, glory, power, all are yours;
  take our lives and gifts, all are yours –
    O Lord, hear our prayer.

74

Father in heaven

HALAD 5 5 5 5 5 5 5 4

3

Words: Daniel Niles
Music: Elena G Maquiso
arranged David Peacock

1 Fa - ther in

hea - ven,_____ grant to your child - ren_____ mer - cy and
(2) -deem - er,_____ may we re - mem - ber_____ your gra - cious
(3) -scend - ing,_____ whose is the bless - ing,_____ strength for the

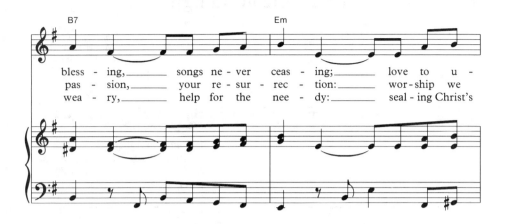

bless - ing,_____ songs ne - ver ceas - ing;_____ love to u -
pas - sion,_____ your re - sur - rec - tion:_____ wor - ship we
wea - ry,_____ help for the nee - dy:_____ seal - ing Christ's

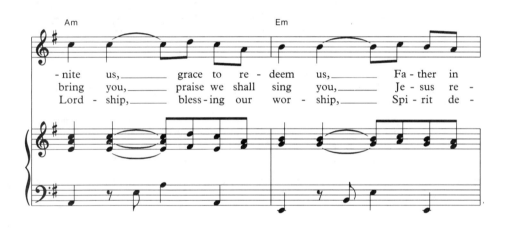

- nite us,_____ grace to re - deem us,_____ Fa - ther in
bring you,_____ praise we shall sing you,_____ Je - sus re -
Lord - ship,_____ bless - ing our wor - ship,_____ Spi - rit de -

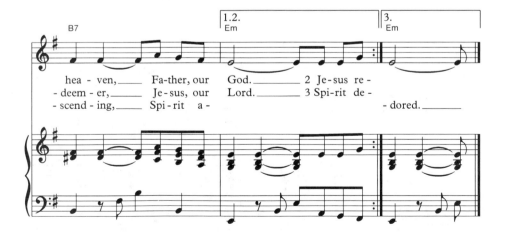

hea - ven,_____ Fa - ther, our God._____ 2 Je - sus re -
- deem - er,_____ Je - sus, our Lord._____ 3 Spi - rit de -
- scend - ing,_____ Spi - rit a - _____ - dored._____

75

Fight the good fight

DUKE STREET   8 8 8 8 (LM)

Words: John Monsell
Music: John Hatton
arranged David Peacock

Confidently ♩ = 120

1 Fight the good fight with
2 Run the straight race through
3 Cast care a - side, lean
4 Faint not, nor fear, his

all your__ might,   Christ   is   your strength,   and
God's   good__ grace,   lift   up   your eyes,   and
on   your__ guide,   his   bound-less mer - cy
arms   are__   near;   he   does not change,   and

Christ   your   right;   lay   hold on life,   and
seek   his   face: life   with its way   be -
will   pro - vide;   trust, and your trust - ing
you   are   dear;   on - ly be - lieve   and

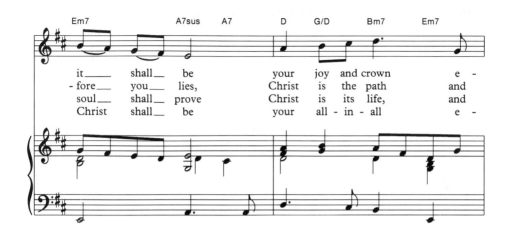

it____ shall____ be your joy and crown e -
- fore____ you____ lies, Christ is the path and
soul____ shall____ prove Christ is its life, and
Christ shall____ be your all - in - all e -

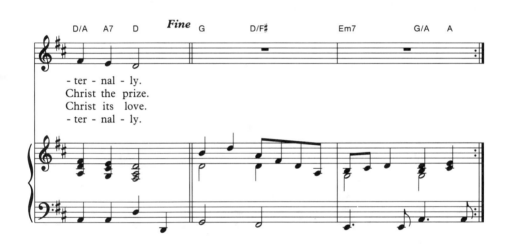

Fine

- ter - nal - ly.
Christ the prize.
Christ its love.
- ter - nal - ly.

Instrumental obligato

Fine

76   Fill now my life

RICHMOND   8 6 8 6 (CM)

Words: Horatius Bonar
Music: adapted from Thomas Haweis
by Samuel Webbe
arranged Christopher Norton

1 Fill now my life, O Lord my God, in
2 Not for the lip of praise a - lone, nor
3 Praise in the com - mon things of life, its

ev - ery part with praise: that my whole
yet the prais - ing heart, I ask, but
go - ings out and in; praise in each

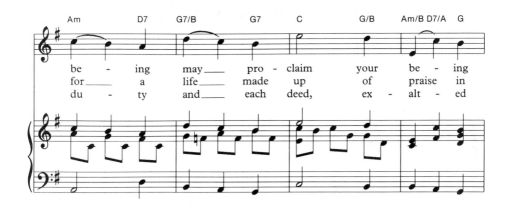

be - ing   may____   pro - claim   your   be - ing
for____   a   life____   made   up   of   praise   in
du - ty   and____   each   deed,   ex - alt - ed

and____   your   ways._____
ev - ery   part:_____
or____   un - seen._____

4   Fill every part of me with praise;
let all my being speak
of you and of your love, O Lord,
poor though I be and weak.

5   Then, Lord, from me you shall receive
the praise and glory due;
and so shall I begin on earth
the song for ever new.

6   So shall no part of day or night
from sacredness be free;
but all my life, with you my God,
in fellowship shall be.

77   Fill your hearts with joy

REGENT SQUARE   8 7 8 7 8 7

Words: from Psalm 147
Timothy Dudley-Smith
Music: Henry Smart
arranged Roger Mayor

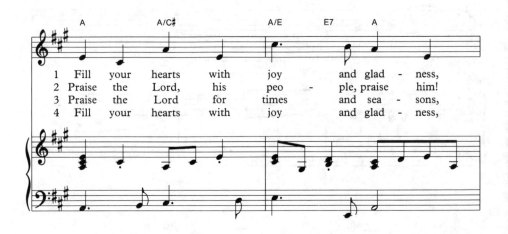

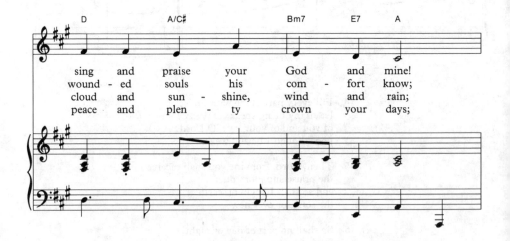

1 Fill your hearts with joy and glad - ness,
2 Praise the Lord, his peo - ple, praise him!
3 Praise the Lord for times and sea - sons,
4 Fill your hearts with joy and glad - ness,

sing and praise your God and mine!
wound - ed souls his com - fort know;
cloud and sun - shine, wind and rain;
peace and plen - ty crown your days;

78   For God so loved the world

LONDONDERRY AIR
11 10 11 10 11 10 11 12

Words: from John 3,
2 Corinthians 8 and Philippians 2
Word & Music
Music: Irish traditional melody
arranged Christopher Norton

With increasing intensity ♩ = 108

For God so loved the world he gave his on-ly Son, who came to die that we might ev-er live; and on a cru-el cross our full re-demp-tion won, that we might know the peace he longs to give: though he was

79   For the beauty of the earth

DIX   7 7 7 7 7 7

Words: F Sandford Pierpoint
Music: Conrad Kocher
arranged Christopher Norton

1 For the__ beau-ty of the earth, for the beau-ty of the skies, for the__ love which from our birth

2 For the__ beau-ty of each hour of the day and of the night, hill and__ vale, and tree and flower,

3 For the__ joy of ear and eye, for the heart and mind's de-light, for the__ mys-tic har-mo-ny

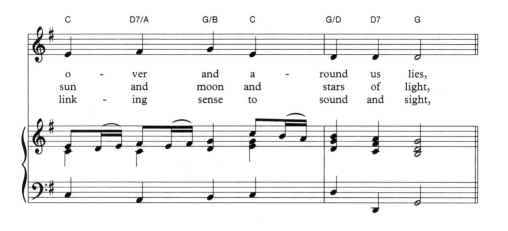

o - ver and a - round us lies,
sun and moon and stars of light,
link - ing sense to sound and sight,

Chorus

Christ our God, to you we raise this our sac - ri -

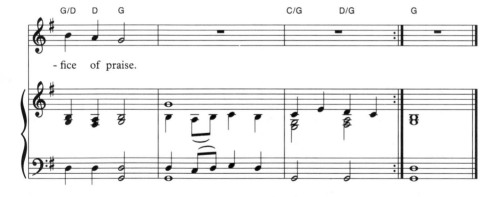

- fice of praise.

4 For the joy of human love,
brother, sister, parent, child,
friends on earth and friends above,
pleasures pure and undefiled,
   Christ our God . . .

5 For each perfect gift divine
to our race so freely given,
joys bestowed by love's design,
flowers of earth and fruits of heaven,
   Christ our God . . .

80 For the bread

CROSS OF JESUS   8 7 8 7

Words: Louis Benson
Music: John Stainer
arranged Christopher Norton

1 For the bread which you have bro-ken,
2 By these pledg - es that you love us,
3 In your ser - vice, Lord, de - fend us,

for the wine which you have poured, for the words which you have spo-ken,
by your gift of peace re - stored, by your call to heaven a - bove us,
help us to__ o - bey your word; in the world to which you send us

now we give you thanks, O Lord.
con-se - crate our lives, O Lord:
let your king-dom come, O Lord!

Music arrangement: © 1993 HarperCollins*Religious*

81   From deep despair to you I call

MOORTOWN   8 6 8 6 (CM)

Words: from Psalm 130
David Preston
Music: Christopher Norton

11

1 From deep des-pair to you I call:
2 O Lord, if you re - cord our sins,
3 Now for the Lord my spi - rit waits,
4 O Is - rael, hope in God the Lord!

Lord, hear me when I cry!   O turn your ear to
who ev - er could be spared?   But mer - cy may be
my hope is in his word;   more than the watch - men
His grace is full and free,   and pays the price to

hear my voice   which pleads with you on high!
found with you,   that you may then be feared.
wait for dawn   my soul waits for the Lord.
ran - som us   from all i - ni - qui - ty.

82   For the fruits of his creation

ALL THROUGH THE NIGHT   8 4 8 4 8 8 8 4

Words: Frederick Pratt Green
Music: Welsh traditional melody
arranged David Peacock

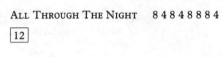

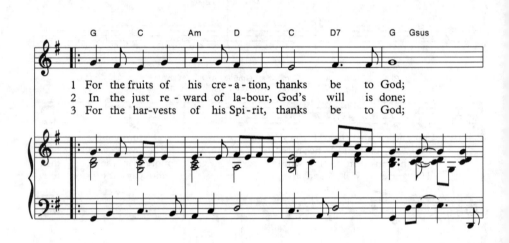

1 For the fruits of his cre-a-tion, thanks be to God;
2 In the just re-ward of la-bour, God's will is done;
3 For the har-vests of his Spi-rit, thanks be to God;

for his gifts to ev-ery na-tion, thanks be to God;
in the help we give our neigh-bour, God's will is done;
for the good we all in-her-it, thanks be to God;

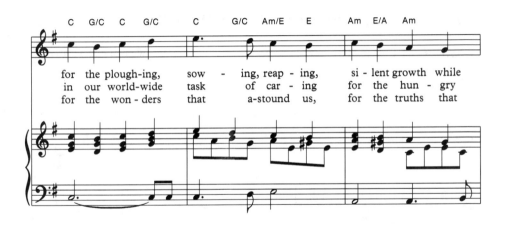

for the plough-ing, sow - ing, reap - ing, si - lent growth while
in our world-wide task of car - ing for the hun - gry
for the won - ders that a-stound us, for the truths that

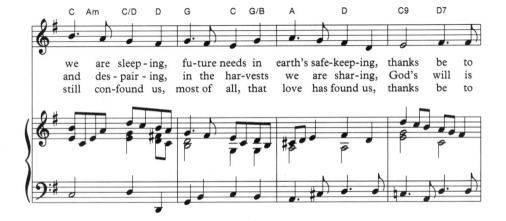

we are sleep - ing, fu-ture needs in earth's safe-keep-ing, thanks be to
and des - pair - ing, in the har-vests we are shar-ing, God's will is
still con-found us, most of all, that love has found us, thanks be to

God.
done.

God.

83 Forgive our sins as we forgive

FORGIVENESS   8 6 8 6 (CM)

Words: Rosamund Herklots
Music: Christopher Norton

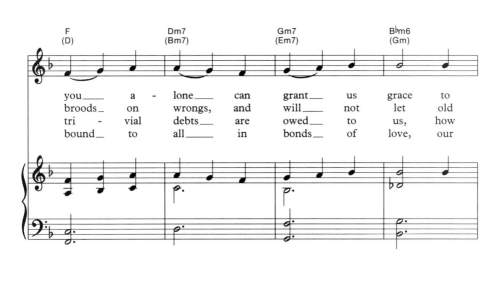

you___ a - lone___ can grant___ us grace to
broods_ on wrongs, and will___ not let old
tri - vial debts___ are owed___ to us, how
bound_ to all___ in bonds_ of love, our

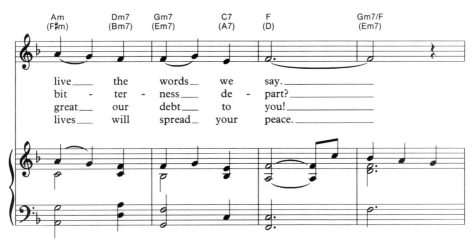

live___ the words___ we say._____
bit - ter - ness___ de - part?_____
great___ our debt___ to you!_____
lives___ will spread_ your peace._____

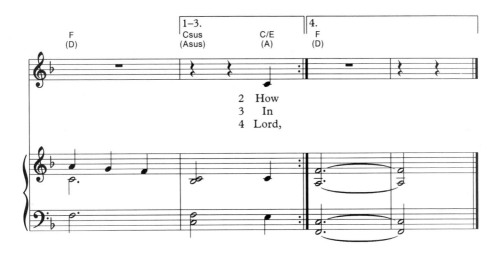

2 How
3 In
4 Lord,

84   Freedom and life are ours

FROM STRENGTH TO STRENGTH
6 6 8 6 D (DSM)

Words: Christopher Idle
Music: Edward Naylor
arranged Roger Mayor

1 Free-dom and life are ours for Christ has set us free! Ne-ver a-gain sub-mit to powers that lead to sla-ver-y: Christ is the

2 Called by the Lord to use our free-dom and be strong, not let-ting li-ber-ty ex- -cuse a life of bla-tant wrong: freed from the

3 Spi-rit of God, come, fill, em-an-ci-pate us all! Speak to us, Word of truth, un- -til be-fore his throne we fall: glo-ry and

Lord who breaks our chains, our bond - age
law's stern hand God's gift of grace to
li - ber - ty our Fa - ther has de -

ends, Christ is the res - cu - er who makes the help-less
prove, know that the law's en - tire de - mand is glad - ly
- creed, and if the Son shall make us free we shall be

slaves_____ his friends.
met_____ by love.
free_____ in - - deed!

Obligato for B♭ instrument

85 From heaven you came

THE SERVANT KING   Irregular

Words and music: Graham Kendrick
Music arranged David Peacock

1 From heaven you came, help-less Babe – en-tered our world your glo - ry veiled, not to be served but to serve, and give your life that we might live.

2 There in the gar - den of tears my hea - vy load he chose to bear; his heart with sor - row was torn, 'Yet not my will but yours,' he said.

3 Come see his hands and his feet, the scars that speak of sac - ri - fice; hands that flung stars in - to space to cru - el nails sur - rend - ered.

4 So let us learn how to serve and in our lives en - throne him, each oth - er's needs to pre - fer – for it is Christ we are serv - ing.

Chorus This is our

Part II

This is our God – the ser-vant king,

God ___ the ser-vant king, ___ he calls us

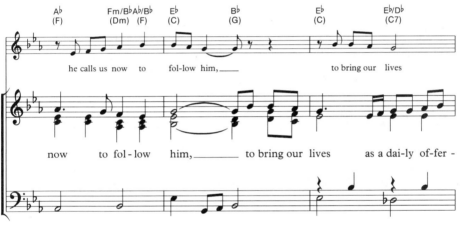

he calls us now to fol-low him, ___ to bring our lives

now to fol-low him, ___ to bring our lives as a dai-ly of-fer-

an off-er-ing of wor-ship to the ser-vant king. king.

- ing ___ of wor-ship to ___ the ser-vant king. king.

86 From the sun's rising

FROM THE SUN'S RISING   Irregular

Words and music: Graham Kendrick
Music arranged Christopher Norton

22

One in a bar feel ♩. = 66

1 From the sun's ris - ing un - to the sun's set - ting
2 To ev - ery tongue, tribe and na - tion he sends us,
3 Come let us join with the church from all na - tions,

Je - sus our Lord shall be great in the earth;
to make dis - ci - ples to teach and bap - tize;
cross ev - ery bor - der, throw wide ev - ery door:

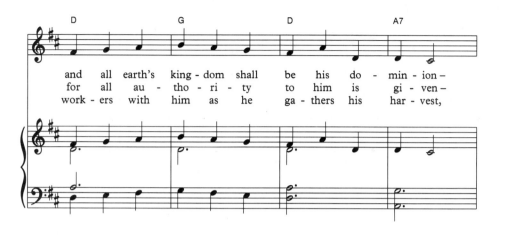

and all earth's king-dom shall be his do - min - ion –
for all au - tho - ri - ty to him is gi - ven –
work - ers with him as he ga - thers his har - vest,

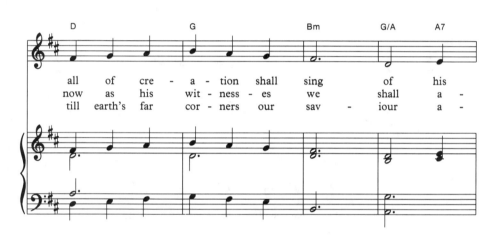

all of cre - a - tion shall sing of his
now as his wit - ness - es we shall a -
till earth's far cor - ners our sav - iour a -

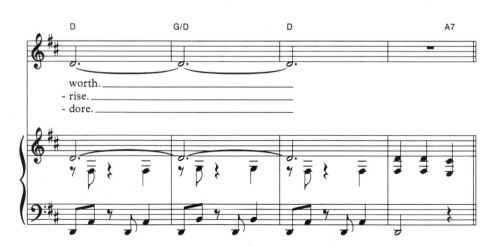

worth._____
- rise._____
- dore._____

87 Glad music fills the Christmas sky

ROCKHAVEN 8 8 8 8 (LM)

Words: Michael Perry
Music: Roger Mayor

an - gels wor - ship high a - bove_ and Ma - ry_ sings her
knows that won - ders have be - gun,_ and trusts for_ all the
yet to_ know his_ hu-man face,_ to watch him die, to

lul - la - by._ 2 Of
fu-ture brings. 3 The
see him rise. 4 Let

4 Let praise be true and love sincere,
   rejoice to greet the saviour's birth;
   let peace and honour fill the earth
   and mercy reign – for God is here!

5 Then lift your hearts and voices high,
   sing once again the Christmas song:
   for love and praise to Christ belong –
   in shouts of joy, and lullaby.

88   Glory be to Jesus

CASWALL   6 5 6 5

Words: from the Italian
Edward Caswall
Music: Friedrich Filitz
arranged Roger Mayor

3

1 Glo - ry be to Je - sus,
2 Grace and life e - ter - nal
3 A - bel's blood for ven - geance

who, in bit - ter pains,
in that blood I find:
plead - ed to the skies,

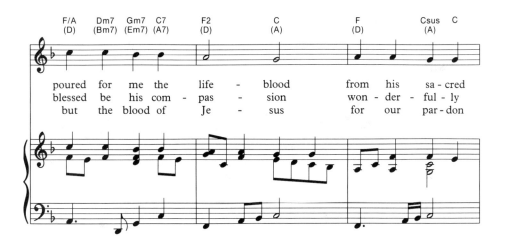

poured for me the life - blood from his sa - cred
blessed be his com - pas - sion won - der - ful - ly
but the blood of Je - sus for our par - don

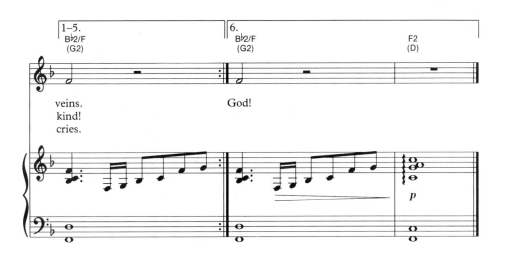

veins.
kind!
cries.

God!

4 When that blood is sprinkled
   on our guilty hearts,
   Satan in confusion
   terror-struck departs.

5 When this earth exulting
   lifts its praise on high,
   angel hosts rejoicing
   make their glad reply.

6 Raise your thankful voices,
   swell the mighty flood;
   louder still and louder
   praise the Lamb of God!

89 Glory in the highest

LAND OF HOPE AND GLORY   11 11 11 11

Words: from *Gloria in excelsis*
Christopher Idle
Music: Edward Elgar
arranged Noël Tredinnick

1

1 Glo-ry in the high-est to the God of
2 Je-sus Christ is ri-sen, God the Fa-ther's
3 Christ the world's true Sav-iour, high and ho-ly

heaven! Peace to all your peo-ple
Son! With the Ho-ly Spi-rit,
one, seat-ed now and reign-ing

through the earth be given! Migh-ty God and
you are Lord a-lone! Lamb once killed for
from your Fa-ther's throne: Lord and God, we

90 Go forth and tell

Go Forth   10 10 10 10

Words: James Seddon
Music: Michael Baughen
arranged Christopher Norton

1 Go   forth and   tell!   O church of God, a - wake!
2 Go   forth and   tell!   God's love em - bra - ces   all;
3 Go   forth and   tell   where still the dark - ness   lies;

God's   sav - ing news   to   all the   na - tions   take;
he   will in   grace   re - spond to   all who   call:
in   wealth or   want,   the   sin - ner   sure - ly   dies:

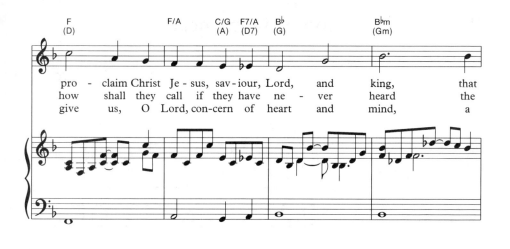

F		F/A	C/G	F7/A	B♭		B♭m	
(D)		(A)	(D7)	(G)		(Gm)		

pro - claim Christ Je - sus, sav - iour, Lord, and king, that
how shall they call if they have ne - ver heard the
give us, O Lord, con - cern of heart and mind, a

F/C	D7♭9	D7	Gm7	C7♭9	C7	F	B♭/F	1–4. F B♭/C C7	5. F
(D)	(B7)		(Em7)	(A7)		(D)	(G)	(D) (G) (A7)	(D)

all the world his wor-thy praise may sing.
gra-cious in - vi - ta-tion of___ his word?
love like yours com - pas-sion-ate___ and kind.

4 Go forth and tell! The doors are open wide:
   share God's good gifts – let no one be denied;
   live out your life as Christ your Lord shall choose,
   your ransomed powers for his sole glory use.

5 Go forth and tell! O church of God, arise!
   go in the strength which Christ your Lord supplies;
   go till all nations his great name adore
   and serve him, Lord and king for evermore.

God be in my head

GOD BE IN MY HEAD   Irregular

Words: after R Pynson
Music: Henry Walford Davies
arranged Christopher Norton

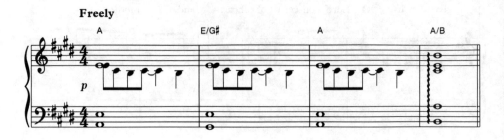

God be in my head and in my un-der-

-stand-ing. God be in my eyes and in my look-ing.

92 God brings us comfort
(Praise God today)

BRAMMIT   10 10 and refrain

Words: from Isaiah 12
Christopher Idle
Music: Christopher Rolinson

3

Majestically, but with motion ♩ = 126

93 God is love

PERSONENT HODIE   6 6 6 6 6 5 5 3 9

Words: Percy Dearmer
Music: *Piae Cantiones* 1582
arranged David Peacock

1 God is love –
2 Je-sus shared
3 To our Lord

his the care, tend - ing each, ev - ery-where;
all our pain, lived and died, rose a - gain,
praise we sing – light and life, friend and king,

God is love – all is there! Je - sus came to
rules our hearts, now as then – for he came to
com - ing down love to bring, pat - tern for our

94 God has spoken

EBENEZER   8 7 8 7 D

Words: George Briggs
Music: Thomas Williams
arranged Christopher Norton

6

Rock ballad ♩ = 88

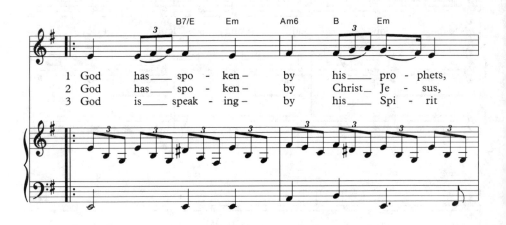

1 God has spo - ken – by his pro - phets,
2 God has spo - ken – by Christ Je - sus,
3 God is speak - ing – by his Spi - rit

spo - ken his un - chang - ing word;
Christ, the ev - er - last - ing Son;
speak - ing to our hearts a - gain;

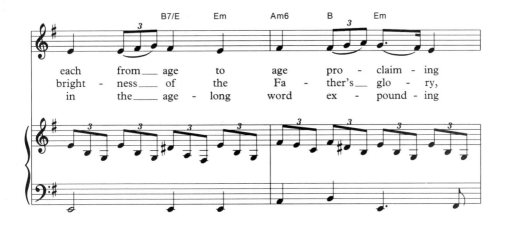

each from___ age to age pro - claim - ing
bright - ness___ of the Fa - ther's___ glo - ry,
in the___ age - long word ex - pound - ing

God the___ one,___ the right - eous Lord;
with the___ Fa - ther ev - er one:
God's own___ mes - sage, now___ as then.

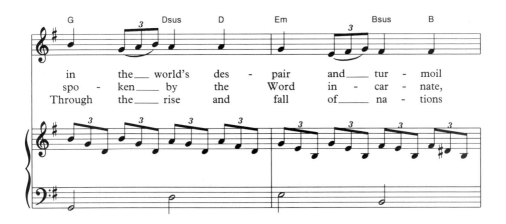

in the___ world's des - pair and___ tur - moil
spo - ken___ by the Word in - car - nate,
Through the___ rise and fall of___ na - tions

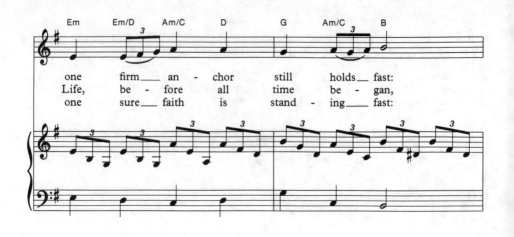

one firm___ an - chor still holds___ fast:
Life, be - fore all time be - gan,
one sure___ faith is stand - ing___ fast:

God is___ king, his throne e - ter - nal,
light of___ light, to earth de - scend - ing,
God a - bides, his word un - chang - ing,

God the___ first___ and God the last.
God, re - vealed as Son___ of Man.
God the___ first___ and   God the last.

95

God is our strength and refuge
(First tune)

DAMBUSTERS MARCH   7 7 7 5 7 7 11

Words: from Psalm 46
Richard Bewes
Music: Eric Coates
arranged Noël Tredinnick

10

Stately ♩ = 64

1 God is our strength and__ re-fuge,
2 There is a flow-ing__ ri - ver

our pre - sent help in__ trou - ble; and we there - fore
with - in God's ho - ly__ ci - ty; God is in the

will not fear, though the earth__ should change!
midst of her – she shall not__ be moved!

95 God is our strength and refuge

(Second tune)

PSALM 46   7 7 7 5 7 7 11

10

Words: from Psalm 46
Richard Bewes
Music: Annie Willis

With increasing intensity ♩ = 60

1 God is our strength and re-fuge, our pre-sent help in trou-ble;

and we there-fore will not fear, though the earth should change!____

Though moun-tains shake and trem-ble, though swirl-ing floods are rag-ing,

96   God is our fortress

EIN 'FESTE BURG   8 7 8 7 6 6 6 6 7

Words: after Martin Luther
Michael Perry
Music: Martin Luther
arranged Christopher Norton

1

Confidently ♩ = 95

1 God is our fort-ress
(2) hope is fixed on
(3) word of God will

and our rock, our migh-ty help in_ dan - ger; he shields us from the
Christ a-lone, the Man, of God's own choos - ing; with-out him no-thing
not_ be slow while de-mon hordes sur - round_ us, though e - vil strike its

bat - tle's shock and thwarts the de - vil's an - ger: for still the prince of
can be won and fight-ing must be_ los - ing: so let the powers ac -
cruel-lest blow and death and hell con - found_ us: for ev - en if dis -

Music arrangement: © 1993 HarperCollins*Religious*

Words: © Michael Perry / Jubilate Hymns

97 God of mercy, God of grace

GOD OF MERCY 7 7 7 7 7 7

9

Words: from Psalm 67
Henry Francis Lyte
Music: Roger Jones
arranged David Peacock

1 God of mer - cy, God of grace, show the bright - ness of your face; shine up-on us, Sav-iour, shine, fill your church with light div -
2 Let the peo - ple praise you, Lord! Be by all who live a - dored; let the na-tions shout and sing glo - ry to their sav-iour
3 Let the peo - ple crown you king! Then shall earth her har-vest bring, God to us his bless-ing give, we to God de - vo - ted

98   God of gods, we sound his praises

HICKLING   8 7 8 7 8 8 8 7

Words: Timothy Dudley-Smith
Music: Roger Mayor

1 God of gods, we sound his prai - ses,
2 Christ-ians in ___ their hearts en - throne him,
3 Hail the Christ, the King of glo - ry,
4 Lord, we look ___ for your re - turn - ing;

high - est heaven its hom - age brings; earth and all ___ cre -
tell his prai - ses wide a - broad; pro - phets, priests, a -
he whose praise the an - gels cry; ___ born to share our
teach us so ___ to walk your ways, hearts and minds your

99   God rest you merry, gentlemen

GOD REST YOU MERRY   Irregular

15

Words: traditional
in this version Jubilate Hymns
Music: English traditional carol
arranged Christopher Norton

Boldly ♩ = 88

1 God
rest you mer - ry, gen - tle - men, let noth - ing you dis -
(2) Beth - le - hem in Ju - dah the ho - ly babe was
(3) God our heaven - ly Fa - ther a ho - ly an - gel

- may! for Je - sus Christ our sav - iour was
born; they laid him in a man - ger on
came; the shep - herds saw the glo - ry and

4 Fear not, then said the angel,
   let nothing cause you fright;
   to you is born a saviour
   in David's town tonight,
   to free all those who trust in him
   from Satan's power and might:
       O tidings of comfort and joy . . .

5 The shepherds at these tidings
   rejoiced in heart and mind,
   and on the darkened hillside
   they left their flocks behind,
   and went to Bethlehem straightway
   this holy child to find:
       O tidings of comfort and joy . . .

6 And when to Bethlehem they came
   where Christ the infant lay:
   they found him in a manger
   where oxen fed on hay,
   and there beside her newborn child
   his mother knelt to pray:
       O tidings of comfort and joy . . .

7 Now to the Lord sing praises,
   all people in this place!
   With Christian love and fellowship
   each other now embrace,
   and let this Christmas festival
   all bitterness displace:
       O tidings of comfort and joy . . .

Either verses 2 and 6 or verses 4 and 5 may be omitted

Melody part for B♭ instruments

100   God, whose almighty word

Moscow   6 6 4 6 6 6 4

Words: John Marriott
Music: Felice de Giardini
arranged David Peacock

9

Flowing ♩ = 100

1 God, whose al - migh - ty word   cha - os and
2 Sav - iour, who came to bring   on your re -
3 Spi - rit of truth and love –   life - giv - ing,
4 Gra - cious and ho - ly Three,   glo - ri - ous

dark - ness heard,   and took their flight:
- deem - ing wing   heal - ing and sight,
ho - ly dove,   speed on your flight!
Tri - ni - ty,   wis - dom, love, might:

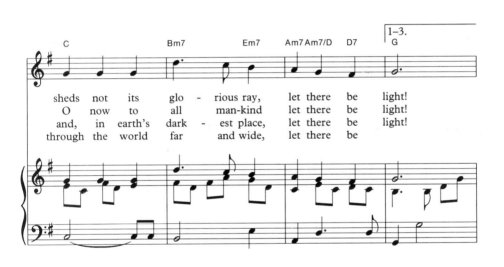

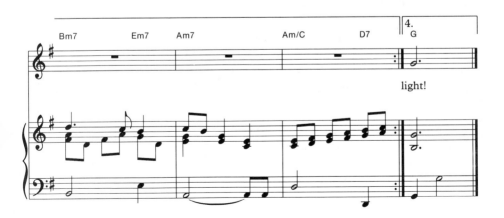

101 God whose love we cannot measure

SONG OF THANKS   8 7 8 7 D

Words: after St Boniface
Michael Perry
Music: Christopher Norton

12

Unhurried ♩ = 86

1 God whose love we can - not mea - sure,
2 In our hearts we bless and praise you –

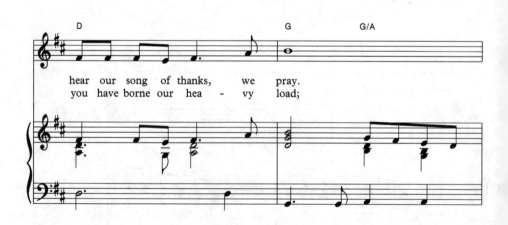

hear our song of thanks, we pray.
you have borne our hea - vy load;

102 Good Christians all, rejoice

IN DULCI JUBILO   6 6 7 7 7 8 5 5

6

Spritely ♩. = 68

Words: from *In dulci jubilo*
John Neale
Music: German carol melody
arranged Roger Mayor

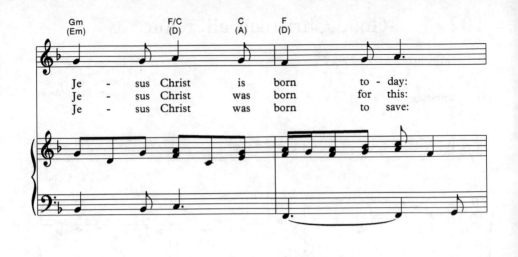

Je - sus Christ is born to - day:
Je - sus Christ was born for this:
Je - sus Christ was born to save:

ox and ass be - fore him bow and
he has o - pened hea - ven's door and
come at his most gra - cious call to

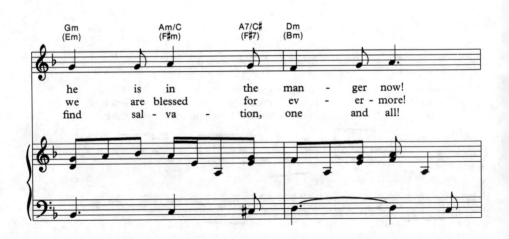

he is in the man - ger now!
we are blessed for ev - er - more!
find sal - va - tion, one and all!

Great is your faithfulness

GREAT IS THY FAITHFULNESS 11 10 11 10 and refrain

Words: Thomas Chisholm
in this version Jubilate Hymns
Music: William Runyan
arranged Roger Mayor

Prayerfully ♩ = 100

1 Great is your faith-ful-ness, O God my Fa-ther, you have ful-filled all your prom-ise to me; you ne-ver fail and your love is un -

2 Sum-mer and win-ter, and spring-time and har-vest, sun, moon and stars in their cour-ses a - bove join with all na-ture in e - lo-quent

3 Par-don for sin, and a peace ev - er - las-ting, your liv - ing pres-ence to cheer and to guide; strength for to - day, and bright hope for to -

104 Guide me, O my great Redeemer

CWM RHONDDA   8 7 8 7 4 7 extended

Words: Peter Williams and others
Music: John Hughes
arranged Christopher Norton

7

Steadily ♩ = 102

1 Guide me, O my great Re - deem - er, pil - grim through this bar - ren land: I am weak, but you_ are_ migh - ty_ hold me with your

2 O - pen now the cry - stal_ foun - tain where the heal - ing wa - ters flow; let the fie - ry, clou - dy_ pil - lar lead me all my_

3 When I tread the verge of_ Jor - dan bid my anx - ious fears sub - side; Death of death, and hell's De - struc - tion, land me safe on_

power-ful hand: Bread of hea - ven, Bread of hea - ven,
jour - ney through. Strong De-liver - er, strong De-liver - er,
Can-aan's side. Songs of prai - ses, songs of prai - ses,

feed me now and ev - er - more! feed me now and
ev - er be my strength and shield. ev - er be my
all my joy shall ev - er be; all my joy shall

ev - er - more!
strength and shield.
ev - er be;

105

Had he not loved us
(First tune)

ROUNDHAY   10 10 10 10

Words: Timothy Dudley-Smith
Music: Christopher Norton

1 Had he not loved us
(2) loved us
(3) loved us

— he had ne - ver come, yet is he love and
— he had ne - ver come; had he not come he
— he had ne - ver come; still were we lost in

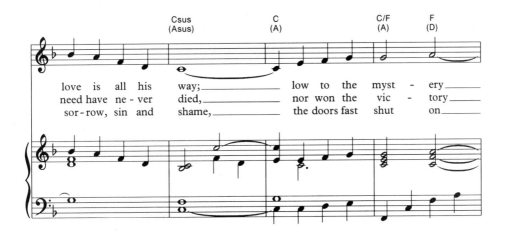

love is all his way;_____ low to the myst - ery_____
need have ne - ver died,_____ nor won the vic - tory_____
sor-row, sin and shame,_____ the doors fast shut on_____

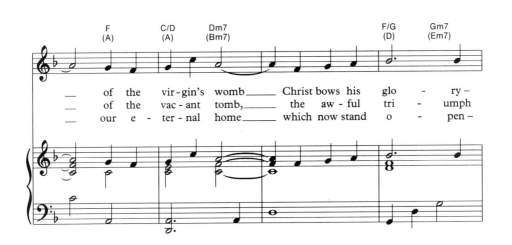

__ of the vir-gin's womb_____ Christ bows his glo - ry –
__ of the vac-ant tomb,_____ the aw - ful tri - umph
__ our e - ter - nal home_____ which now stand o - pen –

born on Christ-mas Day._____ 2 Had he not
of the Cru - ci - fied._____ 3 Had he not
for he loved and came._____

105

Had he not loved us
(Second tune)

ELLERS   10 10 10 10

Words: Timothy Dudley-Smith
Music: Edward Hopkins
arranged Roger Mayor

106   Hail the day that sees him rise

LLANFAIR   7 7 7 7 and Alleluias

Words: Charles Wesley and
Thomas Cotterill
Music: Robert Williams
arranged Roger Mayor

5

With energy ♩ = 128

1 Hail the day that sees him rise   Al - le -
2 There for him high tri - umph waits: Al - le -
3 See! the heaven its Lord re - ceives,   Al - le -

- lu - ia,   to his throne be - yond the skies: al - le -
- lu - ia,   lift your heads, e - ter - nal gates –   al - le -
- lu - ia,   yet he loves the earth he leaves;   al - le -

-lu - ia, Christ, the Lamb for sin - ners given,
-lu - ia, he has con - quered death and_ sin,
-lu - ia, though re - turn - ing to_ his throne,

al - le - lu - ia, en - ters now the high - est heaven:
al - le - lu - ia, take the King of glo - ry_ in:
al - le - lu - ia, still he calls man-kind his own.

al - le - lu - ia! - lu - ia!

4 Still for us he intercedes,   Alleluia,
   his prevailing death he pleads,   alleluia,
   near himself prepares our place,   alleluia,
   he the first-fruits of our race.   alleluia!

5 Lord, though parted from our sight   Alleluia,
   far beyond the starry height,   alleluia,
   lift our hearts that we may rise   alleluia,
   one with you beyond the skies: alleluia!

6 There with you we shall remain,   Alleluia,
   share the glory of your reign;   alleluia,
   there your face unclouded view,   alleluia,
   find our heaven of heavens in you.   alleluia!

107 Hail to the Lord's anointed

CRÜGER   7 6 7 6 D

Words: James Montgomery
Music: Johann Crüger
arranged Christopher Norton

108 Hark! the herald angels sing

MENDELSSOHN   7 7 7 7 D and refrain

Words: Charles Wesley and others
Music: Felix Mendelssohn
arranged Roger Mayor

1 Hark! the her - ald ang - els sing   glo - ry to   the new-born King;
2 Christ, by high - est heaven a - dored, Christ, the ev - er - last - ing Lord:
3 Hail the heaven-born Prince of   peace, hail the Sun   of right-eous-ness:

peace on earth   and mer - cy   mild, God and sin - ners re - con - ciled!
late in time   be-hold him   come, off-spring of   a   vir - gin's womb;
light and life   to all he   brings, risen with heal - ing in   his wings;

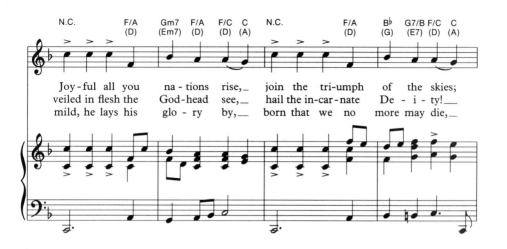

Joy-ful all you na-tions rise,_ join the tri-umph of the skies;
veiled in flesh the God-head see,_ hail the in-car-nate De - i - ty!_
mild, he lays his glo - ry by,_ born that we no more may die,_

with the an-gel - ic host pro-claim, 'Christ is_ born in Beth-le - hem'.
pleased as man with us to dwell, Je - sus our Em-ma-nu - el:
born to raise us from the earth, born to_ give us se-cond birth.

Chorus

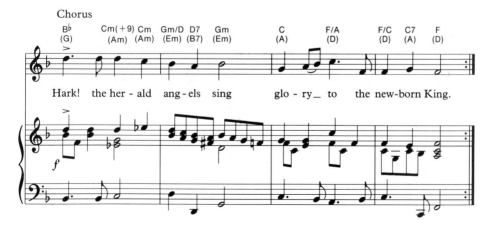

Hark! the her - ald ang-els sing glo - ry_ to the new-born King.

109

He gave his life

SELFLESS LOVE   8 6 8 6 D (DCM)

Words: Christopher Porteous
in this version Jubilate Hymns
Music: Andrew Maries
arranged Christopher Norton

Flowing ♩ = 84

1 He
gave his life in self-less love, for sin-ners once he
came; he had no stain of sin him-self but bore our guilt and

(2) did not come to call the good but sin-ners to re-
-pent; it was the lame, the deaf, the blind for whom his life was

(3) heard him call his Fa-ther's name – then 'Fin-ished!' was his
cry; like them we have for-sa-ken him and left him there to

(4) bo-dy bro-ken once for us is glo-rious now a-
-bove; the cup of bless-ing we re-ceive, a shar-ing of his

110   He healed the darkness of my mind

VISION   8 8 8 8 (LM)

Words: Frederick Pratt Green
Music: Roger Mayor

12

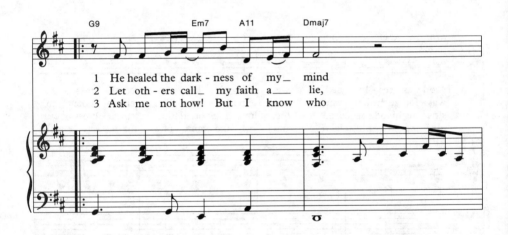

1 He healed the dark-ness of my_ mind
2 Let oth-ers call_ my faith a___ lie,
3 Ask me not how! But I know who

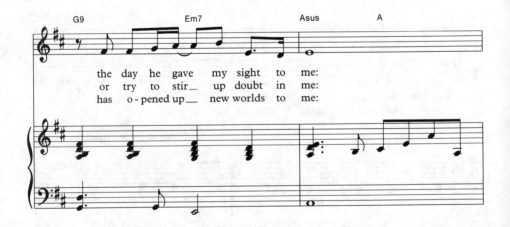

the day he gave my sight to me:
or try to stir_ up doubt in me:
has o-pened up_ new worlds to me:

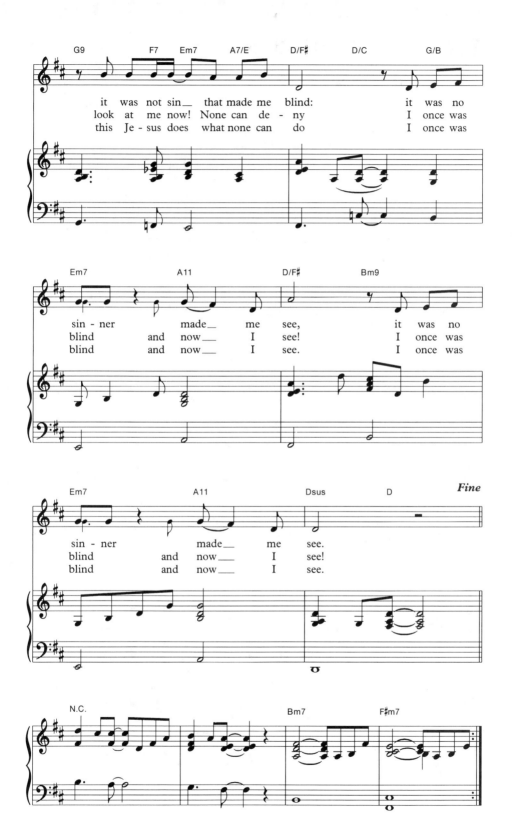

111 He lives in us

WATERSIDE 8 6 8 6 D (DCM)

Words: from Romans 8
Michael Perry
Music: Christopher Norton

1 He lives in us, the Christ of God, his Spi-rit joins with ours; he brings to us the Fa-ther's grace with powers be-yond our

(2) pangs of guilt and fears of death are Sa-tan's stra-ta-gems – by Je-sus Christ who died for us God par-dons: who con-

(3) gave the Son to save us all – no great-er love is known! And shall that love a-ban-don us who have be-come Christ's

May also be sung to the tune RACHEL (129)

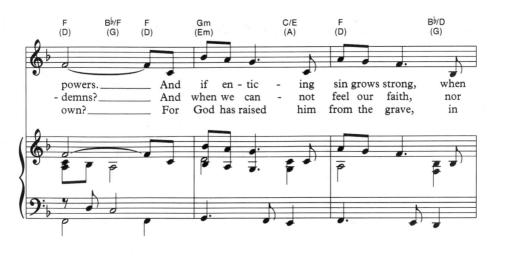

F   Bb/F   F   Gm   C/E   F   Bb/D
(D)   (G)   (D)   (Em)   (A)   (D)   (G)

powers.____ And if en - tic - ing sin grows strong, when
- demns?____ And when we can - not feel our faith, nor
own?____ For God has raised him from the grave, in

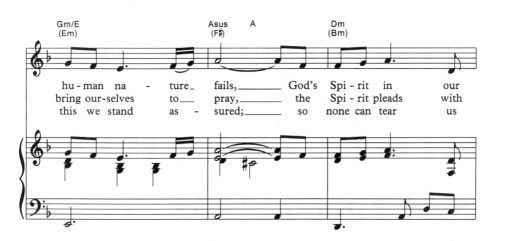

Gm/E   Asus   A   Dm
(Em)   (F#)   (Bm)

hu - man na - ture_ fails,____ God's Spi - rit in our
bring our-selves to_ pray,____ the Spi - rit pleads with
this we stand as - sured;____ so none can tear us

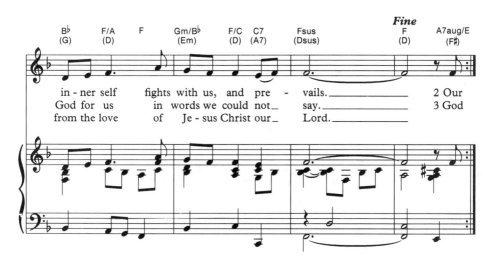

Fine

Bb   F/A   F   Gm/Bb   F/C C7   Fsus   F   A7aug/E
(G)   (D)   (Em)   (D) (A7) (Dsus)   (D)   (F#)

in - ner self fights with us, and pre - vails._____ 2 Our
God for us in words we could not_ say._____ 3 God
from the love of Je - sus Christ our_ Lord._____

112

He stood before the court

St John   666688

11

Words: Christopher Idle
Music: John Calkin
arranged Roger Mayor

1 He
stood be - fore the court on trial in - stead of
us; he met its power to hurt, con-demned to

(2) are the crimes that tell the tale of hu - man
guilt; our sins, our death, our hell – on these the

(3) sen - tence must be passed, the un-known pris - oner
killed; the price is paid at last, the law of

(4) we be judged and tried? In Christ our trial is
done; we live, for he has died, our con - dem -

A7/C♯	D	E7/B	Asus	A	A/G	D/F♯	

face   the   cross: our   king,   ac - cused   of
case   is   built: to   this world's powers their
God   ful - filled: he   takes   our   blame, and
- na - tion   gone: in   Christ   are   we   both

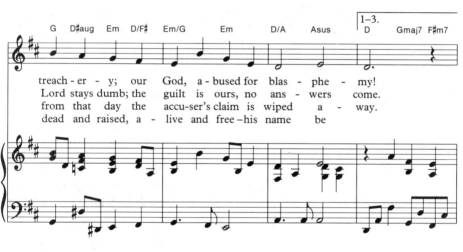

G   D♯aug   Em   D/F♯   Em/G   Em   D/A   Asus | 1–3. D   Gmaj7   F♯m7

treach - er - y;   our   God, a - bused for blas - phe - my!
Lord stays dumb; the   guilt is ours, no   ans - wers   come.
from   that   day   the   accu-ser's claim is wiped   a - way.
dead   and raised, a - live and free –his name   be

Em7   A7 | 4. D   Gmaj7   F♯m7   Em7   G/A   D

2   These
3   The
4   Shall

praised!

113   Heal me, hands of Jesus

SUTTON COMMON   6 6 8 6 (SM)

Words: Michael Perry
Music: Norman Warren

1 Heal me, hands of Je - sus, and
2 Cleanse me, blood of Je - sus, take
3 Know me, mind of Je - sus, and
4 Fill me, joy of Je - sus: an -

search out all my pain; re - store my hope, re -
bit - ter - ness a - way; let me for - give as
show me all my sin; dis - pel the me - mo -
-xi - e - ty shall cease and heaven's se - re - ni -

- move my fear and bring me peace a - gain.
one for - given and bring me peace to - day.
- ries of guilt and bring me peace with - in.
- ty be mine, for Je - sus brings me peace!

114 He was pierced

LIKE A LAMB   Irregular

3

Words and music: Maggi Dawn
Music arranged Christopher Norton

115 He who created light

Moscow 6 6 4 6 6 6 4

9

Words: Michael Saward
Music: Felice de Giardini
arranged David Peacock

Flowing and unhurried ♩ = 100

1 He who cre - a - ted light from his com -
2 He who was born to save, stand-ing at
3 He whose in - spir - ing power sur - ges through
4 He who is three - in - one, God – Fa - ther,

- mand - ing height, his voice was heard.
Laz - arus' grave, his voice was heard.
ev - ery hour, his voice is heard.
Spi - rit, Son – his voice is heard.

Then through sea, sky and earth, lab - our-ing, came to birth,
He who had healed the lame, called to the dead by name,
Strong as the wind he blows, swift as a tor - rent flows,
To him our hearts we raise, sing - ing our hymns of praise,

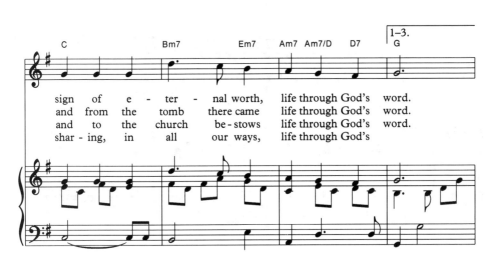

sign of e - ter - nal worth, life through God's word.
and from the tomb there came life through God's word.
and to the church be - stows life through God's word.
shar - ing, in all our ways, life through God's

word.

116

Hear me, O Lord

PAMELA   10 8 10 8

Words: from Psalm 86
Michael Perry
Music: Gareth Green

1 Hear me, O Lord, and re-spond to my prayer,
2 Bring me your joy as I wor-ship you, Lord,
3 Give me a sign of your good-ness, O Lord,

guard well my life, for I love____ you:__
come to my heart, for I need____ you;__
grant me the strength that o-beys____ you:__

no - thing com-pares with the won - ders you do,____
teach me your way, let me walk in your truth –
you are com-pas - sion, a - bound-ing in love,____

for there is no__ god a - bove you.
I can-not fail when I heed you.
you are my king, and I praise you!

OPTIONAL DESCANT for verse 3. (Instrumental or vocal sung to 'Ah')

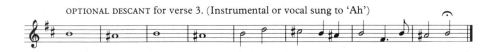

117

Heavenly hosts

BLAENWERN   8 7 8 7 D

9

Words: from Revelation 4, 5
Timothy Dudley-Smith
Music: William Rowlands
arranged Roger Mayor

Thoughtfully ♩ = 110

1 Heaven - ly hosts in cease - less wor - ship 'Ho - ly,
2 All cre - a - tion, all_ re - demp - tion, join to

ho - ly, ho - ly!' cry; 'He who is, who
sing the Sav - iour's worth; Lamb of God whose

was_ and will be, God al - migh - ty, Lord most
blood_ has bought us, kings and priests, to reign on

118   Help us to help each other

St Columbia   8 6 8 6 (CM)

2

Words: Charles Wesley
in this version Jubilate Hymns
Music: Irish traditional melody
arranged David Peacock

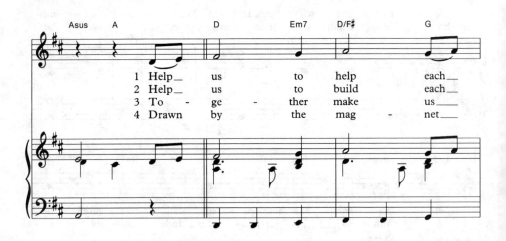

1 Help us to help each
2 Help us to build each
3 To - ge - ther make us
4 Drawn by the mag - net

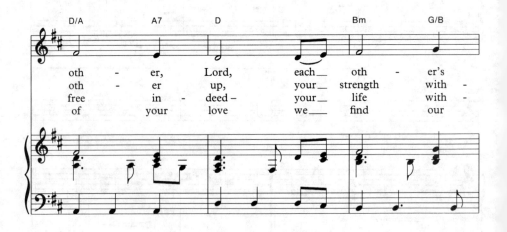

oth - er, Lord, each oth - er's
oth - er up, your strength with -
free in - deed – your life with -
of your love we find our

load   to—— bear;————— that
- in   us—— prove;————— in -
- in   us—— show;————— and
hearts   made— new:————— near -

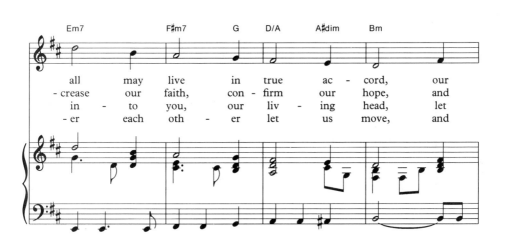

all   may   live   in   true   ac - cord,   our
- crease   our   faith,   con - firm   our   hope,   and
in - to   you,   our   liv - ing   head,   let
- er   each   oth - er   let   us   move,   and

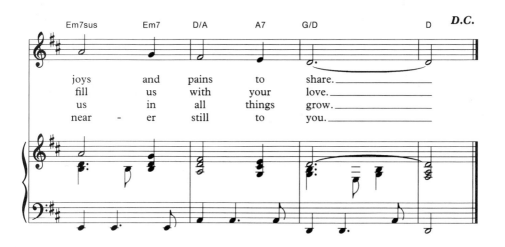

joys   and   pains   to   share.————
fill   us   with   your   love.————
us   in   all   things   grow.————
near - er   still   to   you.————

D.C.

119

Here from all nations

EPIPHANY HYMN   11 10 11 10

Words: from Revelation 7
Christopher Idle
Music: Joseph Thrupp
arranged Christopher Norton

12

Medium slow ♩ = 116

1 Here from all na - tions, all tongues and all
2 These have come out of the hard - est op -
3 Gone is their thirst and no more shall they

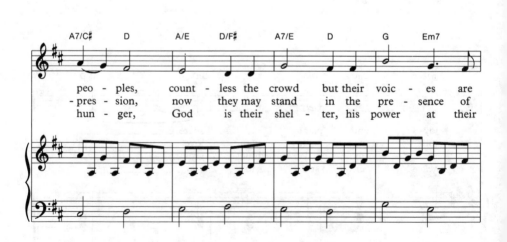

peo - ples, count - less the crowd but their voic - es are
- pres - sion, now they may stand in the pre - sence of
hun - ger, God is their shel - ter, his power at their

one;   vast   is   the   sight_ and ma - jes - tic their
God,   serv - ing their Lord_ day and   night   in his
side;   sun   shall not   pain_ them, no burn - ing will

sing - ing –   'God has the   vic - tory: he reigns   from the
tem - ple,   ran - somed and cleansed   by the Lamb's   pre-cious
tor - ture,   Je - sus the Lamb   is their shep - herd and

throne!'
blood.
guide.

4 He will go with them to clear living water
    flowing from springs which his mercy supplies;
    gone is their grief and their trials are over –
    God wipes away every tear from their eyes.

5 Blessing and glory and wisdom and power
    be to the Saviour again and again;
    might and thanksgiving and honour for ever
    be to our God: Alleluia! Amen.

120 Here, O my Lord

St Agnes   10 10 10 10

Words: Horatius Bonar
Music: James Langran
arranged Christopher Norton

1 Here, O my Lord, I see you face to face,
here faith can touch and han-dle things un - seen;

2 Here I will feed up - on the bread of God,
here drink with you the ro - yal wine of heaven;

3 I have no help but yours, nor do I need
a - no - ther arm but yours to lean up - on;

here   I will grasp with   firm - er hand your grace
here   I will lay   a - side each earth - ly load,
it   is e - nough, my   Lord, e - nough in - deed,

and   all my wea - ri - ness up - on   you   lean.
here   taste a - fresh the calm of   sin   for - given.
my   hope is in your strength, your strength a - lone.

4   Mine is the sin, but yours the righteousness;
      mine is the guilt, but yours the cleansing blood:
      here is my robe, my refuge, and my peace;
      your blood, your righteousness, O Lord my God.

5   Too soon we rise, the symbols disappear;
      the feast, though not the love, is past and done:
      gone are the bread and wine, but you are here,
      nearer than ever, still my shield and sun.

6   Feast after feast thus comes and passes by,
      yet, passing, points to that glad feast above;
      giving sweet foretaste of the festal joy,
      the Lamb's great bridal feast of bliss and love.

121   Holy child, how still you lie

HOLY CHILD   7 7 7 7 D

11

Words: Timothy Dudley-Smith
Music: Michael Baughen
arranged Roger Mayor

Flowing ♩ = 84

1 Ho-ly

child,_____ how still you lie! safe the man-ger, soft the
(3) child,_____ what gift of grace from the Fa - ther free - ly
(5) child,_____ so far from home, all the lost to seek and
(7) child,_____ how still you lie! safe the man-ger, soft the

hay; faint up - on_____ the east-ern sky breaks the
willed! In your in - fant form we trace all God's
save, to what dread - ful death you come, to what
hay; clear up - on_____ the east-ern sky breaks the

Fine

dawn of Christ-mas Day.
pro - mi - ses ful-filled.
dark and si - lent grave!
dawn of Christ-mas Day.

2 Ho-ly child,_____ whose birth-day
4 Ho-ly child,_____ whose hu - man
6 Ho-ly child,_____ be - fore whose

brings shep-herds from their field and fold, an - gel
years span like ours de-light and pain; one in
name powers of dark - ness faint and fall; con-quered,

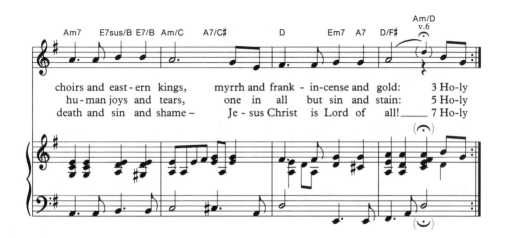

choirs and east-ern kings, myrrh and frank - in-cense and gold: 3 Ho-ly
hu-man joys and tears, one in all but sin and stain: 5 Ho-ly
death and sin and shame – Je - sus Christ is Lord of all!_____ 7 Ho-ly

122   Holy, holy, holy

NICAEA   11 12 12 10

Words: Reginald Heber
Music: John Dykes
arranged Christopher Norton

1 Ho-ly, ho-ly,   ho - ly,
2 Ho-ly, ho-ly,   ho - ly!
3 Ho-ly, ho-ly,   ho - ly!
4 Ho-ly, ho-ly,   ho - ly,

Lord___ God al - migh - ty!   ear - ly   in   the
All   the saints a - dore   you   cast - ing down their
Though the dark-ness hide   you,   though the sin - ful
Lord___ God al - migh - ty!   all your works shall

morn - ing our   song of praise shall be:
gold - en   crowns a - round the glass - y sea,
hu - man   eye your   glo - ry may not see,
praise your name, in   earth and sky and sea:

The traditional version of this text is found in the words edition

123   Holy Spirit, gracious guest

HEAVENLY LOVE   7 7 7 5

23

Words: from 1 Corinthians 13
Christopher Wordsworth
in this version Jubilate Hymns
Music: David Peacock

Quite slow with a strong beat ♩ = 92

1 Ho - ly Spi - rit,   gra - cious guest,
2 Faith that moun - tains   could re - move,
3 Though I as a   mar - tyr bleed,

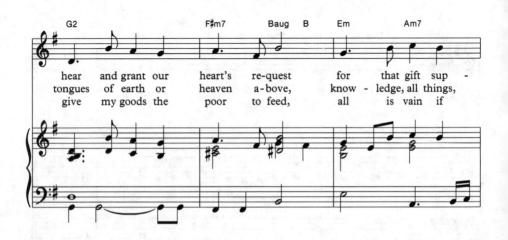

hear and grant our   heart's re - quest   for   that gift sup -
tongues of earth or   heaven a - bove,   know - ledge, all things,
give my goods the   poor to feed,   all   is vain if

- reme and best: ho - ly heaven-ly___ love.
emp - ty prove if I have no___ love.
love I need: there - fore give_ me_ love.

and the best_ is___ love,_____ the best_ is___

love,_____ the best_ is___ love.

4 Love is kind and suffers long,
   love is pure and thinks no wrong,
   love than death itself more strong:
    therefore give us love.

5 Prophecy will fade away,
   melting in the light of day;
   love will ever with us stay:
    therefore give us love.

6 Faith and hope and love we see
   joining hand in hand agree –
   but the greatest of the three,
    and the best is love,
    the best is love,
    the best is love.

124   How can we sing with joy

MARTYRDOM   8 6 8 6 (CM)

Words: Brian Foley
Music: Hugh Wilson
arranged David Peacock

1 How can we sing with joy to God, how can we pray to him, when

(2) can we claim to do God's will when we have turned a-way from

(3) can we praise the love of God which all his works make known, when

Words: © 1971 Faber Music Ltd,
3 Queen Square, London WC1N 3AU.
Reprinted from the *New Catholic Hymnal*
by permission of the publishers

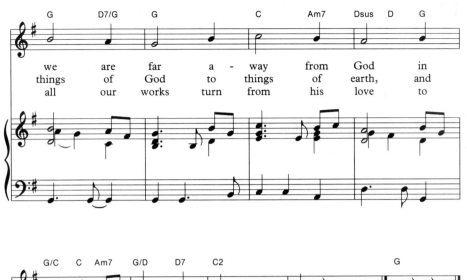

we   are   far   a - way   from   God   in
things   of   God   to   things   of   earth,   and
all   our   works   turn   from   his   love   to

self - ish - ness   and   sin?_____   2 How
willed_ to_ dis - o - bey?_____   3 How
choi - ces_ of   our   own?_____   4 God

4   God knows the sinful things we do,
     the godless life we live,
     yet in his love he calls to us,
     so ready to forgive.

5   So we will turn again to God –
     his ways will be our ways,
     his will our will, his love our love,
     and he himself our praise!

125 How firm a foundation

St Denio   11 11 11 11
9

Words: Richard Keen
in this version Jubilate Hymns
Music: Welsh melody
arranged David Peacock

With confidence ♩ = 102

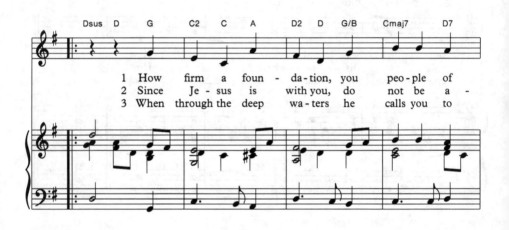

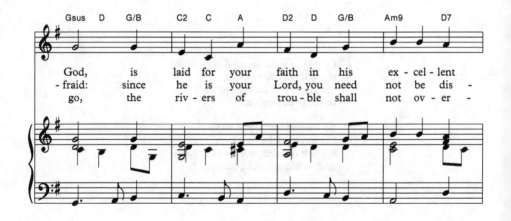

1 How firm a foun - da - tion, you peo - ple of
2 Since Je - sus is with you, do not be a -
3 When through the deep wa - ters he calls you to

God, is laid for your faith in his ex - cel - lent
- fraid: since he is your Lord, you need not be dis -
go, the riv - ers of trou - ble shall not ov - er -

4 When through fiery trials your pathway shall lead,
his grace shall sustain you with all that you need;
the flames shall not hurt you – his only design
your dross to consume and your gold to refine.

5 Whoever has come to believe in his name
will not be deserted, and not put to shame;
though hell may endeavour that Christian to shake
his Lord will not leave him, nor ever forsake.

126 How good is the God we adore

CELESTE 8 8 8 8

Words: Joseph Hart
Music: Lancashire Sunday School Songs
arranged Roger Mayor

'Gospel' (with strong accents) ♩ = 70

good is the God__ we a - dore!
(2) Christ is the first__ and the last;

our__
his__

127   How sure the Scriptures are

DARWALL'S 148TH   6 6 6 6 8 8

Words: Christopher Idle
Music: John Darwall
arranged Roger Mayor

1 How
2 They
3 Let

sure the Scrip - tures are!   God's vi - tal, ur - gent
test each hu - man thought,   re - fin - ing like a
those who hear his voice   con - front - ing them to -

word,   as true as steel, and far more sharp than
fire;   they mea - sure what we ought to do and
- day,   re - ject the tempt - ing choice of doubt - ing

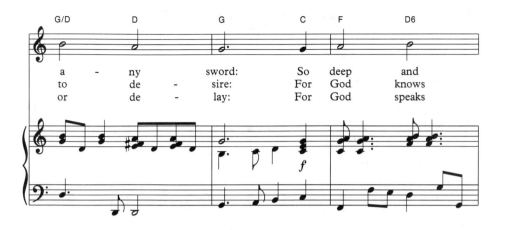

a - ny sword: So deep and
to de - sire: For God knows
or de - lay: For God speaks

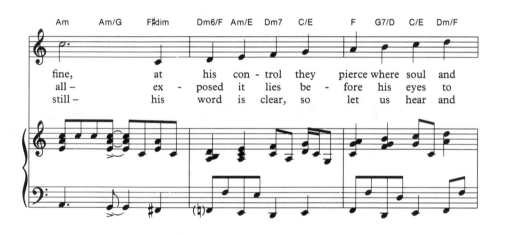

fine, at his con - trol they pierce where soul and
all — ex - posed it lies be - fore his eyes to
still — his word is clear, so let us hear and

spi - rit join.
whom we call.
do his will!

128 How long, O Lord

How Long O Lord   86886

Words: from Psalm 13
Barbara Woollett
Music: Christopher Norton

Moderately with expression ♩ = 60

1 How long, O Lord, will you for-get an ans-wer to my
2 How long, O Lord, will you for-sake and leave me in this
3 How long, O Lord – but you for-give, with mer-cy from a -

prayer? No to-kens of your love I see,
way?— When will you come to my re-lief?
- bove.— I find that all your ways are just,

your face is turned a - way from me: I wres-tle with des -
My heart is o - ver-whelmed with grief, by e - vil night and
I learn to praise you and to trust in your un - fail - ing

1.2.

3.

- pair.
day.
love.

129 How sweet the name of Jesus
(First tune)

RACHEL 8 6 8 6 (CM)

Words: John Newton
Music: Christopher Bowater
arranged Christopher Norton

Worshipfully ♩ = 112

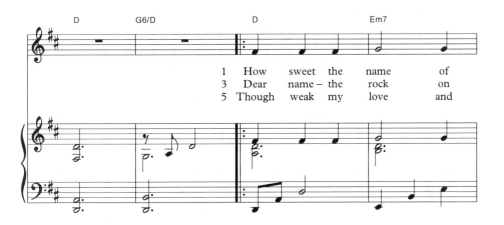

1 How sweet the name of
3 Dear name – the rock on
5 Though weak my love and

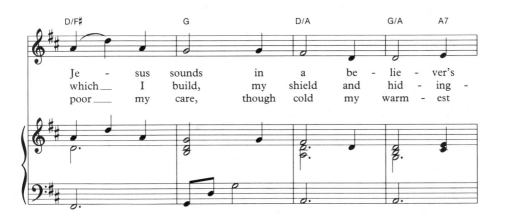

Je - sus sounds in a be - lie - ver's
which__ I build, my shield and hid - ing -
poor__ my care, though cold my warm - est

Music: © 1976 Sovereign Lifestyle Music Ltd,
PO Box 356, Leighton Buzzard, Beds, LU7 8WP, UK

129 How sweet the name of Jesus
(Second tune)

St Peter   8 6 8 6 (CM)

Words: John Newton
Music: Alexander Reinagle
arranged Christopher Norton

12

Unhurried ♩ = 96

1 How
sweet the name of Je - sus sounds in
(2) makes the wound - ed spi - rit whole, and
(3) name - the rock on which I build, my

a be - liev - er's ear! It
calms the troub - led breast; it
shield and hid - ing - place, my

Music arrangement: © 1993 HarperCollins*Religious*

soothes our sor - rows, heals our wounds and drives a - way our
sa - tis - fies the hun - gry soul, and gives the wea - ry
ne - ver - fail - ing trea - sury, filled with bound-less stores of

fear. 2 It
rest. 3 Dear
grace! 4 Je -

4 Jesus, my shepherd, brother, friend,
 my prophet, priest and king;
 my Lord, my life, my way, my end –
 accept the praise I bring.

5 Though weak my love and poor my care,
 though cold my warmest thought:
 yet when I see you as you are,
 I'll praise you as I ought.

6 Till then I would your love proclaim
 with every fleeting breath:
 and may the music of your name
 refresh my soul in death.

130 I am trusting you, Lord Jesus
(First tune)

Words: Frances Havergal
Music: Ethelbert Bullinger
arranged Roger Mayor

BULLINGER 8 5 8 3

With a lilt ♩ = 92

1 I_____ am trust - ing you,_____ Lord
2 I_____ am trust - ing you_____ for
3 I_____ am trust - ing you_____ for

Je - sus, you have died_____ for
par - don – at your feet_____ I
cleans - ing, Je - sus, Son_____ of

me;
bow;
God;

trust - ing you for
for___ your grace and
trust - ing you to

Fine

full___ sal - va - tion great_ and free.
ten - der mer - cy, trust - ing now.
make_ me ho - ly by___ your blood.

4 I am trusting you to guide me –
   you alone shall lead;
   every day and hour supplying
   all my need.

5 I am trusting you for power –
   yours can never fail;
   words which you yourself shall give me
   must prevail.

6 I am trusting you, Lord Jesus –
   never let me fall;
   I am trusting you for ever,
   and for all.

130   I am trusting you, Lord Jesus
(Second tune)

I AM TRUSTING YOU   8 5 8 3 D

Words: Frances Havergal
Music: Roger Jones

1 I am trust-ing you, Lord Je - sus, you have died for me;
3 I am trust-ing you for cleans-ing, Je - sus, Son of God;
5 I am trust-ing you for pow - er – yours can ne - ver fail;

trust - ing you_ for full sal - va - tion great and free.
trust - ing you_ to make me ho - ly by your blood.
words which you_ your-self shall give me must pre-vail.

2 I am trust-ing you for par-don — at your feet I bow;
4 I am trust-ing you to guide me — you a-lone shall lead;
6 I am trust-ing you, Lord Je-sus — ne-ver let me fall;

for your grace and ten - der mer - cy, trust-ing now, trust-ing now._
ev - ery day_ and hour sup-ply - ing all my need, all my need.
I am trust - ing you_ for ev - er, and for all,_ and for all._

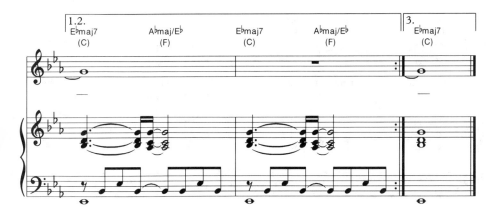

131   I believe in God the Father

DIM OND JESU   8 7 8 7 D

Words: Michael Perry
Music: Robert Lowry
arranged Christopher Norton

9

Thoughtfully ♩ = 90

1 I be - lieve in God the
(3) - lieve in God the

Fa - ther who cre - a - ted heaven and earth, hold-ing all things in his
Spi - rit, wind of heaven and flame of fire, pledge of all that we in -

pow-er, bring-ing light and life to birth. 2 I be -
- he - rit, sent to com - fort and in - spire. 4 Hon-our,

132   I come with joy

MATTHEW   8 6 8 6 (DCM)

Words: Brian Wren
Music: David Peacock

9

Moderately ♩ = 104

1 I come with joy to meet my Lord, for-giv-en, loved, and
(3) Christ breaks bread and bids us share, each proud di-vi-sion
(5) -ge-ther met, to-ge-ther bound, we'll go our dif-ferent

free; in awe and won-der to re-call his
ends; the love that made us makes us one, and
ways; and as his peo-ple in the world we'll

Fine

life laid down for me. 2 I come with Christ-ians
stran-gers now are friends. 4 And thus with joy we
live and speak his praise.

far and near   to   find, as   all   are   fed,   the
meet our Lord; his   pres-ence, al - ways near,   is

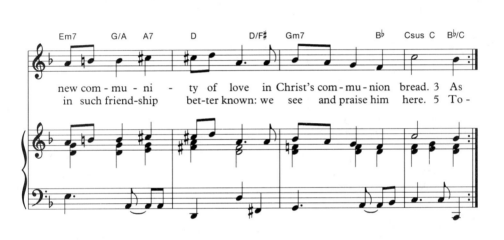

new com - mu - ni   -   ty of   love in Christ's com-mu-nion bread. 3 As
in such friend-ship   bet-ter known: we   see   and praise him   here. 5 To-

Instrumental obligato

vv.1,3,5

Fine vv.2,4

133   I know that my redeemer lives

CHURCH TRIUMPHANT   8 8 8 8 (LM)

3

Words: Samuel Medley
Music: James Elliott
arranged David Peacock

1 I know that my re-
(2) lives, tri-um-phant
(3) lives to help in

-deem-er lives – what com-fort_ this as-sur-ance gives! He
from the grave, he_ lives, e-ter-nal-ly to save; he
time of need, he_ lives, my_ hun-gry soul to feed; he

lives, he lives, who once was dead, he lives, my ev-er-
lives, to bless me with his love, and in-ter-cedes for
lives, and grants me dai-ly breath, he lives, and I shall

- last	- ing	head.			2 He	
me	a -	bove.			3 He	
con -	quer	death.			4 He	

4 He lives, my kind, wise, constant friend,
   who still will guard me to the end;
   he lives, and while he lives I'll sing,
   Jesus, my prophet, priest and king!

5 He lives, my saviour, to prepare
   a place in heaven, and lead me there;
   he lives – all glory to his name,
   Jesus, unchangeably the same.

Instrumental obligato

134   I love you, O Lord

JANE   8 8 8 8 D (DLM)

12

Words: from Psalm 18
Christopher Idle
Music: David Peacock

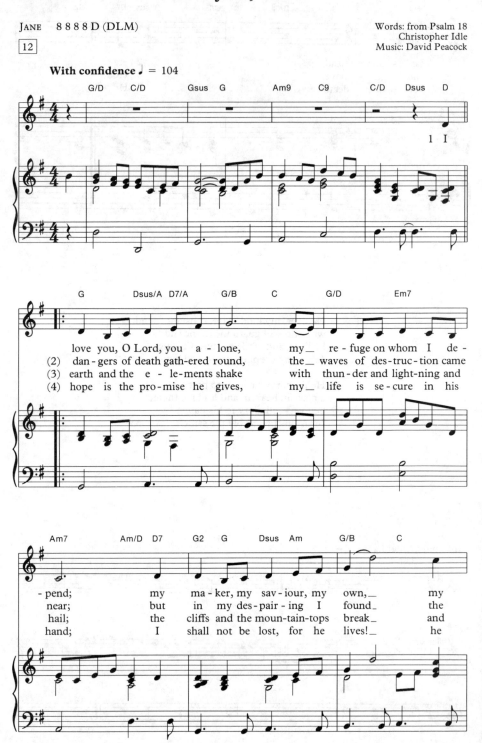

love you, O Lord, you a - lone, my re - fuge on whom I de -
(2) dan - gers of death gath-ered round, the waves of des-truc-tion came
(3) earth and the e - le-ments shake with thun - der and light-ning and
(4) hope is the pro-mise he gives, my life is se-cure in his

- pend; my ma - ker, my sav - iour, my own, my
near; but in my des-pair-ing I found the
hail; the cliffs and the moun-tain-tops break and
hand; I shall not be lost, for he lives! he

G/D Em7   Am7 Am7/D   Gsus   G   Eb

hope and my trust with-out end: the Lord is my strength and my
Lord who re-leased me from fear: I   called for his help   in my
mor - tals are fee - ble and pale.   His   jus - tice is   full   and com -
comes to my aid – I shall stand!   Lord God, you are power - ful to

Ab   Gm7   C   Fm   Cm/Eb Gm/A   C/D   D

song,   de - fend - er and guide of my ways;   my
pain,   to   God my sal - va - tion I cried: he
- plete,   his   mer - cy to   us has no   end;   the
save,   your Spi - rit will spur me to   pray;   your

G   Dsus/A A7   G/B   C   G/D   C/D

mas - ter to whom I be - long,   my God who shall have   all my
brought me his com-fort a - gain,   I   live by the strength he sup -
clouds are a path for his feet,   he comes on the wings of the
Son has de - feat - ed the grave: I   trust and I praise you to -

Gsus   G   Am9   C9   C/D   Dsus   D   G2

praise.   2 The
- plied.   3 The
wind.   4 My
- day!

135 I cannot tell why

LONDONDERRY AIR
11 10 11 10 11 10 11 12

Words: William Fullerton
Music: Irish traditional melody
arranged Christopher Norton

Lyrically ♩ = 108

1 I can-not

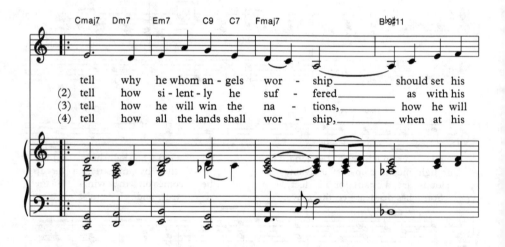

tell   why   he whom an - gels   wor -   ship_____ should set his
(2) tell   how   si - lent - ly   he   suf -   fered_____ as with his
(3) tell   how   he will win the   na -   tions,_____ how he will
(4) tell   how   all the lands shall   wor -   ship,_____ when at his

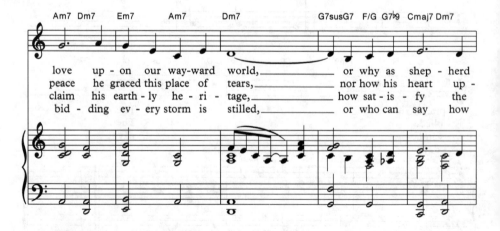

love   up - on   our way-ward   world,_____ or why as   shep - herd
peace   he graced this place of   tears,_____ nor how his heart   up -
claim   his earth - ly   he - ri -   tage,_____ how sat - is - fy   the
bid - ding   ev - ery storm is   stilled,_____ or who can   say   how

Music arrangement: © 1993 HarperCollins*Religious*

he should seek the wan - derers,_____ to bring them back in -
-on the cross was bro - ken,_____ the crown of pain to
needs and as - pi - ra - tions_____ of east and west, of
great the ju - bi - la - tion_____ when all our hearts with

- to his flock and fold._____ But this I know, that he was born of
three and thir - ty years._____ But this I know, he heals the bro - ken-
sin - ner and of sage._____ But this I know, all flesh shall see his
love for him are filled._____ But this I know, the skies will sound his

Ma - ry_____ when Beth-lehem's man - ger was his on - ly home,_____
- heart-ed_____ and stays our sin and calms our lurk-ing fear,_____
glo - ry,_____ and he shall reap the har-vest he has sown,_____
prai - ses,_____ and my - riad, my - riad hu-man voic-es sing,_____

136   If Christ had not been raised

I HEARD THE VOICE   8 6 8 6 D

Words: from 1 Corinthians 15
Christopher Idle
Music: Roger Jones
arranged David Peacock

Slow rock ♩ = 68

1 If Christ had not_ been raised from death
2 If Christ still lay_ with - in the tomb
3 If Christ had not_ been tru - ly raised

our faith would be__ in vain,
then death would be__ the end,
his church would live_ a lie;

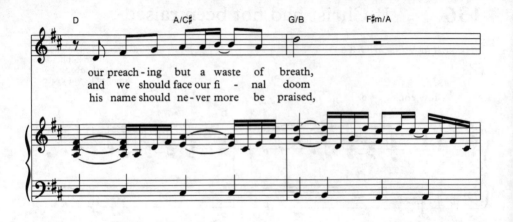

our preach - ing but a waste of breath,
and we should face our fi - nal doom
his name should ne - ver more be praised,

our sin and guilt re - main.
with nei - ther guide nor friend.
his words de - serve to die.

But now the Lord is risen in - deed;
But now the Sav-iour is raised up,
But now our great Re-deem - er lives;

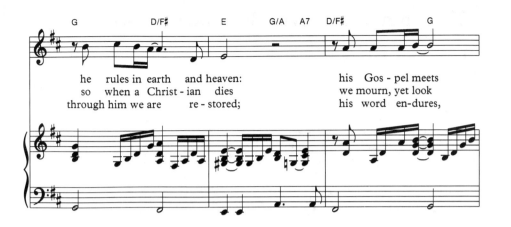

he   rules in earth   and heaven: his Gos - pel meets
so   when a Christ - ian   dies   we mourn, yet look
through him we are   re - stored;   his word en-dures,

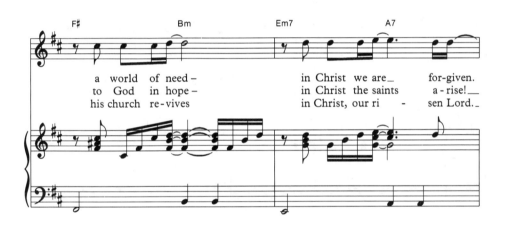

a   world   of need –   in Christ we are_   for-given.
to   God   in hope –   in Christ the saints   a - rise!__
his church re -vives   in Christ, our ri -   sen Lord._

137 Immortal, invisible, God only wise

St Denio 11 11 11 11

Words: Walter Smith
in this version Jubilate Hymns
Music: Welsh melody
arranged David Peacock

1 Im - mor - tal, in - vi - si - ble, God on - ly
2 Un - rest - ing, un - hast - ing, and si - lent as
3 To all you are giv - ing, to life great and
4 We wor - ship be - fore you, great Fa - ther of

wise, in light in - ac - ces - si - ble hid from our
light, nor want - ing, nor wast - ing, you rule us in
small, in all you are liv - ing, the true life of
light, while an - gels a - dore you, all veil - ing their

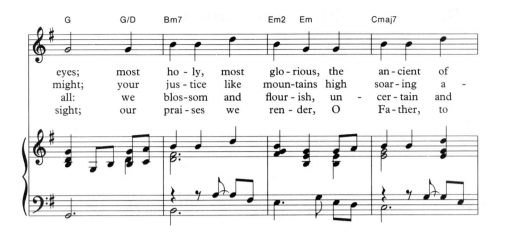

eyes; most ho - ly, most glo - rious, the an - cient of
might; your jus - tice like moun - tains high soar - ing a -
all: we blos - som and flour - ish, un - cer - tain and
sight; our prai - ses we ren - der, O Fa - ther, to

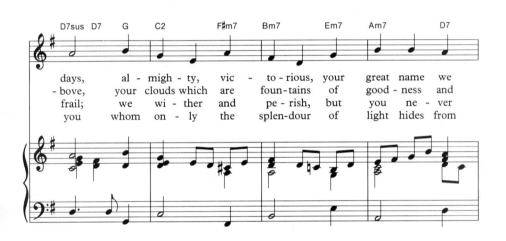

days, al - migh - ty, vic - to - rious, your great name we
- bove, your clouds which are foun - tains of good - ness and
frail; we wi - ther and pe - rish, but you ne - ver
you whom on - ly the splen - dour of light hides from

praise.
love.
fail.

view.

138   In awe and wonder

ANGELIC SPIRITS   8 6 8 6 (CM)

Words: Michael Saward
Music: Christopher Norton

May also be sung to the tune MY GOD, HOW WONDERFUL, (200)

burn - ing love__ are yours,_____ and yours a -
ma - jes - ty__ you hear_____ their cease - less
heaven and earth, you reign_____ in realms of

- lone.   2 An -
cry: 3 'O
light.'   4 Your

4 Your holiness inspires our fear,
   evokes, and heals, our shame;
   your boundless wisdom, awesome power,
   unchangeably the same.

5 Salvation comes from you alone
   which we can never win;
   your love revealed on Calvary
   is cleansing for our sin.

6 There is no grace to match your grace,
   no love to match your love,
   no gentleness of human touch
   like that of heaven above.

7 On earth we long for heaven's joy
   where, bowed before your throne,
   we know you, Father, Spirit, Son,
   as God, and God alone.

139 In the cross of Christ I glory

ALL FOR JESUS 8 7 8 7

3

Words: after John Bowring
in this version Word & Music
Music: John Stainer
arranged Roger Mayor

Worshipfully ♩ = 92

1 In the cross of Christ I glo - ry
2 When earth's sor-rows o - ver-take me,
3 When the sun of bliss is beam-ing
4 Joy and sor-row, pain and plea-sure

tow-ering o - ver wrecks of time; all the light of sa - cred sto - ry
hopes de-ceive and fears an-noy, ne - ver shall the cross for - sake me —
light and life up - on my way, from the cross his ra-diance stream-ing
by the cross are sanc - ti - fied; peace is there be - yond all mea - sure

ga - thers round his head sub-lime.
Christ shall bring me peace and joy.
adds more lus - tre to the day.
through the grace of

Christ who died.

140   In heavenly armour

THE BATTLE BELONGS TO THE LORD
Irregular

Words and music: Jamie Owens-Collins
Music arranged Geoff Baker

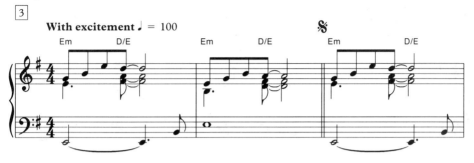

With excitement ♩ = 100

1   In hea-ven-ly ar - mour we'll en - ter the land— the
2 When the po-wer of dark-ness comes in___ like a flood, the
3 When your e - ne-my pres-ses in hard,_ do not fear— the

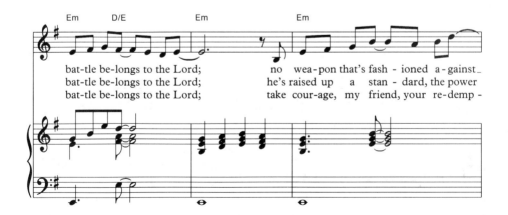

bat-tle be-longs to the Lord;   no wea-pon that's fash - ioned a-gainst_
bat-tle be-longs to the Lord;   he's raised up a stan - dard, the power
bat-tle be-longs to the Lord;   take cour-age, my friend, your re-demp-

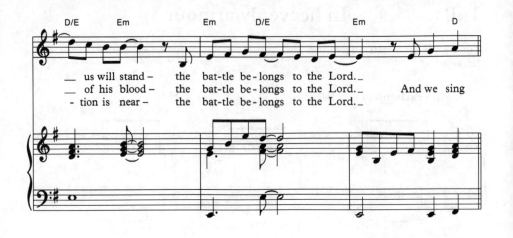

_ us will stand – the bat-tle be-longs to the Lord._
_ of his blood – the bat-tle be-longs to the Lord._ And we sing
- tion is near – the bat-tle be-longs to the Lord._

repeat 3rd time

glo – ry, hon - our, po-wer and strength to the Lord;

_ we sing glo – ry, hon - our,

1.2. **D.S.**

po-wer and strength to the Lord!

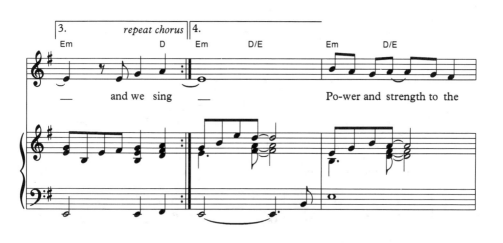

3. *repeat chorus* **4.**

— and we sing — Po-wer and strength to the

Lord, po-wer and strength to the Lord!

rall.

141   In heavenly love abiding
(First tune)

IN HEAVENLY LOVE   7 6 7 6 D

Words: Anna Waring
in this version Jubilate Hymns
Music: Christopher Bowater
arranged Christopher Norton

Music: © 1990, Sovereign Lifestyle Music Ltd,
PO Box 356, Leighton Buzzard, Beds LU7 8WP, UK

no - thing chang - es___ here:_____ the storm may roar a -
no - thing can I__ lack:_____ his wis - dom is for
threat-ening clouds have_ been:_____ my hope I can - not

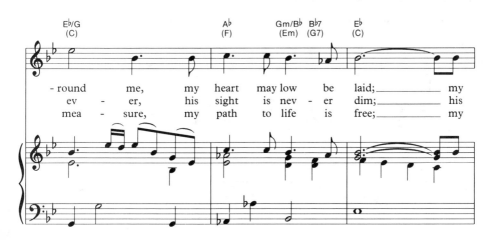

- round me, my heart may low be laid;_____ my
ev - er, his sight is nev - er dim;_____ his
mea - sure, my path to life is free;_____ my

Fa - ther's arms sur - round me,_____ how can___ I be a - fraid?
love de - serts me nev - er_____ and I_____ will walk with him.
sav - iour has my trea - sure,___ and he___ will walk with me.

Chorus

In heaven-ly love a-bid - ing, no change my heart shall fear;_____ and safe is such con- -fid - ing, for no - thing chang - es here.

2 Where -
3 Green

141 In heavenly love abiding
(Second tune)

PENLAN   7 6 7 6 D

Words: Anna Waring
in this version Jubilate Hymns
Music: David Jenkins
arranged Christopher Norton

heaven - ly love a - bid-ing,_____ no
(2) -ev - er he may guide me_____ no
(3) pas - tures are be - fore me,_____ which

change my heart shall fear;_____ and
want shall turn me back;_____ my
yet I have not seen;_____ bright

142 In silent pain the eternal Son

IN SILENT PAIN   8 6 8 6 8 8 8 6

Words: Christopher Idle
Music: David Peacock

1 In silent pain the eternal Son
hangs derelict and still;
in darkened day his work is done,
ful-

(2) died that we might die to sin
and live for righteousness;
the earth is stained, to make us clean
and

(3) strife he came, to bring a sword, the
truth to end all lies;
to rule in us, our patient Lord, un-

143   It came upon the midnight clear

NöEL   8 6 8 6 D

Words: Edmund Sears
in this version Jubilate Hymns
Music: English traditional melody
arranged David Peacock

144   It is a thing most wonderful

GIDEON   8 8 8 8 (LM)

Words: William How
in this version Jubilate Hymns
Music: Thomas Southgate
arranged Roger Mayor

1 It is a thing most won - der - ful - al - most too won - der - ful to be - that

2 And yet I know that it is true: he came to this poor world be - low, and

3 I can - not tell how he could love a child so weak and full of sin; his

4 I sometimes think about the cross,
   and shut my eyes, and try to see
   the cruel nails, and crown of thorns,
   and Jesus crucified for me.

5 But, even could I see him die,
   I could but see a little part
   of that great love which, like a fire,
   is always burning in his heart.

6 How wonderful it is to see
   my love for him so faint and poor,
   but yet more wonderful to know
   his love for me so free and sure.

7 And yet I want to love you, Lord:
   O teach me how to grow in grace,
   that I may love you more and more
   until I see you face to face!

145   Jesus Christ gives life

LIFE AND GLADNESS   8 7 8 7 8 7

Words: Michael Saward
Music: Alistair Goudie

146 Jesus Christ is risen today

EASTER HYMN   7 7 7 7 and alleluias

Words: Unknown
Music: *Lyra Davidica*
arranged Roger Mayor

16

Joyfully ♩ = 124

1 Je - sus Christ is   risen to - day,_
2 Hymns of joy then   let us sing_ Al - le - lu - ia,
3 But the pains which he en - dured

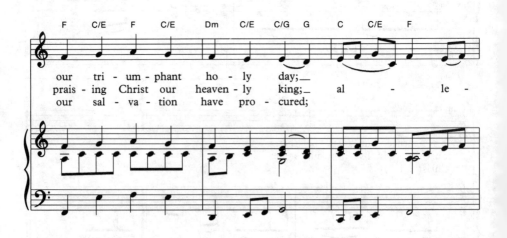

our tri - um - phant   ho - ly   day;_
prais - ing Christ our heaven - ly king;_ al - le -
our sal - va - tion   have pro - cured;

147   Jesus Christ the Lord is born

PUER NOBIS   7 6 7 7

16

Words: after German authors
Michael Perry
Music: from *Piae Cantiones*
arranged David Peacock

1 Je - sus Christ the Lord is born,
2 'Go to Beth - le - hem to - day,
3 Held with - in a cat - tle stall,

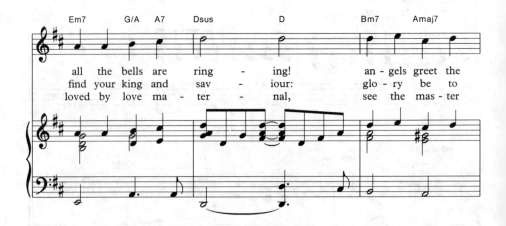

all the bells are ring - ing! an - gels greet the
find your king and sav - iour: glo - ry be to
loved by love ma - ter - nal, see the mas - ter

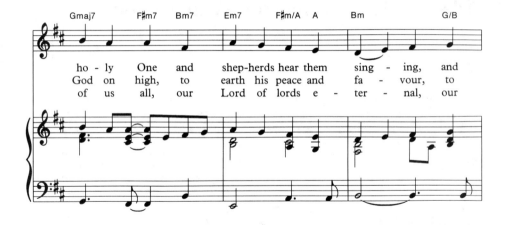

ho - ly   One   and   shep-herds hear them   sing - ing,   and
God   on   high,   to   earth his peace and   fa - vour,   to
of   us   all,   our   Lord of lords e - ter - nal,   our

Fine

shep-herds hear them   sing - ing.
earth his peace and   fa - vour!'
Lord of lords e - ter - nal.

4   Soon shall come the wise men three,
    rousing Herod's anger;
    mother's hearts shall broken be
        and Mary's son in danger,
        and Mary's son in danger.

5   Death from life and life from death,
    our salvation's story:
    let all living things give breath
        to Christmas songs of glory,
        to Christmas songs of glory!

148   Jesus, come! for we invite you

LIFE AND GLADNESS   8 7 8 7 8 7

Words: from John 2
Christopher Idle
Music: Alistair Goudie

1 Je-sus, come! ____ for we in-vite ____ you, guest and mas - ter, friend and Lord; now, as once ____ at Ca - na's
2 Je-sus, come! ____ trans-form our plea - sures, guide us in - to paths un-known; bring your gifts, ____ com-mand your
3 Je-sus, come ____ in new cre - a - tion, heaven brought near ____ in power di-vine; give your un - ex - pect - ed
4 Je-sus, come! ____ sur-prise our dull - ness, make us will - ing to re-ceive more than we can ____ yet i-

149 Jesus comes with clouds descending

HELMSLEY 8 7 8 7 4 7 extended

Words: after John Cennick
Charles Wesley and
Martin Madan
in this version Jubilee Hymns
Music: English melody
arranged Christopher Norton

1 Je - sus__ comes with clouds__ de - scend-ing: see the Lamb for sin - ners slain!__ Thou-sand thou - sand saints__ at - tend - ing

2 Ev - ery__ eye__ shall then__ be - hold__ him robed in awe - some ma - je - sty;__ those who jeered at__ him__ and sold__ him,

3 All the__ wounds of__ cross__ and pas - sion still his glo - rious bo - dy__ bears;__ cause of__ end - less ex - ul - ta - tion

4 Yes, A - -men! Let__ all_____ a - dore__ you high on your e - -ter - nal__ throne;__ crowns and__ em - pires fall__ be - fore__ you –

150   Jesus, good above all other

QUEM PASTORES LAUDAVERE   8 8 8 7

9

Words: from the Latin
verses 1 and 2 John Neale
verses 3 and 4 Percy Dearmer
Music: German carol melody
arranged Roger Mayor

1 Je - sus, good a - bove_ all oth - er,
2 Je - sus, cra - dled in a man - ger,
3 Je - sus, for your peo - ple dy - ing,
4 Lord, in all our do - ings guide us:

gen - tle child_ of gen - tle mo - ther;
keep_ us free_ from sin and dan - ger;
ris - en mas - ter, death de - fy - ing;
pride_ and hate_ shall not di - vide us;

Eb	Ab/C	Bb	Ab	Bb		G/B	Cm
(C)	(F)	(G)	(F)	(G)		(E)	(Am)

in a sta - ble born our bro - ther,
and to all, both friend and stran - ger,
Lord of heaven, your grace sup - ply - ing,
we'll go on with you be - side us,

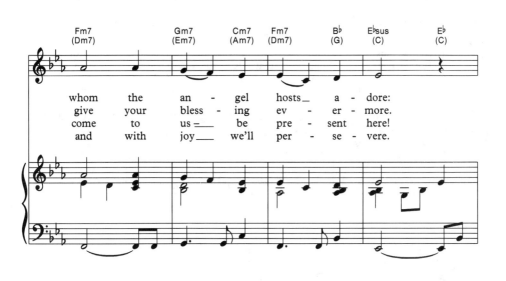

Fm7	Gm7	Cm7	Fm7	Bb	Ebsus	Eb
(Dm7)	(Em7)	(Am7)	(Dm7)	(G)	(C)	(C)

whom the an - gel hosts __ a - dore:
give your bless - ing ev - er - more.
come to us __ be pre - sent here!
and with joy __ we'll per - se - vere.

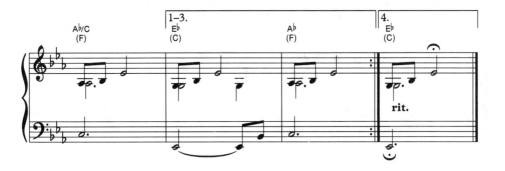

Ab/C	1-3. Eb	Ab	4. Eb
(F)	(C)	(F)	(C)

rit.

151   Jesus is king

JESUS IS KING   10 10 10 10

Words and music: Wendy Churchill
Music arranged David Peacock

1 Jesus is king, and we will ex-tol him,
2 We have a hope that is stead-fast and cer - tain,
3 We come to him our Priest and A-pos - tle,
4 'O Holy One, our hearts do a-dore you;

give him the glo - ry, and hon - our his
gone through the cur - tain and touch - ing the
clothed in his glo - ry and bear - ing his
thrilled with your good - ness we give you our

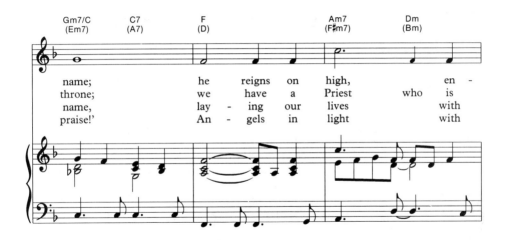

name;   he reigns on high,   en -
throne;   we have a Priest who is
name,   lay - ing our lives with
praise!'   An - gels in light with

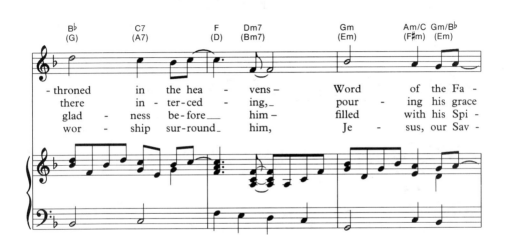

- throned in the hea - vens – Word of the Fa -
there in - ter-ced - ing, pour - ing his grace
glad - ness be-fore him – filled with his Spi -
wor - ship sur-round him, Je - sus, our Sav -

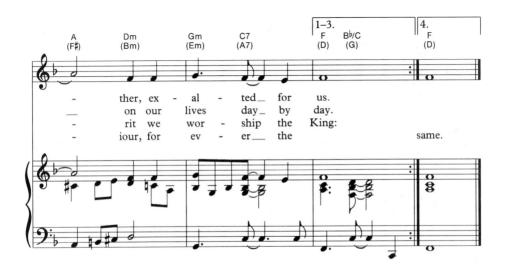

ther, ex - al - ted for us.
on our lives day by day.
rit we wor - ship the King:
iour, for ev - er the same.

152 Jesus, Jesus fill us with your love

CHEREPONI 4 5 5 7 7 7 9

Words: Tom Colvin
Music: Ghana Folk song
arranged Betty Pulkingham

6

With a gentle lilt ♩ = 60

Chorus

Je - sus,_____ Je - sus,_____ fill us with your love; show us how to serve the neigh-bours we have from you.

Verse

1 Kneels at the feet of his friends,
2 Neigh-bours are rich folk and poor;
3 These are the ones we should serve,
4 Lov - ing puts us on our knees,

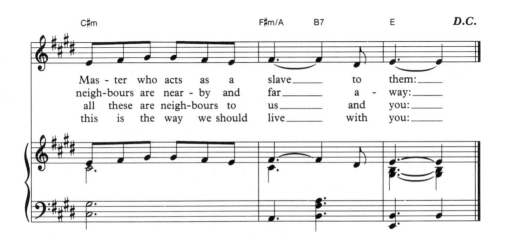

This folk song may be sung in four-part harmony, using chords on the right-hand piano part (basses sing melody). Sing the verses in unison. A very effective arrangement is achieved when voices sing alone, and a hand-drum is used to create poly-rhythms.

153   Jesus lives! Your terrors now

ST ALBINUS   7 8 7 8 and Alleluia

Words: after Christian Gellert
Frances Cox
in this version Jubilate Hymns
Music: Henry Gauntlett
arranged David Peacock

1 Je-sus lives! Your ter-rors now
2 Je-sus lives! –hence-forth is death
3 Je-sus lives! – for us he died:

can, O death, no
but the gate of
then, a - lone to

more ap - pal us:
life im - mor - tal;
Je - sus liv - ing,

Je - sus lives! –by
this shall calm our
this shall calm our
pure in heart may

this we know
trem-bling breath
we a - bide,

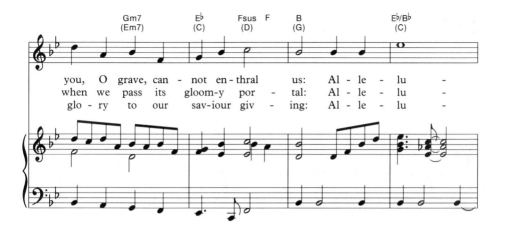

you, O grave, can - not en - thral us: Al - le - lu -
when we pass its gloom-y por - tal: Al - le - lu -
glo - ry to our sav-iour giv - ing: Al - le - lu -

- ia!
- ia!
- ia!

4 Jesus lives! – this bond of love
   neither life nor death shall sever,
   powers in hell or heaven above
   tear us from his keeping never:
      Alleluia!

5 Jesus lives! – to him the throne
   over all the world is given;
   may we go where he is gone,
   rest and reign with him in heaven:
      Alleluia!

154 Jesus, lover of my soul
(First tune)

ABERYSTWYTH   7 7 7 7 D

Words: Charles Wesley
Music: Joseph Parry
arranged Christopher Norton

1 Je - sus, lov - er of my soul, let me to your
2 O - ther re - fuge have I none, all my hope in
3 You, O Christ, are all I want, more than all in
4 Plen - teous grace with you is found, grace to wash a -

pre - sence fly, while the ga - thering wa - ters roll,
you I see: leave, O leave me, not a - lone;
you I find: raise the fal - len, cheer the faint,
- way my sin: let the heal - ing streams a - bound;

while the_ tem-pest still is high. Hide me, O my Sav-iour, hide,
still sup-port and com-fort me. All my trust on you is_ stayed,
heal the_ sick and lead the blind. Just and ho - ly is your name,
make and keep me clean with - in. Liv-ing Foun-tain, now im - part

till the storm of life is_ past; safe in - to the ha-ven, guide
all my help from you I_ bring: co-ver my de-fence-less head
I am all un - wor-thi-ness; false and full of sin I am,
all your life and pu - ri - ty; spring for ev - er in my heart,

and re - ceive my soul at last.
with the_ sha - dow of your wing.
you are_ full_ of truth and grace.
rise to_ all_ e - ter - ni - ty!

154

Jesus, lover of my soul
(Second tune)

HOLLINGSIDE   7 7 7 7 D

Words: Charles Wesley
Music: John Pykes
arranged Christopher Norton

1 Je - sus, lov - er of my soul, let me to your pre - sence fly, while the gath - ering wa - ters roll, while the tem - pest

2 O - ther re - fuge have I none, all my hope in you I see: leave, O leave me, not a - lone; still sup - port and

3 You, O Christ, are all I want, more than all in you I find: raise the fal - len, cheer the faint, heal the sick and

4 Plen - teous grace with you is found, grace to wash a - way my sin: let the heal - ing streams a-bound; make and keep me

155 Jesus, saviour, holy child
(Rocking Carol)

Hajej, Nynej, Jezisku   10 7 8 8 8 8

Words: Michael Perry
Music: Czech carol melody
arranged David Peacock

3

1 Je - sus, sav - iour, ho - ly child, sleep to - night, slum - ber deep till morn - ing light. Lul - la - by, our joy, our trea - sure,

2 From your Fa - ther's home you come to this earth, by your low - ly man - ger birth! Child of God, our na - ture shar - ing;

3 Now to hea - ven's glo - ry song we re - ply with a Christ - mas lul - la - by. Hush, the e - ter - nal Lord is sleep - ing

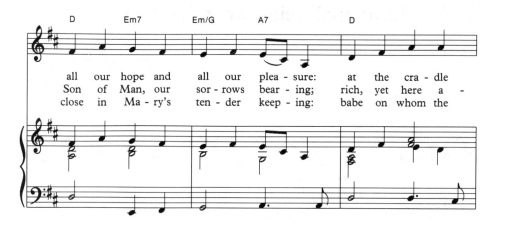

all our hope and all our plea - sure: at the cra - dle
Son of Man, our sor - rows bear - ing; rich, yet here a -
close in Ma - ry's ten - der keep - ing: babe on whom the

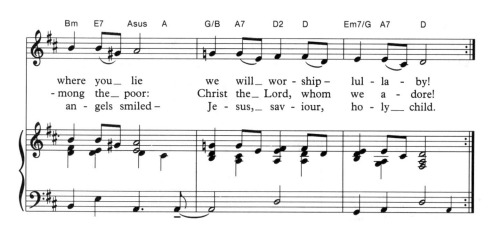

where you_ lie we will_ wor - ship – lul - la - by!
- mong the_ poor: Christ the_ Lord, whom we a - dore!
an - gels smiled – Je - sus,_ sav - iour, ho - ly _ child.

Instrumental obligato

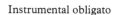

156   Jesus shall reign where'er the sun

TRURO   8 8 8 8 (LM)

Words: Isaac Watts
in this version Jubilate Hymns
Music: from Thomas William's
Psalmodia Evangelica
arranged Roger Mayor

7

With energy ♩ = 100

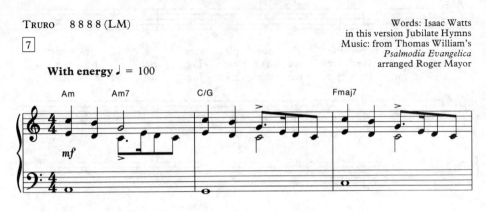

1 Je - sus shall reign where-'er the sun does
2 Peo - ple and realms of ev - ery tongue de -
3 Bless-ings a - bound where Je - sus reigns – the

its   suc - ces - sive__ jour - neys run;   his
- clare his love__ in__ sweet - est song,   and
pri - soner leaps__ to__ lose his chains,   the

king - dom stretch from shore to___ shore till moons shall rise and
child - ren's voi – ces shall pro - claim their ear - ly bless - ings
wea - ry find e - ter - nal___ rest, the hun - gry and the

Fine

set no more.
on his name.
poor are blessed.

4 To him shall endless prayer be made,
   and princes throng to crown his head;
   his name like incense shall arise
   with every morning sacrifice.

5 Let all creation rise and bring
   the highest honours to our king;
   angels descend with songs again
   and earth repeat the loud 'Amen!'

157

Jesus, stand among us
(First tune)

LISTEN TO MY PRAYER   6 5 6 5

Words: William Pennefather
Music: Christopher Norton

1 Je - sus, stand a - mong us   in your ri - sen
2 Breathe the Ho - ly Spi - rit   in - to ev - ery
3 Thus with quick-ened foot-steps   we'll pur-sue our

power;   let this time of wor - ship
heart;   bid the fears and sor - rows
way,   watch-ing for the dawn-ing

be a hal-lowed hour.   of e - ter - nal
from each soul de - part.

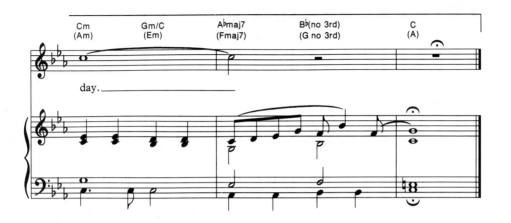

day.

Instrumental obligato

157

Jesus, stand among us
(Second tune)

NORTH COATES   6 5 6 5

Words: William Pennefather
Music: Friedrich Filitz
arranged Roger Mayor

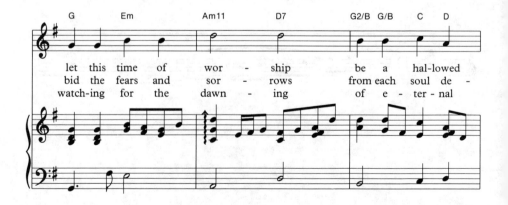

1   Je - sus, stand a- mong us   in your ri - sen power; let this time of wor - ship be a hal-lowed

2   Breathe the Ho - ly   Spi - rit in - to ev - ery heart; bid the fears and sor - rows from each soul de -

3   Thus with quick-ened   foot - steps we'll pur - sue our way, watch-ing for the dawn - ing of e - ter - nal

hour.
- part.

day.

rall.

Instrumental obligato

Obligato for B♭ instruments

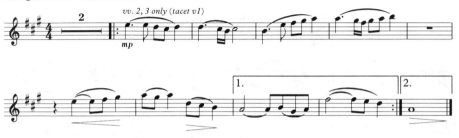

158   Jesus, the joy of loving hearts

MARYTON   8 8 8 8 (LM)

Words: from the Latin
Ray Palmer
Music: Henry Smith
arranged Christopher Norton

1 Je - sus, the joy of lov - ing hearts,
2 Your truth un - changed has ev - er stood,
3 We taste of you, the liv - ing bread,

true source of life, our lives sus - tain:
you res - cue those who on you call:
and long to feast up - on you still;

4 Our restless spirits long for you,
  whichever way our lot is cast,
  glad when your gracious smile we view,
  blessed when our faith can hold you fast.

5 Jesus, for ever with us stay,
  make all our moments calm and bright;
  chase the dark night of sin away,
  spread through the world your holy light.

159   Jesus! the name high over all

LYDIA   8 6 8 6 (CM) extended

Words: Charles Wesley
Music: Thomas Phillips
arranged David Peacock

1

Joyfully ♩ = 132

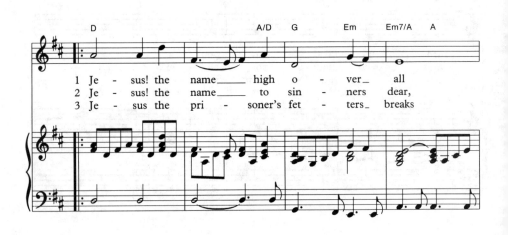

1 Je - sus! the name____ high o - ver__ all
2 Je - sus! the name____ to sin - ners dear,
3 Je - sus the pri - soner's fet - ters__ breaks

in   hell or__ earth____ or sky;   an - gels a -
the   name to__ sin - ners given;   it scat - ters
and   brui - ses__ Sa - tan's head;   power in - to

-gain be - fore it fall_____ and de - vils fear and fly,_____ and
all their guil - ty fear,_____ it turns their hell to heaven,_____ it
strength-less souls he speaks____ and life in - to the dead,_____ and

de - vils____ fear_ and_ fly.
turns their_ hell_ to____ heaven!
life_ in - to__ the___ dead.

Lamb!

4 O that the world might taste and see
   the riches of his grace!
   The arms of love that welcome me
      would everyone embrace,
      would everyone embrace.

5 His righteousness alone I show,
   his saving grace proclaim;
   this is my work on earth below,
      to cry 'Behold the Lamb!'
      to cry 'Behold the Lamb!'

6 Happy if with my final breath
   I may but gasp his name,
   preach him to all, and cry in death,
      'Behold, behold the Lamb!'
      'Behold, behold the Lamb!'

160 Jesus the saviour comes

LITTLE CORNARD   666688

Words: Margaret Clarkson
Music: Martin Shaw
arranged Christopher Norton

18

Strongly ♩ = 130

1 Je - sus the sav - iour comes!   Greet him with joy - ful song,
2 Je - sus the sav - iour comes!   Lord o - ver life and death;
3 Je - sus the sav - iour comes!   sov-ereign and Lord of all;

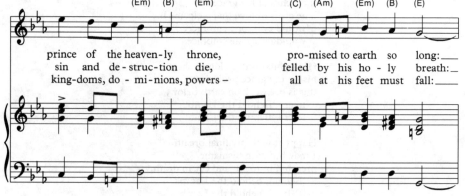

prince of the heaven - ly   throne,   pro - mised to earth so   long:___
sin and de - struc - tion   die,   felled by his ho - ly   breath:___
king-doms, do - mi - nions, powers –   all at his feet must   fall:___

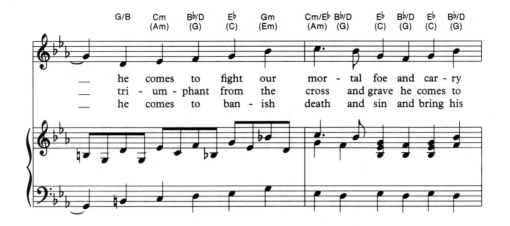

he comes to fight our mor - tal foe and car - ry
tri - um - phant from the cross and grave he comes to
he comes to ban - ish death and sin and bring his

all our sin and woe.
heal and bless and save.
great sal - va - tion in.

4 Lord of the Christmas crib,
   Lord of the cross of shame,
   humbly we worship you,
   proudly we take your name:
   be all our joy till advent drums
   and trumpets cry, 'The saviour comes!'

5 Then with your ransomed hosts,
   faultless before your face,
   sons of the living God,
   born of redeeming grace,
   your love we'll sing, your power we'll praise:
   your name adore through endless days!

161   Joy to the world

ANTIOCH   8 6 8 6 (CM)

Words: Isaac Watts
Music: George Handel
arranged Christopher Norton

1 Joy to the world! The Lord has come: let earth re - ceive her king,____ let ev - ery heart_ pre -
2 Joy to the earth! The sav - iour reigns: your sweet - est songs em - ploy____ while fields and streams and
3 He rules the world with truth and grace, and makes the na - tions prove____ the glo - ries of___ his

-pare_ him_ room_____ and heaven and na - ture sing, and_
hills_ and_ plains_____ re - peat the sound-ing_ joy, re -
right - eous - ness,_____ the won-ders of his_ love, the_

heaven and na - ture sing, and heaven, and heaven_ and na - ture
- peat the sound-ing joy, re - peat,____ re - peat____ the sound-ing
won - ders of his love, the won - ders, won - ders of his

sing!
joy.
love.

162 Judge eternal, throned in splendour

RHUDDLAN 878787

23

Words: Henry Holland
in this version Jubilate Hymns
Music: Welsh traditional melody
arranged Roger Mayor

1 Judge e - ter - nal, throned in splen-dour, Lord of lords and
2 Wea - ry peo - ple still are long - ing for the hour that
3 Crown, O Lord, your own en - dea - vour, cleave our dark-ness

King of kings, with your liv - ing fire of judge - ment
brings re - lease, and the ci - ty's crowd-ed cla - mour
with your sword, cheer the faint and feed the hun - gry

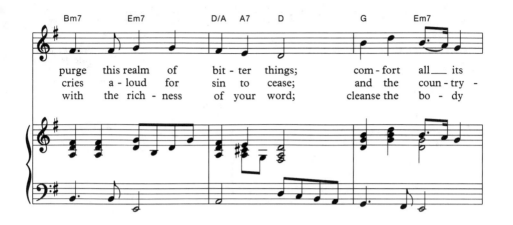

purge this realm of bit - ter things; com - fort all___ its
cries a - loud for sin to cease; and the coun - try -
with the rich - ness of your word; cleanse the bo - dy

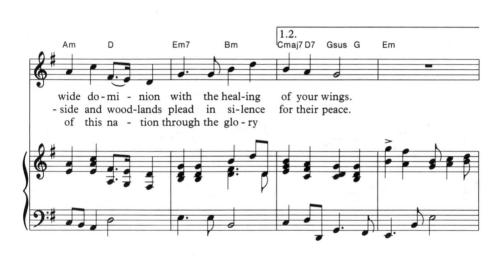

wide do - mi - nion with the heal-ing of your wings.
- side and wood-lands plead in si - lence for their peace.
of this na - tion through the glo - ry

of the Lord.

163   Just as a lost and thirsty deer

THIRSTING FOR GOD   8 8 8 8 (LM)

From Psalm 42
Words and music: John Bell
and Graham Maule
arranged Roger Mayor

1 Just   as   a   lost   and   thir - sty
2 Both   day   and   night   I   cry   a -
3 Bro - ken and   hurt   I   call   to
4 Why   am   I   now   so   lost   and

deer   longs   for   the   cool   and   run - ning
- loud;   tears   have be - come   my   on - ly
mind   how   in   the   past   I   served the
low;   why   am   I   trou - bled and   con -

G
(E)　　　　　Gm
　　　　　　(Em)　　E♭maj7
　　　　　　　　　　(C)　　　F
　　　　　　　　　　　　　　(D)　　　Dm7
　　　　　　　　　　　　　　　　　　(Bm7)

stream,　　　　　I　　thirst　for　you,　　　the
food　　　　　　while　all　a - round　　　cruel
Lord,　　　　　wor - shipped and　walked　with
- fused?　　　　Giv - en　no　ans - wer,

E♭
(C)　　　　Cm7
　　　　　(Am7)　　Dsus
　　　　　　　　　(Bsus)　　D
　　　　　　　　　　　　　(B)　　　Gm
　　　　　　　　　　　　　　　　(Em)　　Am7
　　　　　　　　　　　　　　　　　　　(F♯m7)

liv - ing　　　God,　　　　　an - xious　to
voi - ces　　　ask,　　　　'Where　is　your
hap - py　　　crowds,　　　sing - ing　and
still　I　　　hope　　　　and　trust　my

Cm7
(Am7)　　　　　　　　Dsus
　　　　　　　　　　(Bsus)　　Dm7
　　　　　　　　　　　　　　(Bm7)　　　G
　　　　　　　　　　　　　　　　　　(E)

know　　　　that　you　are　　　near.
God,　　　　where　is　your　　　God?'
shout - ing　praise　to　　　　God.
Sav - iour　and　my　　　　　God.

164 Just as I am

WOODWORTH 8 6 8 6 extended

Words: Charlotte Elliott
in this version Jubilate Hymns
Music: William Bradbury
arranged David Peacock

2

Sensitively ♩ = 90

C/D   G/D   G/A   A7   D

1 Just   as   I
(2) as   I
(3) as   I

Dmaj7   Em7/D   D   A

am,____ with - out____ one plea   but   that____ you
am,____ with - out____ de - lay   your   call____ of
am,____ though tossed____ a - bout   with   ma - ny a

Em7   G/A   G/D   D   G/A A7   D

died   to   set   me   free,   and_ at   your
mer - cy   I   o - bey –   your blood   can
con - flict,   ma - ny a   doubt,   fight - ings   with –

4 Just as I am, poor, wretched, blind!
   Sight, riches, healing of the mind –
   all that I need, in you to find,
       O Lamb of God, I come, I come.

5 Just as I am! You will receive,
   will welcome, pardon, cleanse, relieve:
   because your promise I believe,
       O Lamb of God, I come, I come.

6 Just am I am! Your love unknown
   has broken every barrier down:
   now to be yours, yes, yours alone,
       O Lamb of God, I come, I come.

7 Just as I am! Of that free love
   the breadth, length, depth and height to prove,
   here for a time and then above,
       O Lamb of God, I come, I come.

165 King of glory, king of peace

GWALCHMAI 7 4 7 4 D

Words: George Herbert
in this version Word & Music
Music: Joseph Jones
arranged Christopher Norton

11

1 King of glory, king of peace I will love you;
since your mer - cies_ nev - er cease, faith shall prove

2 Prais - es with my ut - most art I will bring you;
songs of tri - umph from my heart I will sing

3 Seven whole days_ not one in seven_ I will praise you;
wor - ship lifts the_ heart to heaven, love o - beys

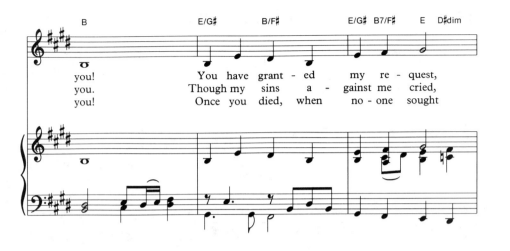

you!   You have grant-ed   my re-quest,
you.   Though my sins a-gainst me cried,
you!   Once you died, when no-one sought

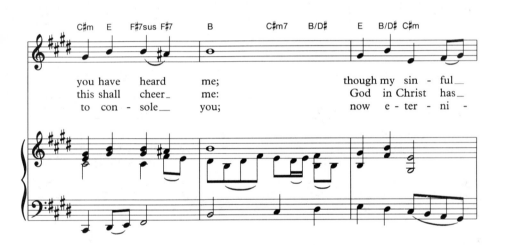

you have heard me;   though my sin-ful
this shall cheer me: God in Christ has
to con-sole you;   now e-ter-ni-

soul trans-gressed,   you have spared me.
jus-ti-fied   and will clear me.
-ty's too short   to ex-tol you!

166 King of the universe

KING OF THE UNIVERSE   11 10 12 10

Words: Michael Saward
Music: Alistair Goudie
arranged David Peacock

wise and just cre - a - tor, hope of the na - tions:
bow with-in your pres - ence, Lord of the na - tions: we
ba - sis of all or - der, guide to the na - tions:

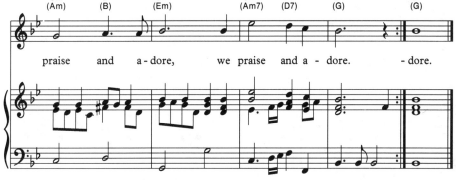

praise and a-dore, we praise and a - dore. - dore.

4 Justice and righteousness, holy, unswerving –
all that is tainted shall burn in your flame;
sword-bearing deity, punisher of evil,
judge of the nations: we praise and adore,
we praise and adore.

5 Ruler and potentate, sage and lawgiver,
humbled before you, unworthy we bow:
in our extremity, show us your forgiveness,
merciful Father: we praise and adore,
we praise and adore.

167 Lead us, heavenly Father

MANNHEIM   8 7 8 7 8 7

Words: James Edmeston
in this version Jubilate Hymns
Music: Friedrich Filitz
arranged Roger Mayor

1 Lead us, heaven-ly Fa-ther, lead us
2 Sav-iour, by your grace re-store us –
3 Spi-rit of our God, de-scend-ing,

through this world's tem-pest-uous sea;
all our weak-ness-es are plain:
fill our hearts with ho-ly peace –

guard us, guide us,
you have lived on
love with ev-ery

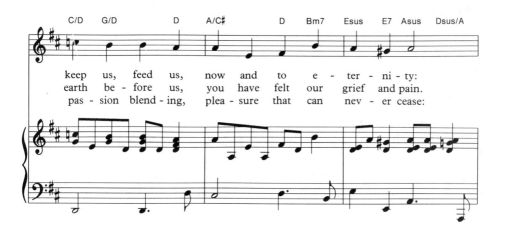

keep us, feed us, now and to e - ter - ni - ty:
earth be - fore us, you have felt our grief and pain.
pas - sion blend - ing, plea - sure that can nev - er cease:

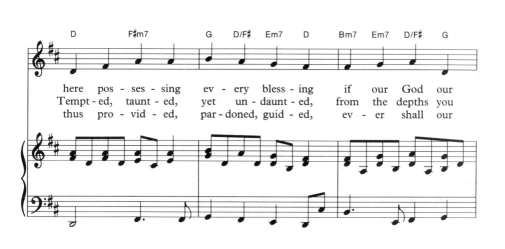

here pos - ses - sing ev - ery bless - ing if our God our
Tempt - ed, taunt - ed, yet un - daunt - ed, from the depths you
thus pro - vid - ed, par - doned, guid - ed, ev - er shall our

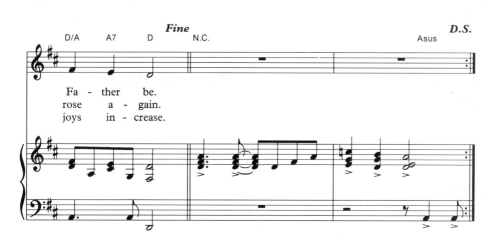

Fa - ther be.
rose a - gain.
joys in - crease.

168   Led like a lamb

YOU'RE ALIVE   Irregular   Words and music: Graham Kendrick

1 Led like a lamb to the slaugh - ter in
2 At break of dawn – poor Ma - ry, still
3 At the right hand of the Fa - ther, now

si - lence and shame,   there on your back you car - ried a world of
weep-ing, she came: when through her grief she heard your voice now
seat - ed on high,   you have be - gun your e - ter - nal_ reign of

vio - lence and pain,   bleed-ing,_   dy - ing,_
speak-ing her name,   A 'Ma - ry!'_   B 'Mas-ter!'_
jus - tice and joy: Glo - ry,_   glo - ry,_

The congregation may divide at A and B in verse 2.
If dividing between men and women, the men should sing part A

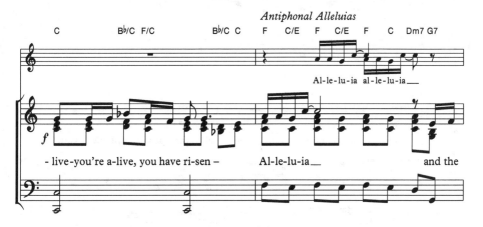

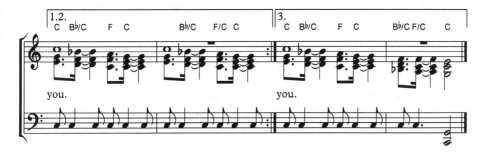

169 Let the people praise you

LET THE PEOPLE PRAISE YOU   7 6 7 6 and refrain

From Psalm 67
Words and music: Christopher Rolinson

The congregation may divide at A and B

Fine

all the peo-ple praise_____ you.

1 May your ways be known on earth, and your power to
2 We'll be glad and sing for joy, for you rule with
3 For you are a gra-cious God, we de-light to

save us:__ then the peo-ples of the world shall
jus - tice;__ then the ends of all the earth shall
praise you:_ then our land shall see the fruits of

D.C.

fear you,_ shall fear you.
fear you,_ shall fear you.
bless - ing,__ your bless - ing.

170 Let trumpets sound
(Hark, the glad sound)

COMMITMENT 8 6 8 6 D (DCM)

14

Words: Phillip Doddridge
Music: Joe Pinson
arranged David Peacock

With strength ♩ = 110

1 Let

trum - pets sound! The Sav-iour comes,   the   Sav-iour pro-mised
(3) comes the bro - ken heart to bind,   the   wound-ed soul to

long: let   ev - ery heart pre-pare a throne   and_
cure;   and   with   the trea-sures of his grace   to en-

171   Let us love and sing

LET US LOVE   8 7 8 7 7 7

Words: John Newton
Music: Christopher Norton

1 Let us love and sing and won - der; let us
praise the sav - iour's name! he has hushed the law's loud

2 Let us love the Lord who bought us, dy - ing
for our re - bel race; called us by his word and

3 Let us sing, though fierce temp - ta - tion threat - ens
hard to drag us down; for the Lord, our strong sal -

4 Let us won - der at the glo - ry God will
lav - ish on his own; saved by grace, we tell the

172   Let us sing to the God of salvation

GIVE ME JOY   Irregular

Words: from Psalm 95
Richard Bewes
Music: traditional
arranged Roger Mayor

1 Let us sing to the God of sal-
  (2) hand are the earth's deep-est
  (3) wor - ship the Lord our
  (4) -day be the time when you

-va-tion, let us sing to the Lord our rock; let us
pla-ces, and the strength of the hills is his; all the
ma-ker, let us kneel to the Lord our God; for we
hear him! May our hearts not be hard or cold, lest we

come to his house with thanks-giv-ing,___ let us
sea is the Lord's, for he made it – by his
all are the sheep of his pas-ture – he will
stray from the Lord in re-bel-lion___ as his

173 Like the murmur of the dove's song

BRIDEGROOM 8 7 8 7 6

Words: Carl P Daw Jr
Music: Peter Cutts

1 Like the mur - mur of the dove's song, like the chal-lenge of her flight, like the
2 To the mem - bers of Christ's Bo - dy, to the bran-ches of the Vine, to the
3 With the heal - ing of di - vi - sion, with the cease-less voice of prayer, with the

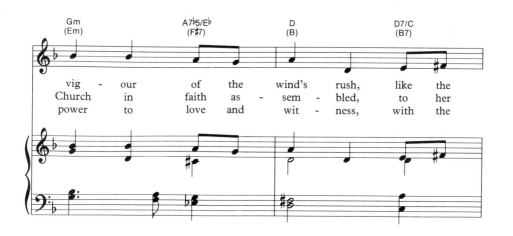

vig - our of the wind's rush, like the
Church in faith as - sem - bled, to her
power to love and wit - ness, with the

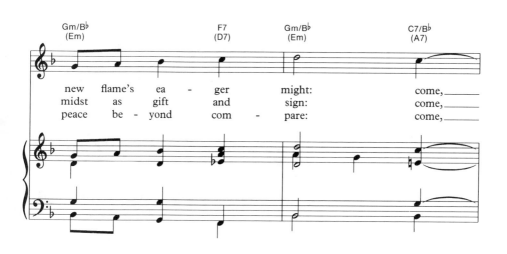

new flame's ea - ger might: come,_____
midst as gift and sign: come,_____
peace be - yond com - pare: come,_____

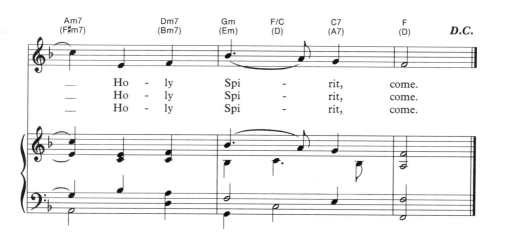

— Ho - ly Spi - rit, come.
— Ho - ly Spi - rit, come.
— Ho - ly Spi - rit, come.

174   Lord, as I wake

LORD AS I WAKE   8 8 8 8 (LM)

6

Words: from Psalm 5
Brian Foley
Music: Roger Mayor

1 Lord, as I wake I turn to you,
2 There is no bless-ing, Lord, from you
3 Your lov-ing gifts of grace to me,
4 Lord, make my life a life of love,

your-self the first thought of___ my day;
for those who make their will___ their way,
those fav-ours I could ne - ver earn,
keep me from sin in all___ I do;

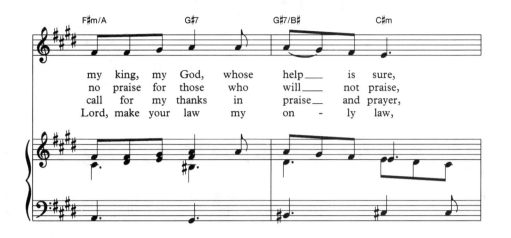

my king, my God, whose help____ is sure,
no praise for those who will____ not praise,
call for my thanks in praise__ and prayer,
Lord, make your law my on - ly law,

your-self the help for which I pray.
no peace for those who will__ not pray.
call me to love you in____ re-turn.
your will my will, for love__ of you.

175 Lord, be my vision

SLANE   10 10 10 10

[2]

Words: from the Irish
Mary Byrne and Eleanor Hull
in this version Jubilate Hymns
Music: Irish traditional melody
arranged Christopher Norton

Prayerfully ♩ = 90

1 Lord, be my vi - sion, su - preme in my heart;
2 Lord, be my wis - dom and be my true word;
3 Lord, be my breast-plate, my sword for the fight;

bid ev - ery ri - val give way and de - part:
I ev - er with you and you with me, Lord:
be my strong arm - our, for you are my might.

you my__ best__ thought in the day or the night,_____
you my__ great fa - ther and I your true child,_____
You are__ my__ shel - ter and you my high tower =_____

wa - king or sleep - ing, your pre - sence my light.
once far a - way, but by__ love re - con - ciled.
raise me to hea - ven, O__ Power of my power.

4 I need no riches, nor earth's empty praise –
   you my inheritance through all my days;
   all of your treasure to me you impart,
   high King of heaven, the first in my heart.

5 High King of heaven, when battle is done,
   grant heaven's joy to me, bright heaven's sun;
   Christ of my own heart, whatever befall,
   still be my vision, O Ruler of all.

176   Lord, for the years

LORD OF THE YEARS   11 10 11 10

Words: Timothy Dudley-Smith
Music: Michael Baughen
arranged Christopher Norton

1 Lord, for the years your love has kept and guid - ed,
2 Lord, for that word, the word of life which fires us,
3 Lord, for our land, in this our ge - ne - ra - tion,

urged and in - spired us, cheered us on＿ our way,
speaks to our hearts and sets our souls a - blaze;
spi - rits op - pressed by plea-sure, wealth and care;

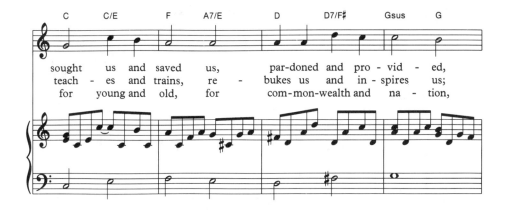

sought us and saved us, par-doned and pro - vid - ed,
teach - es and trains, re - bukes us and in - spires us;
for young and old, for com-mon-wealth and na - tion,

Lord of the years, we bring our thanks to - day.
Lord of the word, re - ceive your peo - ple's praise.
Lord of our land, be pleased to hear our prayer.

4 Lord, for our world; when we disown and doubt him,
loveless in strength, and comfortless in pain;
hungry and helpless, lost indeed without him;
Lord of the world, we pray that Christ may reign.

5 Lord, for ourselves; in living power remake us –
self on the cross and Christ upon the throne,
past put behind us, for the future take us,
Lord of our lives, to live for Christ alone.

177 Lord, I was blind

BODMIN   8 8 8 8 (LM)

9

Words: William Matson
in this version Jubilate Hymns
Music: Alfred Scott-Gatty
arranged Roger Mayor

Prayerfully ♩ = 92

1 Lord, I was blind; I could not see
2 Lord, I was deaf; I could not hear
3 Lord, I was dumb; I could not speak

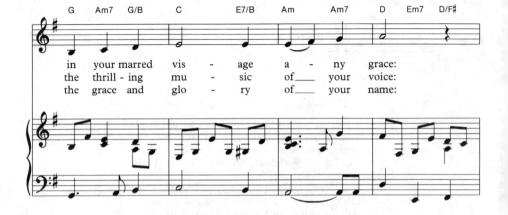

in   your marred   vis – age   a – ny   grace:
the   thrill - ing   mu – sic   of   your   voice:
the   grace and   glo – ry   of   your   name:

but now the beau - ty of_____ your face_____
but now I hear you and_____ re - joice,_____
but now as touched with liv - ing flame_____

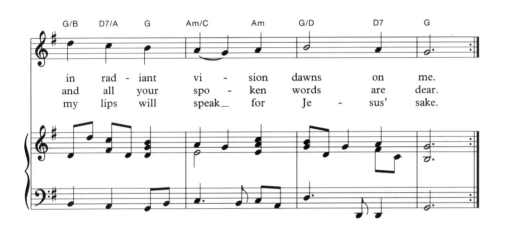

in rad - iant vi - sion dawns on me.
and all your spo - ken words are dear.
my lips will speak_ for Je - sus' sake.

4 Lord, I was dead; I could not move
my lifeless soul from sin's dark grave:
but now the power of life you gave
has raised me up to know your love.

5 Lord, you have made the blind to see,
the deaf to hear, the dumb to speak,
the dead to live – and now I break
the chains of my captivity!

178 Lord Jesus Christ

LIVING LORD   9 8 8 8 8 3

Words and music: Patrick Appleford
Music arranged Noël Tredinnick

Verse 3 should be omitted when there is no communion

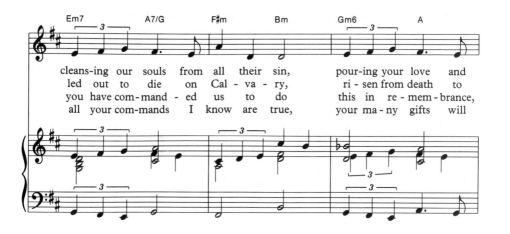

cleans-ing our souls from all their sin,   pour-ing your love   and
led out to die on Cal - va - ry,   ri - sen from death   to
you have com-mand - ed us to do   this in re - mem - brance,
all your com-mands I know are true,   your ma - ny gifts   will

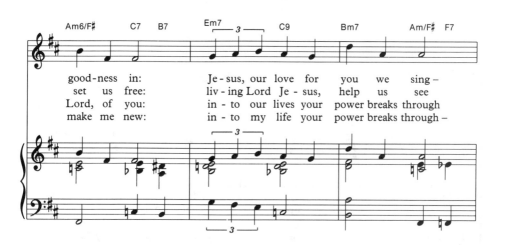

good-ness in: Je - sus, our love for   you   we   sing —
set us free: liv - ing Lord Je - sus, help us   see
Lord, of you: in - to our lives your   power breaks through
make me new: in - to my life your   power breaks through —

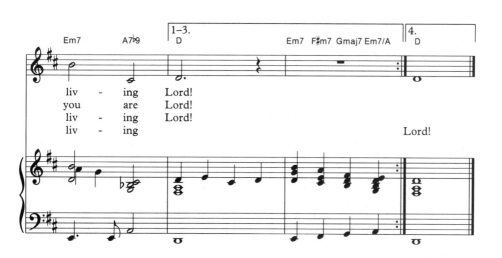

1–3.
liv - ing   Lord!
you   are   Lord!
liv - ing   Lord!
liv - ing   Lord!

179   Like a mighty river flowing

OLD YEAVERING   8 8 8 7

Words: Michael Perry
Music: Noël Tredinnick
arranged David Peacock

4.   Like the morning sun ascended,
     like the scents of evening blended,
     like a friendship never ended
       is the perfect peace of God.

5.   Like the azure ocean swelling,
     like the jewel all-excelling,
     far beyond our human telling
       is the perfect peace of God.

May also be sung to the tune QUEM PASTORES LAUDAVERE (150)

180   Lord of the church

LONDONDERRY AIR   11 10 11 10 D

Words: Timothy Dudley-Smith
Music: Irish traditional melody
arranged Christopher Norton

11

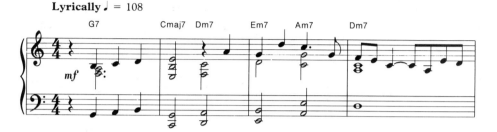

1 Lord of the church, we pray for our re - new - ing:
(2) church, we seek a Fa-ther's bless - ing,
(3) church, we long for our u - ni - ting,

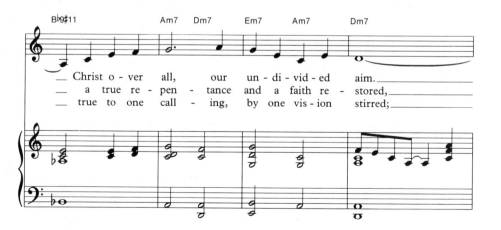

— Christ o - ver all, our un - di - vid - ed aim.
— a true re - pen - tance and a faith re - stored,
— true to one call - ing, by one vis - ion stirred;

181   Lord of the cross of shame

CROSS OF SHAME   6 6 11 D

Words: Michael Saward
Music: Michael Baughen
arranged David Peacock

1 Lord of the cross of shame, _____ set my cold
2 Lord of the emp - ty tomb, _____ born of a
3 Lord of my life to - day, _____ teach me to

heart a - flame   with love to you,   my
vir - gin's womb,   tri - umph - ant o - ver
live and pray   as one who knows the

May also be sung to the tune COME DOWN (159)

182   Lord, the light of your love

SHINE JESUS SHINE   Irregular

Words and music: Graham Kendrick
Music arranged Christopher Norton

1 Lord, the light of your love is shin - ing, in the midst of the dark - ness, shin - ing: Je - sus, light of the world, shine up - on__ us; set us free by the truth you now bring__ us –

2 Lord, I come to your awe - some pres - ence, from the sha - dows in - to your ra - diance; by your Blood I may en - ter your bright - ness: search me, try me, con - sume all my dark - ness –

3 As we gaze on your king - ly bright - ness so our fa - ces dis - play your like - ness, ev - er chang - ing from glo - ry to glo - ry: mir - rored here, may our lives tell your sto - ry –

183   Lord, you need no house

WAXHAM   5 6 6 4

12

Words: from Acts 17
Christopher Idle
Music: Roger Mayor

Thoughtfully ♩ = 82

1 Lord,   you_ need   no   house,   no man- ger
2 Lord,   you_ need   no   gift,   for all   things
3 Lord,   you_ need   no   skill   to make   your_

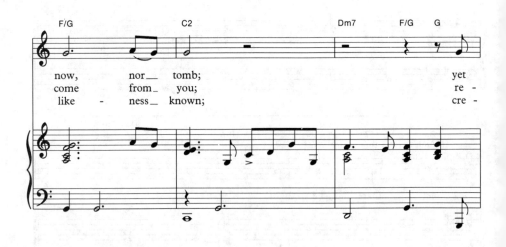

now,   nor_ tomb;   yet
come   from_ you;   re -
like - ness_ known;   cre -

184   Lord, you sometimes speak in wonders

CLEVELAND   8 7 8 7 10

Words: Christopher Idle
Music: Christopher Johnson
arranged Roger Mayor

1 Lord, you some-times speak in won - ders,
2 Lord, you some-times speak in whis - pers,
3 Lord, you some-times speak in si - lence,

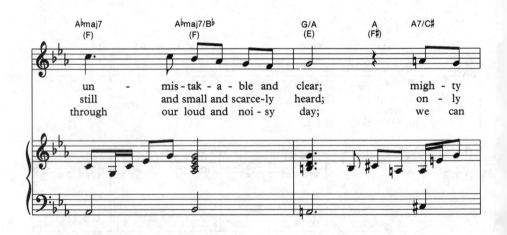

un - mis - tak - a - ble and clear;
still and small and scarce-ly heard;
through our loud and noi - sy day;

migh - ty
on - ly
we can

The original version of this hymn text comprises the first four lines of each verse.
The fifth line was added by the composer to fit this particular musical setting.

signs   to prove your pres-ence, o - ver - com-ing doubt and fear: O___
those who want   to   lis - ten catch the   all - im - port - ant word: O___
know and trust you bet - ter when we   quiet-ly wait and pray: O___

Lord,   you some-times speak in   won-ders.
Lord,   you some-times speak in   whis-pers
Lord,   you some-times speak in   si - lence.

Je - sus.

4 Lord, you often speak in Scripture –
   words that summon from the page,
   shown and taught us by your Spirit
   with fresh light for every age:
      O Lord, you often speak in Scripture.

5 Lord, you always speak in Jesus,
   always new yet still the same:
   teach us now more of our Saviour;
   make our lives display his name:
      O Lord, you always speak in Jesus.

185

Lord, you were rich

BERGERS 989898

Words: Frank Houghton
in this version Jubilate Hymns
Music: French traditional melody
arranged David Peacock

1 Lord, you were rich be - yond all splen - dour,
2 You are our God be - yond all prais - ing,
3 Lord, you are love be - yond all tell - ing,

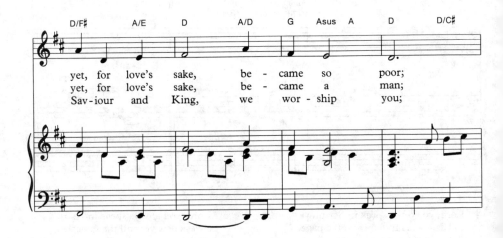

yet, for love's sake, be - came so poor;
yet, for love's sake, be - came a man;
Sav - iour and King, we wor - ship you;

186   Lord, your church on earth is seeking

ODE TO JOY   8 7 8 7 D

Words: Hugh Sherlock
and Michael Saward
Music: Ludwig Van Beethoven
arranged Christopher Norton

1

Medium tempo ♩ = 120

1 Lord, your church on earth is seek-ing power and wis-dom from a-bove: teach us all the art of speak-ing
2 You re-lease us from our bond-age, lift the bur-dens caused by sin; give new hope, new strength and cour-age,
3 In the streets of ev-ery ci-ty where the bruised and lone-ly live, we will show the sav-iour's pi-ty

Words: © Methodist Publishing House,
20 Ivatt Way, Westwood, Peterborough PE3 7PG

187   Lord, your word shall guide us

RAVENSHAW   6 6 6 6

Words: Henry Baker
in this version Jubilate Hymns
Music: Michael Weisse
arranged Roger Mayor

1 Lord, your word shall guide us and with truth pro-
2 When our foes are near us, then your word shall
3 When the storms dis-tress us and dark clouds op-

-vide us: teach us to re-
cheer us — word of con- so-
-press us, then your word pro-

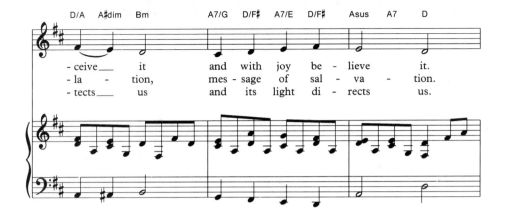

| D/A | A#dim | Bm | | A7/G | D/F# | A7/E | D/F# | Asus | A7 | D |

- ceive___ it and with joy be - lieve it.
- la - tion, mes - sage of sal - va - tion.
- tects___ us and its light di - rects us.

1–5.
Em7   A6   A7

6.
Em7   A6   A7   Dsus   D

rall.

p

4   Who can tell the pleasure,
who recount the treasure
by your word imparted
to the simple-hearted?

5   Word of mercy, giving
courage to the living;
word of life, supplying
comfort to the dying:

6   O that we discerning
its most holy learning,
Lord, may love and fear you –
evermore be near you!

188 Love divine, all loves excelling

BLAENWERN 8 7 8 7 D

Words: Charles Wesley
Music: William Rowlands
arranged Roger Mayor

1 Love divine, all loves excelling, joy of heaven, to earth come down: fix in us your humble dwelling, all your faithful mercies

2 Come, almighty to deliver, let us all your grace receive; suddenly return, and never, never more your temples

3 Finish then your new creation: pure and sinless let us be; let us see your great salvation, perfect in eterni-

189   Love is his word

CRESSWELL   8 8 9 7 10 7

Words: Luke Connaughton
Music: Anthony Milner
arranged Roger Mayor

1 Love is his word,   love is his way,   feast-ing with all,
2 Love is his way,   love is his mark,   shar-ing his last
3 Love is his mark,   love is his sign,   bread for our strength,

fast-ing a-lone,   liv-ing and dy-ing,   ris-ing a-gain,
Pass-o-ver feast,   Christ at his ta-ble,   host to the twelve,
wine for our joy,   'This is my bo-dy,   this is my blood' —

Verses 2, 3 and 4 may be omitted when there is no communion

love, on-ly love, is his way:
love, on-ly love, is his mark:
love, on-ly love, is his sign:

Rich - er than gold is the

love of my Lord, bet - ter than splen - dour and

wealth. wealth.

4 Love is his sign, love is his news,
   'Do this,' he said, 'lest you forget.'
   All his deep sorrow, all his dear blood –
   love, only love, is his news:
       Richer than gold . . .

5 Love is his news, love is his name,
   we are his own, chosen and called,
   family, children, cousins and kin,
   love, only love, is his name:
       Richer than gold . . .

6 Love is his name, love is his law,
   hear his command, all who are his:
   'Love one another, I have loved you' –
   love, only love, is his law.
       Richer than gold . . .

7 Love is his law, love is his word:
   love of the Lord, Father and Word,
   love of the Spirit, God ever one,
   love, only love, is his word:
       Richer than gold . . .

190   Loved with everlasting love

DIM OND JESU   7 7 7 7 D

Words: George Robinson
Music: Robert Lowry
arranged Christopher Norton

191 Low in the grave he lay

CHRIST AROSE   6 5 6 4 and refrain

Words and music: Robert Lowry
Music arranged Roger Mayor

1 Low in the grave he lay,
2 Vain - ly they guard his bed,
3 Death can - not keep his prey,

Je - sus my sav - iour, wait - ing the
Je - sus my sav - iour; vain - ly they
Je - sus my sav - iour; he tore the

com - ing day, Je - sus my Lord!
seal the dead, Je - sus my Lord!
bars a - way, Je - sus my Lord!

192   Make me a channel of your peace

ST FRANCIS   Irregular

From the traditional prayer
Words and music: Sebastian Temple
Music arranged Christopher Norton

3   **Prayerfully** ♩ = 78

1 Make me a chan-nel of your peace:_____ where
2 Make me a chan-nel of your peace:_____ where
3 Make me a chan-nel of your peace:_____ it

there is hat-red let me bring your love,_____ where
there's des-pair in life let me bring hope,_____ where
is in par-don - ing that we are par - doned,_____ in

there is in-jur-y, your par-don, Lord,_____ and
there is dark-ness,_____ on - ly light,_____ and
giv-ing of our-selves that we re - ceive,_____ and in

193   Mary came with meekness

NOEL NOUVELET   6 5 6 5 D

Words: Paul Wigmore
Music: French traditional melody
arranged David Peacock

1 Ma - ry came with meek - ness,   Je - sus Christ to bear,
2 An - gels came with prai - ses,   Je - sus Christ to name,
3 Shep - herds came with tremb - ling,   Je - sus Christ to see;
4 Wise men came with trea - sure,   Je - sus Christ to bless –

doo . . .   doo ba-ba-ba!

laid the Lord of glo - ry   in a__ man - ger there.
hea-ven's choirs ex - alt - ing   him who bears our shame.
king who, at their bid - ding,   would their shep-herd be.
he who shares all bless - ings   heaven and earth pos - sess.

doo . . .   do-be-do-be . . .

194 Mary sang a song

MARY SANG A SONG   9 9 9 9

Words: from Luke 1 (*Magnificat*)
Michael Perry
Music: Christopher Norton

Verse lyrics:

1 Ma - ry sang a song, a song __ of love, mag - ni - fied the migh - ty Lord __ a - bove;
2 'God the Lord has done great things __ for me, looked up - on my life's hu - mi - li - ty;
3 'To the hum - ble soul our God __ is kind, to the proud he brings un - ease __ of mind.

me - lo - dies of praise his name____ ex - tol
hap - py they shall call me from____ this day –
Who up - lifts the poor, pulls down____ the strong?

from the ve - ry depths of Ma - ry's soul:
mer - ci - ful is he whom we____ o - bey.
God a - lone has power to right____ the wrong!

4 'He who has been Israel's strength and stay
   fills the hungry, sends the rich away;
   God has shown his promise firm and sure,
   faithful to his people evermore.'

5 This was Mary's song as we recall,
   mother to the saviour of us all:
   magnify his name and sing his praise,
   worship and adore him, all your days!

195

Man of sorrows

MAN OF SORROWS   7 7 7 8

Words and music: Philipp Bliss
Music arranged Christopher Norton

3

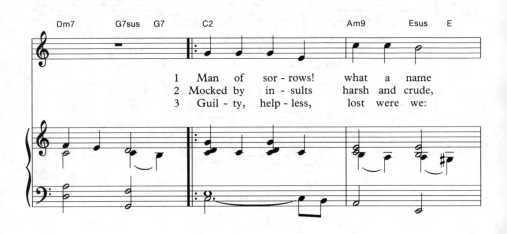

1 Man of sor - rows! what a name
2 Mocked by in - sults harsh and crude,
3 Guil - ty, help - less, lost were we:

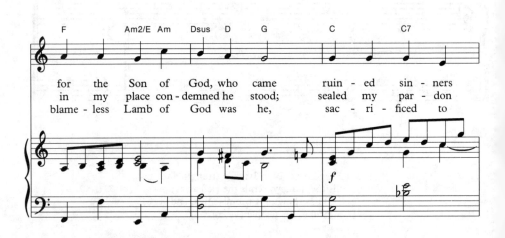

for the Son of God, who came ruin - ed sin - ners
in my place con - demned he stood; sealed my par - don
blame - less Lamb of God was he, sac - ri - ficed to

to	re -	claim:	Al -	le - lu	-	ia!	what	a	sav -	iour!
with	his	blood:	Al -	le - lu	-	ia!	what	a	sav -	iour!
set	us	free:	Al -	le - lu	-	ia!	what	a	sav -	iour!

4   Lifted up was he to die:
     'It is finished!' was his cry;
     now in heaven exalted high:
      Alleluia! what a saviour!

5   When he comes, our glorious king,
     all his ransomed home to bring;
     then again this song we'll sing:
      'Alleluia! what a saviour!'

196   May the grace of Christ our saviour

EBENEZER   8 7 8 7 D

6

Words: from 2 Corinthians 13
John Newton
Music: Thomas Williams
arranged Christopher Norton

Rock ballad ♩ = 88

1 May the grace of Christ our sav - iour

and the Fa - ther's bound - less love,

with the Ho - ly Spi - rit's fa - vour,

197 Meekness and majesty

THIS IS YOUR GOD   12 11 12 11 and refrain

Words and music: Graham Kendrick
Music arranged Christopher Norton

9

Thoughtfully ♩ = 106

1 Meek-ness and ma-jes-ty, man-hood and de-i-ty, in per-fect
2 Fa-ther's pure ra-di-ance, per-fect in in-no-cence, yet learns o-
3 Wis-dom un-search-a-ble, God the in-vi-si-ble, love in-des-

har-mo-ny — the man who is God: Lord of e-ter-ni-ty
-be-di-ence to death on a cross: suffer-ing to give us life,
-truc-ti-ble in frail-ty ap-pears: Lord of in-fi-ni-ty,

dwells in hu-man-i-ty, kneels in hu-mil-i-ty— and— wash-es our
conquer-ing through sac-ri-fice and, as they cru-ci-fy,— prays, 'Fa-ther, for-
stoop-ing so ten-der-ly, lifts our hu-man-i-ty— to the heights of his

198   Morning has broken

BUNESSAN   10 9 10 9

19

Words: Eleanor Farjeon
Music: Gaelic melody
arranged Christopher Norton

Flowing ♩ = 115

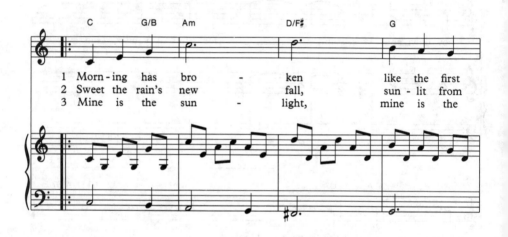

1 Morn-ing has bro - ken   like the first
2 Sweet the rain's new   fall,   sun - lit from
3 Mine is the sun - light,   mine is the

morn - ing;   black-bird has spo - ken
hea - ven,   like the first dew fall
morn - ing   born of the one light

Words: © David Higham Associates,
5–8 Lower John Street, Golden Square, London W1R 3PE

199   May the mind of Christ my saviour

St Leonards   8 7 8 5

Words: Katie Wilkinson
in this version Jubilate Hymns
Music: Arthur Barham Gould
arranged David Peacock

Worshipfully ♩ = 88

1 May the mind of Christ my sav-iour
2 May the word of God en - rich me
3 May the peace of God my Fa-ther

live in me from day to day, by his love and power con - trol-ling
with his truth, from hour to hour; so that all may see I tri-umph
in my life for ev - er reign, that I may be calm to com-fort

1–4.
all_ I do_ and say.
on - ly through his power.
those in grief_ and pain.

5.
- lone.

4 May the love of Jesus fill me
    as the waters fill the sea,
    him exalting, self abasing –
        this is victory!

5 May his beauty rest upon me
    as I seek to make him known;
    so that all may look to Jesus,
        seeing him alone.

200 My God, how wonderful you are

MY GOD, HOW WONDERFUL   8 6 8 6 (CM)

3

Words: Frederick Faber
in this version Jubilate Hymns
Music: Roger Jones

Worshipfully ♩ = 74

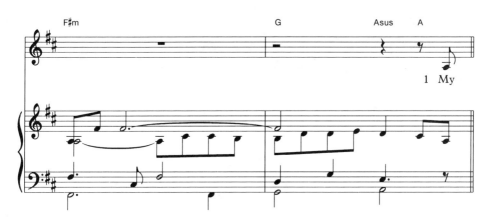

1 My

God,_____ how won-der-ful you are,_____ your ma-jes-
(3) won - der-ful, how beau-ti-ful_____ the sight of
(5) I_____ may love you too, O Lord,__ though you are
(7) God,_____ how won-der-ful you are,_____ your ma-jes-

201 My hope is built

ST CATHERINE   888888

9

Words: Edward Mote
in this version Jubilate Hymns
Music: Henri Hémy
arranged Roger Mayor

Confidently ♩ = 110

1 My hope is built_ on no - thing less
2 When wea - ry in_ this earth - ly race,
3 His vow, his cov - en - ant_ and blood
4 When the last trum - pet's voice_ shall sound,

than Je - sus' blood and right - eous - ness;
I rest on his un - chang - ing grace;
are my de - fence a - gainst_ the flood;
O may I then in him_ be found!

202　My Lord, I did not choose you

ROEWEN　7 6 7 6 D

12

Words: Josiah Conder
Music: Roger Mayor

Flowing smoothly ♩ = 104

Lord, I did not choose_ you for that could ne - ver
(2) -less your grace had called_ me and taught my open - ing

be; my heart would still re - fuse you had
mind the world would have en - thralled me, to

Music: © Roger Mayor / Jubilate Hymns

203
My Lord of light

BARBARA ALLEN   8 7 8 7

Words: Christopher Idle
Music: English traditional melody
arranged Roger Mayor

Gently flowing ♩ = 86

Lord of light   who made the worlds,   in   wis-dom you have
(2) Lord of love   who knew no   sin,   a   sin-ner's death en -
(3) Lord of life   who came in   fire   when Christ was high   a -
(4) Lord of lords,   one   Tri - ni - ty,   to   your pure name   be

spo - ken;__   but those who heard   your   wise com-mands   your
- dur - ing:__   for   us you wore   a__   crown of thorns,   a
- scend-ed:__   your burn-ing love   is__   now re-leased,   our
giv - en__   all   glo - ry now   and   ev - er-more,   all

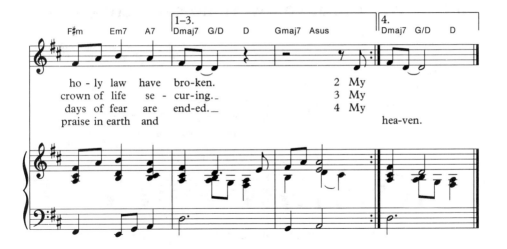

ho - ly law have bro-ken.   2 My
crown of life se - cur-ing.   3 My
days of fear are end-ed.   4 My
praise in earth and   hea-ven.

Instrumental obligato

Obligato for B♭ instruments

204 My Lord, you wore no royal crown

Royal Crown 8 8 8 8 (LM)

Words: Christopher Idle
Music: Christopher Norton

1 My Lord, you wore no roy-al crown;
you did not wield the powers of state,
nor did you need a scho-lar's gown or priest-ly robe, to make___ you great.

2 You ne-ver used a kill-er's sword
to end an un-just ty-ran-ny;
your on-ly wea-pon was your word, for truth a-lone could set___ us free.

3 You did not live a world a-way
in her-mit's cell or des-ert cave,
but felt our pain and shared each day with those you came to seek___ and save.

4 You made no mean or cunning move,
chose no unworthy compromise,
but carved a track of burning love
through tangles of deceit and lies.

5 You came unequalled, undeserved,
to be what I was meant to be;
to serve instead of being served,
to pay for my iniquity.

6 So when I stumble, set me right;
command my life as you require;
let all your gifts be my delight
and you, my Lord, my one desire.

205 My Lord, what love is this

AMAZING LOVE 6 5 6 3 and refrain

Words and music: Graham Kendrick
Music arranged Christopher Norton

12

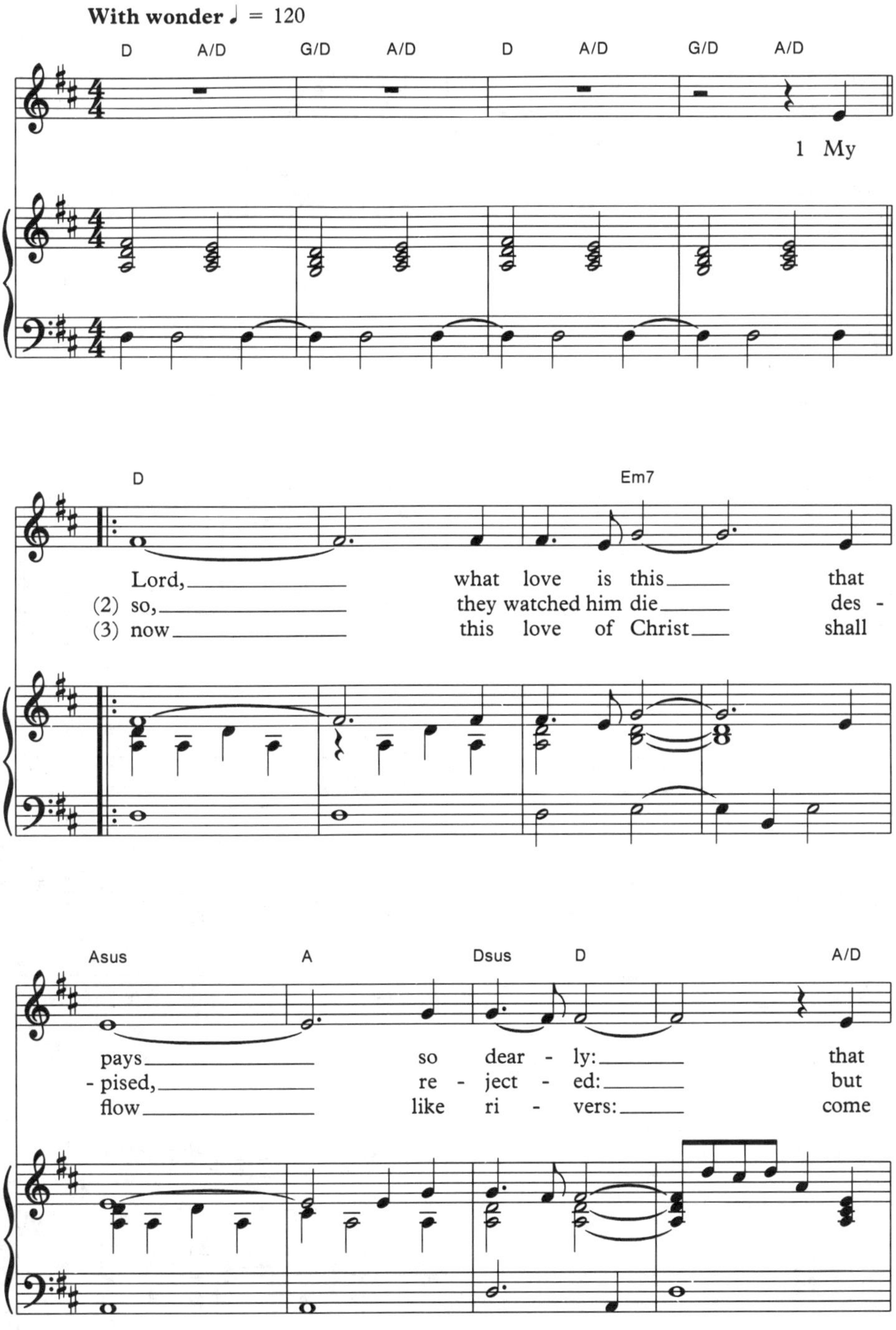

With wonder ♩ = 120
D A/D G/D A/D D A/D G/D A/D
1 My
D Em7
Lord, what love is this that
(2) so, they watched him die des -
(3) now this love of Christ shall
Asus A Dsus D A/D
pays so dear - ly: that
- pised, re - ject - ed: but
flow like ri - vers: come

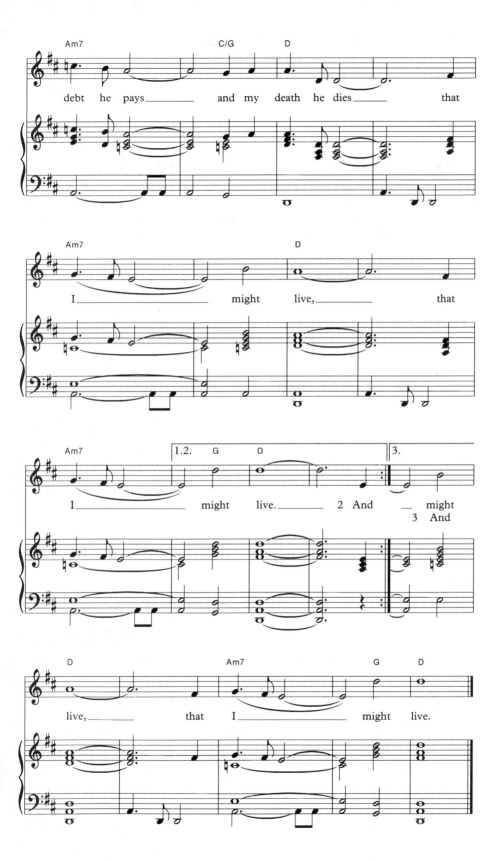

206 My song is love unknown

LOVE UNKNOWN   6 6 6 6 8 8

Words: Samuel Crossman
in this version Jubilate Hymns
Music: John Ireland
arranged Christopher Norton

12

Thoughtfully ♩ = 98

1 My song is love un-known, my sav-iour's love for
2 He came from hea-ven's throne sal-va-tion to be-
3 Some-times they crowd his way and his sweet prai-ses

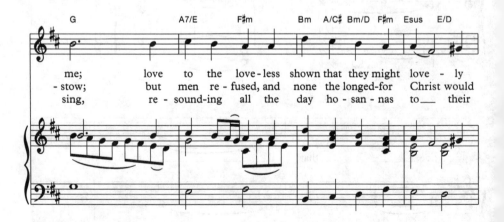

me;   love to the love-less shown that they might love-ly
-stow;   but men re-fused, and none the longed-for Christ would
sing,   re-sound-ing all the day ho-san-nas to__ their

| | be:
know:
king: | | | but
this
then | who am I,
is my friend,
'cru - ci - fy' | | that for my
my friend in -
is all their |

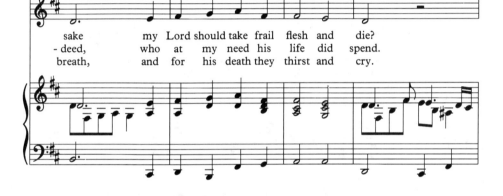

| | sake
- deed,
breath, | | my Lord should take frail flesh and die?
who at my need his life did spend.
and for his death they thirst and cry. |

4 Why, what has my Lord done
to cause this rage and spite?
he made the lame to run,
and gave the blind their sight:
what injuries! yet these are why
the Lord most high so cruelly dies.

5 With angry shouts, they have
my dear Lord done away;
a murderer they save,
the prince of life they slay!
yet willingly he bears the shame
that through his name all may be free.

6 In life no house, no home,
my Lord on earth may have;
in death no friendly tomb
but what a stranger gave.
What may I say? Heaven was his home
but mine the tomb in which he lay.

7 Here might I stay and sing
of him my soul adores;
never was love, dear King,
never was grief like yours! –
this is my friend in whose sweet praise
I all my days could gladly spend.

One or more of verses 4, 5 and 6 may be omitted

207 Name of all majesty

MAJESTAS 6 6 5 5 6 6 6 4

Words: Timothy Dudley-Smith
Music: Michael Baughen
arranged David Peacock

Majestically ♩ = 106

1 Name of all ma - jes - ty, fa - thom-less mys - te-ry,
2 Child of our des - ti - ny, God from e - ter - ni-ty,
3 Sav - iour of Cal - va - ry, cost - li - est vic - to-ry,
4 Source of all sove-reign-ty, light, im - mor - ta - li-ty,

king of the a - ges by an - gels a - dored;
love of the Fa - ther on sin - ners out - poured;
dark - ness de - feat - ed and E - den re - stored;
life ev - er - last - ing and hea - ven as - sured;

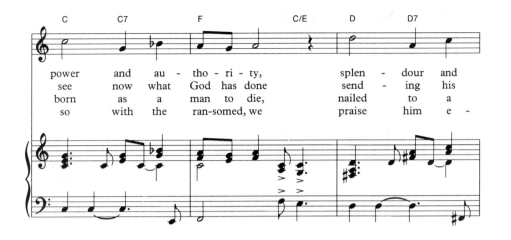

power and au - tho - ri - ty, splen - dour and
see now what God has done send - ing his
born as a man to die, nailed to a
so with the ran-somed, we praise him e -

dig - ni - ty, bow to his mas-ter - y –
on - ly Son, Christ the be - lov - èd One –
cross on high, cold in the grave to lie –
- ter - nal - ly, Christ in his ma - jes - ty –

Je - sus is Lord!
Je - sus is Lord!
Je - sus is Lord!
Je - sus is Lord!

208 New every morning is the love

LAUNDE   8 8 8 8 (LM)

Words: John Keble
Music: Roger Jones
arranged David Peacock

1 New ev - ery morn-ing is the love__
2 New mer - cies, each re-turn-ing day,__
3 If in our dai - ly life our mind_

our wak - ing and_ up - ris - ing prove:_
sur-round your peo - ple as they pray:_
be set to hal - low all we find,__

through sleep and dark-ness safe-ly brought,_____ re - stored to life__
new dan-gers past, new sins for-given,_____ new thoughts of God,
new trea-sures still,_ of count-less price,_____ God will pro-vide_

_____ and power and thought.
_____ new hopes of heaven.
_____ for sac - ri - fice._

4   The trivial round, the common task,
    will give us all we ought to ask:
    room to deny ourselves, a road
    to bring us daily nearer God.

5   Prepare us, Lord, in your dear love
    for perfect rest with you above,
    and help us, this and every day,
    to grow more like you as we pray.

209   No weight of gold or silver

BLACKDOWN   7 6 7 6 D

Words: Timothy Dudley-Smith
Music: Andrew Maries
arranged Christopher Norton

Worshipfully ♩ = 96

1 No_ weight of gold or sil - ver can_
mea - sure hu - man worth; no_ soul se - cures its
ran - som with all the wealth of_ earth: no

(2) sins, our griefs and trou - bles, he_
bore and made his own; we_ hid our fa - ces
from_ him, re - ject - ed and a - lone; his

(3) Christ the past is o - ver, a_
new world now_ be - gins; with_ him we rise to
free - dom who_ saves us from our_ sins: we

210   Not the grandeur of the mountains

FAITHFUL LOVE   8 7 8 7 D

Words: Michael Perry
Music: Andrew Maries

1 Not the gran - deur of the moun - tains, nor the
2 Not the streams that fill the val - leys, nor the
3 Yet these all con - vey his beau - ty and pro -

splen - dour of the sea, can ex - cel the cease - less
clouds that drift a - long, can de - light me more than
- claim his power and grace — for they are a - mong the

won - der of my Sav-iour's love to me:
Je - sus or re - place my grate - ful song: for his
to - kens of the love up - on his face:

love to me is faith - ful, and his mer - cy is di -

- vine; and his truth is ev - er - last - ing, and his

per - fect peace is mine._____

211   Now at last

IRSTEAD   11 9

Words: from Luke 2
Michael Saward
Music: Roger Mayor

1 Now at last,— your ser-vant can de-part—
2 My own eyes— have wit-nessed your sal-va-
3 Light for all,— re-veal-ing you to ev-

— in peace, for your word— is
- tion, Lord, which is seen— through-
- ery land. Glo-rious sight – your

fi - nal - ly___ ful - filled.
-out the whole wide world.
peo - ple Is - rael's

hope, your peo - ple Is - rael's

hope, your peo - ple Is - rael's hope.

rall.

212   Now let us learn of Christ

PARKSTONE   6 6 6 6

Words: Christopher Idle
Music: David Peacock

1 Now let us   learn of   Christs: _____
(2) love in   Christ _____
(3) grow in   Christ _____
(4) stand in   Christ _____

_____ he speaks, and   we shall   find _____
_____ as   he   has   first loved   us; _____
_____ and look   to   things a - bove, _____
_____ in   ev - ery   trial we   meet, _____

_____ he light - ens   our   dark   mind; _____
_____ as   he en - dured the   cross, _____
_____ and speak the   truth in   love; _____
_____ in   all   his   strength com - plete; _____

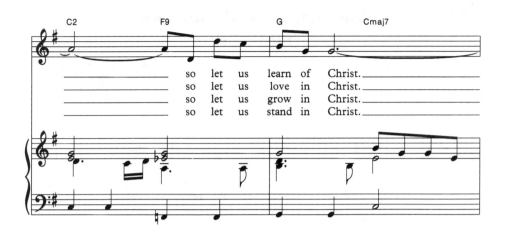

so let us learn of Christ.
so let us love in Christ.
so let us grow in Christ.
so let us stand in Christ.

2 Now let us
3 Now let us
4 Now let us

Instrumental obligato

213

Now thank we all our God
(First tune)

GRACIAS 6 7 6 7 6 6 6 6

Words: after Martin Rinkart
Catherine Winkworth
Music: Geoffrey Beaumont
arranged David Peacock

Jazz-swing style ('push' chords ad lib.) ♩ = 124

1 Now thank we all our God with
(2) may this boun-teous God through
(3) praise and thanks to God who

hearts and hands and voi - ces; who won-drous things has
all our life be near us; with ev - er joy - ful
reigns in high - est hea - ven; to Fa - ther and to

done! in whom this world re - joi - ces;
hearts, and hea - ven's peace to cheer us;
Son and Spi - rit now be giv - en:

Music: © W Paxton & Co Ltd 1957, transferred to Novello & Co Ltd,
3, Primrose Mews, 1a, Sharpleshall Street, London NW1 8YL

who from our mo-thers' arms, has blessed us on our
and keep us in his grace, and guide us when per -
to the e - ter - nal God, whom heaven and earth a -

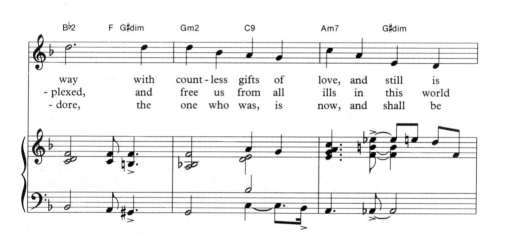

way with count-less gifts of love, and still is
- plexed, and free us from all ills in this world
- dore, the one who was, is now, and shall be

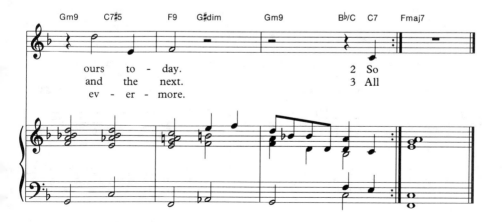

ours to - day. 2 So
and the next. 3 All
ev - er - more.

213   Now thank we all our God
(Second tune)

NUN DANKET   6 7 6 7 6 6 6 6

12

Words: after Martin Rinkart
Catherine Winkworth
Music: Johann Crüger
arranged Roger Mayor

214

O Breath of life

SPIRITUS VITAE   9 8 9 8

Words: Elizabeth Head
Music: Mary Hammond
arranged Roger Mayor

23

1 O   Breath of   life, come sweep - ing
2 O   Wind of   God, come bend us,
3 O   Breath of   love, come breathe with -

through   us,   re - vive your   church with life and
break   us   till   hum - bly   we con - fess our
- in   us,   re - new - ing   thought and will and

power;   O   Breath of   life, come, cleanse, re -
need;   then,   in   your   ten - der - ness   re -
heart;   come,   love of   Christ, a - fresh to

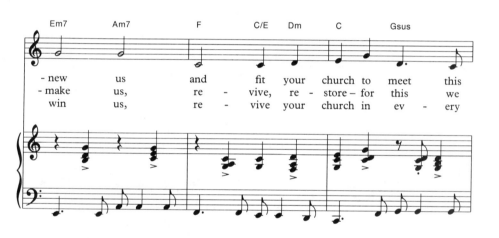

- new   us   and   fit   your   church to   meet   this
- make   us,   re - vive,   re - store – for   this   we
  win   us,   re - vive your church in   ev - ery

hour.   part!
plead.

215 O come, all ye faithful

ADESTE FIDELES Irregular

Words: after John Wade
Frederick Oakley and others
Music: John Wade
arranged David Peacock

7

Joyfully ♩ = 116

1 O come, all ye faith - ful, joy - ful and tri - um - phant; O
2 God from God, Light from light
3 Sing, choirs of an - gels, sing in ex - ul - ta - tion!
4 Yea, Lord, we greet thee, born for our sal - va - tion;
OR, ON CHRISTMAS DAY: born this hap - py morn - ing;

come ye, O come ye to Beth - le - hem;
lo, he ab - hors not the vir - gin's womb!
Sing, all ye ci - ti - zens of hea - ven a - bove,
Je - sus, to thee be glo - ry given!

come and be - hold him, born the king of an - gels! O
Ve - ry___ God, be - got-ten, not cre - a - ted.
'Glo - ry to God___ in the___ high - est!'
Word of the Fa - ther now in flesh ap - pear - ing.

come, let us a - dore him, O come, let us a -

- dore him, O come, let us a - dore him,___

Christ___ the Lord!

216   O come, O come, Emmanuel

VENI EMMANUEL   8 8 8 8 8 8

23

Words: from the Latin
John Neale and others
in this version Jubilate Hymns
Music: from a fifteenth century melody
arranged Roger Mayor

come, O come, Em - ma - nu - el and
(2) come, true Branch of Jes - se, free your
(3) come, bright Day-break, come_____ and cheer our

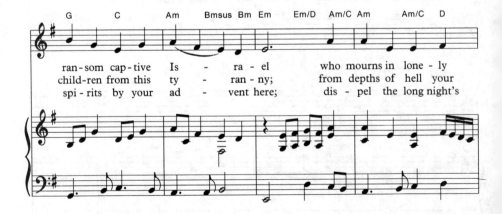

ran - som cap - tive Is - ra - el who mourns in lone - ly
child - ren from this ty - ran - ny; from depths of hell your
spi - rits by your ad - vent here; dis - pel the long night's

4 O come, strong Key of David, come
and open wide our heavenly home;
make safe the way that leads on high
and close the path to misery:
    Rejoice, rejoice . . .

5 O come, O come, great Lord of might
who long ago on Sinai's height
gave all your tribes the ancient law
in cloud and majesty and awe:
    Rejoice, rejoice . . .

217   O for a heart to praise my God

SAWLEY   8 6 8 6 (CM)

Words: Charles Wesley
Music: James Walch
arranged Roger Mayor

sprin - kled with__ the blood so free - ly
Christ is heard__ to speak, where Je - sus
life nor death__ can part from him who

shed for me.
reigns a - lone.
dwells with - in.

love!

rall.

mp

4 A heart in every thought renewed,
and full of love divine;
perfect and right and pure and good –
your life revealed in mine.

5 Your nature gracious Lord, impart –
come quickly from above,
write your new name upon my heart,
your new best name of love!

218   O for a thousand tongues to sing

LYNGHAM   8 6 8 6 extended

Words: Charles Wesley
Music: Thomas Jarman
arranged Christopher Norton

1 O for a thou - sand tongues to___ sing my great re-deem-er's praise, my great___ re - deem - er's praise, the glo-ries of___ my God___ and

the triumphs of his grace, the
king, the triumphs of his grace, the triumphs of his
triumphs of his grace, the triumphs of his
grace, the triumphs of his grace, the triumphs of his
grace!

2 Jesus, the name that charms our fears
and bids our sorrows cease:
this music in the sinner's ears
is life and health and peace.

3 He breaks the power of cancelled sin,
he sets the prisoner free;
his blood can make the foulest clean,
his blood availed for me.

4 He speaks – and, listening to his voice,
new life the dead receive,
the mournful broken hearts rejoice,
the humble poor believe.

5 Hear him, you deaf! his praise, you dumb,
your loosened tongues employ;
you blind, now see your saviour come,
and leap, you lame, for joy!

6 My gracious Master and my God,
assist me to proclaim
and spread through all the earth abroad
the honours of your name.

219   O God beyond all praising

THAXTED   13 13 13 13 13 13

Words: Michael Perry
Music: Gustav Holst
arranged Christopher Norton

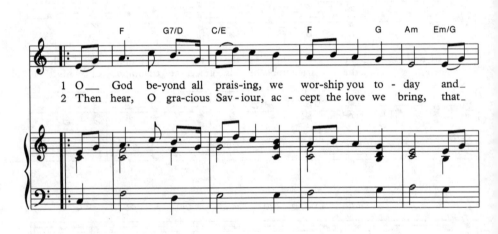

1 O__ God be-yond all prais-ing, we wor-ship you to - day and__
2 Then hear, O gra-cious Sav-iour, ac - cept the love we bring, that__

sing the love a - maz - ing that songs can-not re - pay; for__
we who know your fa - vour may serve you as our king; and__

220   O God, our help in ages past

St Anne   8 6 8 6 (CM)

Words: Isaac Watts
Music: William Croft
arranged Roger Mayor

7

1 O God, our help in a - ges past, our
(2) - neath the sha - dow of your throne your
(3) - fore the hills in or - der stood, or

hope for years to come, our shel - ter from the
peo - ple lived se - cure; suf - fi - cient is your
earth from dark - ness came, from ev - er - last - ing

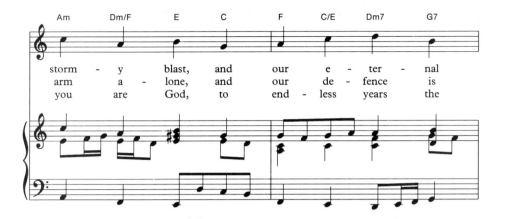

storm - y blast, and our e - ter - nal
arm a - lone, and our de - fence is
you are God, to end - less years the

home: 2 Be - home!
sure. 3 Be -
same. 4 A

4 A thousand ages in your sight
   are like an evening gone;
   short as the watch that ends the night,
   before the rising sun.

5 Time, like an ever-rolling stream,
   will bear us all away;
   we pass forgotten, as a dream
   dies with the dawning day.

6 O God, our help in ages past,
   our hope for years to come:
   be our defence while life shall last,
   and our eternal home!

221 O Jesus, I have promised

THORNBURY 7 6 7 6 D

Words: John Bode
Music: Basil Harwood
arranged Christopher Norton

23

Steadily ♩ = 120

1 O Je-sus, I have pro - mised to serve you to__ the
(2) let me feel you near me — the world is ev - er
(3) let me hear you speak - ing in ac - cents clear and
(4) let me see your foot - marks and in them place my

end — be now and ev - er near me, my
near; I see the sights that daz - zle, the
still; a - bove the storms of pas - sion, the
own: my hope to fol - low tru - ly is

222 O little town of Bethlehem
(First tune)

FOREST GREEN   8 6 8 6 D (DCM)

Words: Phillips Brooks
Music: English traditional melody
arranged David Peacock

222   O little town of Bethlehem
(Second tune)

ENMORE   8 6 8 6 D (DCM)

Words: Phillips Brooks
Music: Philip Trumble

1 O   lit - tle town of   Beth-le-hem,
2 For Christ is born of   Ma - ry
3 How   si - lent-ly, how   si-lent-ly
4 O   ho - ly child of   Beth-le-hem,

how still   we   see   you   lie!   A - bove your deep and
and, gath-ered all   a - bove   while mor - tals sleep, the
the won-drous gift   is   given!   So God im-parts to
de-scend to us,   we   pray;   cast out our sin and

dream-less sleep the   si - lent stars go   by:
an - gels keep their   watch of won - dering love:
hu - man hearts the   bless-ings of his heaven:
en - ter in, be   born in us   to - day!

yet in your dark streets shin - ing   is ev - er - last - ing light;
O morn-ing stars, to - ge - ther   pro-claim the ho - ly birth,
no ear may hear his com - ing,   but in this world of sin,
We hear the Christ-mas an - gels   the great glad tid - ings tell –

the hopes and fears   of   all   the years
and prai - ses sing   to   God   the king,
where meek souls will   re - ceive   him – still
O come to us,   a - bide   with us,

are met   in   you to - night.
and peace to   all the   earth.
the dear Christ en - ters   in.
our Lord Em - ma - nu - el.

223   O Lord my God

O Lord My God   8 8 4 8 8 5 5 3

From Psalm 22
Words and music: John Bell and Graham Maule
Music arranged Roger Mayor

224   O Lord, the clouds are gathering

O LORD THE CLOUDS   Irregular

Words and music: Graham Kendrick
arranged Christopher Norton

1 O__ Lord,__ the clouds are gath-er-ing, the fire of judge-ment
2 O__ Lord,__ ov-er the na-tions now, where is the dove of
3 O__ Lord,__ dark powers are poised to flood our streets with hate and
4 Yet, O Lord,__ your glo-rious cross shall tower tri-umph-ant in this

burns.__ How we have fall-en! O__ Lord,__ you stand ap-
peace?__ Her wings are bro-ken! O__ Lord, while pre-cious
fear.__ We must a-wak-en! O__ Lord, let love re-
land,__ e-vil con-found-ing; through the fire,__ your suf-fering

-palled to see your laws of love so scorned, and lives so bro-ken.
child-ren starve, the tools of war in-crease,_ their bread is sto-len.
-claim the lives that sin would sweep a-way,__ and let your king-dom come!
church dis-play the glo-ries of her Christ,_ prai-ses re-sound-ing.

Chorus

B have mer-cy, Lord,____ for-give us, Lord. Re-

A Have mer-cy, Lord,____ For-give us, Lord,____ Re-

The congregation divides at A and B

225 O Lord, the refuge

O LORD, THE REFUGE   11 10 11 10

Words: from Psalm 90
Basil Bridge
Music: Christopher Norton

Not too fast ♩ = 78

Capo 3(D)

Lord,   the re - fuge of each ge - ne - ra - tion,___   you
(2) thou - sand years like yes - ter - day in pass - ing,___   our
(3) Ho - ly Lord, for - give our self - de - ceiv - ing =___   our
(4) rush - es on: give us a heart of wis - dom___   that

reigned   be - fore the u - ni - verse be - gan;_   we bear your
fleet - ing lives like half - re - mem - bered dreams,   or weeds that
sec - ret sins are clear be - fore your face: grant us re -
seeks   your will and fol - lows your com - mands;   show us your

	A (F#)				A7/D (F#7)	Dm (Bm)	Bm7♭5 (G#m7)	Bdim (G#dim)

stamp,   the marks of your cre - a - tion,   and yet how
flower   at noon but die by eve - ning –   so, Lord, to
- lease,   the joy of those be - liev - ing__   they are re -
deeds,   your glo - ry to our child - ren,__   work out your

F/C   Gm/C   **1–3.** F   B♭2/F   **4.** F
(D)   (Em)   (D)   (G)   (D)

frail we are,__ how brief life's span!   2 One
you our tran - sient glo - ry seems.   3 O
- stored by your e - ter - nal grace.   4 Time
time-less pur - pose through our   hands.

Instrumental obligato

mp   **1–3.**   **4.**   *dim.*

226 O Lord, who came from realms above

HEREFORD   8 8 8 8 (LM)

Words: Charles Wesley
in this version Jubilate Hymns
Music: Samuel Wesley
arranged Roger Mayor

Lord,— who came— from realms— a - bove— the
(2) let— it for— your glo — ry burn— with
(3) - sus,— con - firm— my heart's de - sire— to
(4) let— me prove— your per - fect will,— my

pure— ce - les - tial fire to im - part,— kin -
in - ex - tin - guish - ab - le blaze,— and
work— and speak and think— for you;— still
acts— of faith and love— re - peat,— till

227 O love that will not let me go

ST MARGARET 88886

Words: after George Matheson
in this version Word & Music
Music: Albert Peace
arranged Christopher Norton

1 O love that will not let me
(2) light that fol-lows all my
(3) joy that seeks for me through
(4) cross that rais-es up my

go,— re-vive your love-li-ness in me:— I
way,— re-new your ra-di-ance in me:— I
pain,— re-store your hope-ful-ness to me;— I
head,— re-move the sin-ful-ness from me:— I

give you back the life I owe__ that in your o - cean depths its
wel - come your life - giv - ing ray__ that in your sun - shine's blaze each
trace the rain-bow through the rain__ and trust your pro - mise once a -
lay in dust life's glo - ry dead,__ and from the ground there blos-soms

flow may rich - er, full - er be.
day may bright - er, fair - er be.
- gain: that dawn shall tear - less be.
red, life that shall end - less be.

2 O
3 O
4 O

228   O Spirit of the living God

WAREHAM   8 8 8 8 (LM)

Words: James Montgomery
Music: William Knapp
arranged Roger Mayor

Prayerfully ♩ = 100

1 O
Spi - rit of the liv - ing God, in
(2) tongues of fire and hearts of love to
(3) dark - ness turn to ra - diant light, con -

all the ful - ness of your grace, wher -
preach the re - con - cil - ing word; a -
-fu - sion va - nish from your path; those

Music arrangement: © Roger Mayor / Jubilate Hymns

4 O Spirit of our God, prepare
   the whole wide world the Lord to meet;
   breathe out new life, like morning air,
   till hearts of stone begin to beat:

5 Baptize the nations; far and near
   the triumphs of the cross record;
   till Christ in glory shall appear
   and every race declare him Lord!

229   O Trinity, O Trinity

FELICITY   8 6 8 6 7 7 8 8

Words: Michael Saward
Music: Andrew Maries

6

Not dragging, with a lightness ♩ = 62

C   Dm7/C   C2   C   F/C   F/G   C   F/C   C   F/C

1 O   Tri - ni - ty,   O
2 O   Ma - jes - ty,   O
3 O   Vir - gin - born,   O

C   Dm7   C/E   F   Dm7   C/E   Dm7/F   C/G   G   F/G

Tri - ni - ty,   the   un - cre - a - ted   One;____   O
Ma - jes - ty,   the   Fa - ther of___ our   race;____   O
Vir - gin - born,   of   hu - man - kind_ the   least;____   O

C   F/C   C   F/C   C   D7/A   G/B   C   G/D

Un - i - ty,   O   Un - i - ty,   of   Fa - ther, Spi - rit,
Mys - te - ry,   O   Mys - te - ry,   we   can - not see_ your
Vic - tim torn,   O   Vic - tim torn,   both   spot - less lamb_ and

Son: _____ you are with-out____ be - gin - ning, your
face: _____ your jus - tice is____ un - swerv - ing, your
priest: _____ you died and rose___ vic - tor - ious, you

Chorus

life___ is ne - ver end - ing;
love___ is o - ver - power - ing: and though our tongues are
reign_ a - bove_ all - glo - rious;

earth_ bound clay, light them_ with flam - ing fire to - day.

4 O Wind of God, O Wind of God,
   invigorate the dead;
  O Fire of God, O Fire of God,
   your burning radiance spread:
  your fruit our lives renewing,
  your gifts, the church transforming;
  and though . . .

5 O Trinity, O Trinity,
   the uncreated One;
  O Unity, O Unity,
   of Father, Spirit, Son:
  you are without beginning,
  your life is never ending;
  and though . . .

230   O worship the King

HANOVER   10 10 11 11

9

Words: after William Kethe
Robert Grant
Music: William Croft
arranged Roger Mayor

shield and de - fend - er, the An - cient of Days,
cha - riots of wrath the deep thun - der-clouds form,
- tab - lished it fast by a change-less de - cree,

pa -
and
and

- vil - ioned in splen - dour and gird - ed with praise.
dark is his path on the wings of the storm.
round it has cast like a gar - ment the sea.

4 Your bountiful care what tongue can recite?
   it breathes in the air, it shines in the light;
   it streams from the hills, it descends to the plain,
   and sweetly distils in the dew and the rain.

5 We children of dust are feeble and frail –
   in you we will trust, for you never fail;
   your mercies how tender, how firm to the end!
   our maker, defender, redeemer and friend.

6 O measureless Might, unchangeable Love,
   whom angels delight to worship above!
   your ransomed creation with glory ablaze,
   in true adoration shall sing to your praise!

231   O worship the Lord

Was Lebet   12 10 12 10

Words: John Monsell
Music: melody adapted by
J H Rheinhardt
arranged Christopher Norton

1 O wor-ship the Lord in the
2 Low at his feet lay your
3 Fear not to en-ter his

beau — ty of ho – li-ness, bow down be – fore him, his
bur – den of care-ful-ness, high on his heart he will
courts in the slen – der-ness of the poor wealth you would

glo – ry pro-claim; with gold of o – be-dience and
bear it for you, com – fort your sor – rows and
count as your own; truth in its beau – ty and

Music arrangement: © 1993 HarperCollins*Religious*

in - cense of low - li - ness, kneel and a - dore him – the
ans - wer your prayer - ful-ness, guid - ing your steps in the
love in its ten - der-ness – these are the offer - ings to

Lord is his name. (5 O)
way that is true.
bring to his throne.

4 These, though we bring them in trembling and fearfulness,
  he will accept for the Name that is dear;
  mornings of joy give for evenings of tearfulness,
  trust for our trembling and hope for our fear.

5 O worship the Lord in the beauty of holiness,
  bow down before him, his glory proclaim;
  with gold of obedience and incense of lowliness,
  kneel and adore him – the Lord is his name.

232 Once in royal David's city

IRBY   878777

Words: Cecil Alexander
Music: Henry Gauntlett
arranged Roger Mayor

1

Unhurried ♩ = 82

1 Once in roy - al Da - vid's city stood a
2 He came down to earth from heaven who is
3 And through all his won - drous child - hood he would

low - ly cat - tle shed, where a mo - ther laid her
God and Lord of all; and his shel - ter was a
hon - our and o - bey, love and watch the gen - tle

Verse 3 may be omitted

Music arrangement: © Roger Mayor / Jubilate Hymns

ba - by in a man - ger for___ his___
sta - ble and his cra - dle was__ a___
mo - ther in whose ten - der arms__ he___

bed: Ma - ry was that mo - ther mild,__ Je - sus
stall: with the poor and meek and low - ly lived on
lay: Chris - tian child - ren all should be___ kind, o -

Fine

Christ, her lit - tle__ child.
earth our sav - iour ho - ly.
- be - dient, good as__ he. ___

4 For he is our childhood's pattern:
day by day like us he grew;
he was little, weak and helpless –
tears and smiles like us he knew:
and he feels for all our sadness,
and he shares in all our gladness.

5 And our eyes at last shall see him,
through his own redeeming love;
for that child, so dear and gentle,
is our Lord in heaven above:
and he leads his children on
to the place where he has gone.

6 Not in that poor lowly stable
with the oxen standing by,
we shall see him, but in heaven,
set at God's right hand on high:
there his children gather round
bright like stars, with glory crowned.

233
One thing I know

MORAR MURPHY 9 8 9 8

Words: Michael Perry
Music: Christopher Rolinson

1 One thing I know, that Christ has healed me –
  though I was blind, yet now I see;

2 One thing I pray – that in my weak - ness,
  God's per - fect might will make me strong;

3 One thing I do – put sin be - hind me,
  press for the goal to win the prize;

4 One faith, one Lord, one new cre - a - tion,
  one hope of our e - ter - ni - ty!

234 Peace be with you all

CHELSTON 7 7 7 7

Words: Michael Saward
Music: David Peacock

3

Slow 2 to a bar feel ♩ = 60

1 'Peace be

with you all,' we sing; peace from
(2) -ge - ther in his name, weld - ed
(3) bro - ken for our food; wine we
(4) emp - ty hands, we bow to re -

Christ, our Lord and king,_____ he it
by the Spi - rit's flame;_____ at his
share in gra - ti - tude._____ His the
- ceive our sav - iour now_____ and, re -

| Dm7 | F/G | Em7 | Am | Am7/G |

is who makes us____ one,_____ God's e -
ta - ble here we___ kneel_____ and his
flesh and blood he__ gave_____ for the
- newed in mind and__ heart,_____ in the

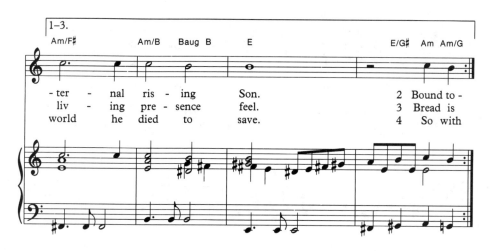

1–3.

| Am/F♯ | Am/B | Baug B | E | E/G♯ Am Am/G |

- ter - nal ris - ing Son. 2 Bound to -
liv - ing pre - sence feel. 3 Bread is
world he died to save. 4 So with

4.

| F2 | F/G | G7 | Csus | C |

peace of Christ de - part._____

235

Praise God
(First tune)

COME TOGETHER 8 8 8 8 (LM)

9

Words: after Thomas Ken
in this version Jubilate Hymns
Music: Jimmy Owens
arranged David Peacock

Worshipfully ♩ = 104

Praise God from whom all bless-ings flow, in heaven a-bove and earth be-low: one God, three per-sons, we a-dore to him be praise for ev-er-more! Praise-more.

235

Praise God
(Second tune)

TALLIS' CANON   8 8 8 8 (LM)

Words: after Thomas Ken
in this version Jubilate Hymns
Music: Thomas Tallis
arranged David Peacock

1

Lively ♩ = 110

Praise God from whom all bless-ings flow, in heaven a-bove and earth be-low: one God, three per-sons, we a-dore — to him be praise for ev-er-more!

236   Praise him, praise him

NICAEA   12 13 12 10

11

Words: from Psalm 148
Michael Perry
Music: John Dykes
arranged Christopher Norton

1 Praise him, praise him, praise him, praise him, powers and do-min-a-tions; praise his name in glo-rious light, you crea-tures of the

2 Praise him, praise him, praise him, praise him, o-cean depths and wa-ters; e-le-ments of earth and heaven, your sev-eral prai-ses

3 Praise him, praise him, praise him, praise him, saints of God who fear him; to the high-est name of all, con-cer-ted an-thems

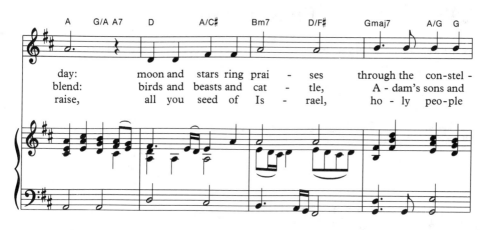

day: moon and stars ring prai - ses   through the con-stel -
blend: birds and beasts and cat - tle,   A - dam's sons and
raise,   all you seed of Is - rael,   ho - ly peo-ple

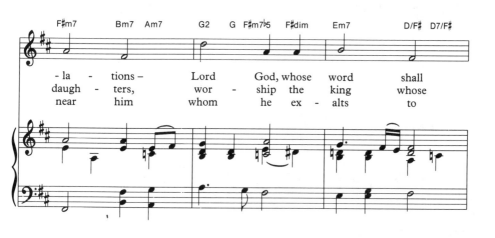

- la - tions -   Lord   God, whose word   shall
daugh - ters,   wor - ship the king   whose
near him   whom   he ex - alts   to

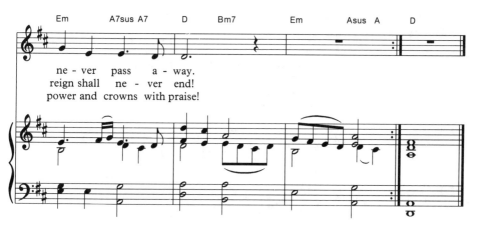

ne - ver pass a - way.
reign shall ne - ver end!
power and crowns with praise!

237

Praise my soul

PRAISE MY SOUL   8 7 8 7 8 7

Words: from Psalm 103
Henry Francis Lyte
Music: John Goss
arranged David Peacock

1 Praise my soul, the king of hea - ven;
2 Praise him for his grace and fa - vour
3 Fa - ther - like, he tends and spares
4 An - gels, help us to a - dore

to his feet your tri - bute bring!
to our fa - thers in dis - tress;
us; all our hopes and fears he knows,
him — you be - hold him face to face;

Ran-somed, healed, re - stored, for - gi - ven,
praise him still the same as ev - er,
in his hands he gent - ly bears us,
sun and moon, bow down be - fore him,

who like me his praise should sing?
slow to blame and swift to bless,
res - cues us from all our foes,
praise him, all in time and space,

Al - le - lu - ia,
Al - le - lu - ia,
Al - le - lu - ia,
Al - le - lu - ia,

al - le - lu - ia! praise the ev - er - last - ing king!
al - le - lu - ia! glo - rious in his faith - ful - ness!
al - le - lu - ia! wide - ly as his mer - cy flows.
al - le - lu - ia! praise with us the

God of grace!

238   Praise our God with shouts of joy

PRAISE OUR GOD   7 7 7 7 D

Words: from Psalm 66
Christopher Idle
Music: David Peacock

1 Praise our God   with   shouts of joy,_
3 God has tamed   the   rag - ing seas,
5 God has not_   des - pised my prayer

sing the glo   -   ry   of   his name;   join   to lift _   his
carved a high   -   way through the tide,   paid   the cost_   of
nor kept back   his   love for me;_   he   has raised me

prai - ses high,   through the world   his   love pro - claim.
our re - lease,   come him - self_   to   be our guide.
from des - pair –   to   our God_   all   glo - ry be!_

239   Praise the Lord of heaven

LORD OF HEAVEN   6 5 6 5 D

Words: from Psalm 148
Timothy Dudley-Smith
Music: Christopher Norton

1 Praise the Lord of hea-ven,___ praise him in___ the height;___ praise him, all___ his an-gels,___ praise him, hosts of light.___ Sun and moon to-ge-

2 Earth and o-cean praise___ him;___ moun-tains, hills___ and trees;___ fire and hail___ and tem-pest,___ wind and storm and seas.___ Praise him, fields and for-

3 Now by prince and peo-ple___ let his praise be told;___ praise him, men___ and maid-ens,___ praise him, young and old.___ He, the Lord of glo-

- ther,_____ shin - ing stars a - flame,_
- ests,_____ birds on flash - ing wings,_
- ry!_____ We, his praise pro - claim!_

plan - ets in their cour - ses,_____ mag - ni - fy_ his name –
praise him, beasts and cat - tle,_____ all cre - a - ted things –
High a - bove all hea - vens_____ mag - ni - fy_ his name –

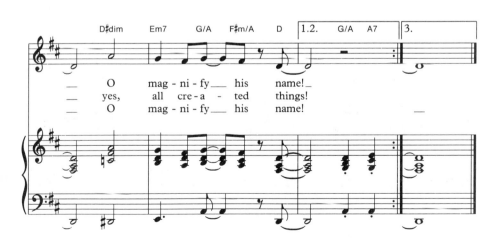

_ O mag - ni - fy_ his name!_
_ yes, all cre - a - ted things!
_ O mag - ni - fy_ his name!

240   Praise the Lord, you heavens

AUSTRIA   8 7 8 7 D

23

Words: from Psalm 148
Foundling Hospital Collection
Music: Croatian folk tune
arranged Christopher Norton

1 Praise the Lord, you heavens, a - dore him – praise him, an - gels
2 Praise the Lord, for he is glo - rious, ne - ver shall his

in the height! Sun and moon, re - joice be - fore him;
pro - mise fail: God has made his saints vic - tor - ious,

241   Praise to the Holiest

GERONTIUS   8 6 8 6 (CM)

Words: John Newman
Music: John Dykes
arranged Roger Mayor

Flowing ♩ = 118

1 Praise to the Hol - iest in the height,
2 Oh lov - ing wis - dom of our God!
3 Oh wis - est love! that flesh and blood,

and in the depth be praise; in all his
when all was sin and shame, a sec - ond
which did in A - dam fail, should strive a -

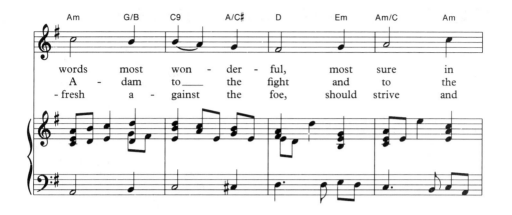

words   most   won - der - ful,   most   sure   in
A -   dam   to___ the   fight   and   to   the
- fresh   a -   gainst   the   foe,   should   strive   and

all   his   ways!   ways!
res -   cue   came.
should pre -   vail;

4   And that the highest gift of grace
    should flesh and blood refine:
    God's presence and his very self,
    and essence all-divine.

5   Oh generous love! that he who came
    as man to smite our foe,
    the double agony for us
    as man should undergo:

6   And in the garden secretly,
    and on the cross on high,
    should teach his brethren, and inspire
    to suffer and to die.

7   Praise to the Holiest in the height,
    and in the depth be praise;
    in all his words most wonderful,
    most sure in all his ways!

242   Praise to the Lord, the almighty

LOBE DEN HERREN   14 14 4 7 8

Words: from Psalm 103
Catherine Winkworth and others
Music: from the *Stralsund Songbook*
arranged Christopher Norton

1 Praise to the Lord, the al-
2 Praise to the Lord, a-bove
3 Praise to the Lord, who shall
4 Praise to the Lord – O let

-migh-ty, the king of cre-a - tion!
all things so migh-ti-ly reign - ing;
pros-per our work and de-fend us;
all that is in me a-dore him!

O my soul, praise him, for he is your health and sal -
keep-ing us safe at his side, and so gent-ly sus -
sure-ly his good - ness and mer-cy shall dai-ly at -
All that has life and breath, come now with prai-ses be -

243   Put peace into each other's hands

ST COLUMBIA   8 7 8 7

2

Words: Fred Kaan
Music: Irish traditional melody
arranged David Peacock

1 Put peace in-to each oth-er's hands and like a trea-sure hold

2 Put peace in-to each oth-er's hands with lov-ing ex-pec-ta -

3 Put peace in-to each oth-er's hands, like bread we break for shar -

D.C.

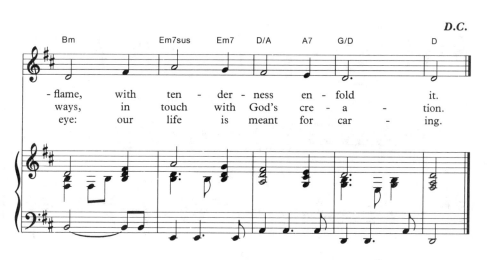

4 As at communion, shape your hands
   into a waiting cradle;
   the gift of Christ receive, revere,
   united round the table.

5 Put Christ into each other's hands:
   he is love's deepest measure;
   in love make peace, give peace a chance
   and share it like a treasure.

244 Rejoice, rejoice!

REJOICE, REJOICE   Irregular

Words and music: Graham Kendrick
Music arranged Christopher Norton

245   Rejoice, the Lord is king

GOPSAL   6 6 6 6 8 8

Words: Charles Wesley
Music: George F Handel
arranged Roger Mayor

With strength, medium tempo ♩ = 128

1 Re-joice, the Lord is king! Your Lord and king a-dore—
2 Je-sus, the sav-iour, reigns, the God of—truth and love;
3 His king-dom can-not fail, he rules both—earth and heaven;

mor-tals, give thanks and sing, and
when he had purged our stains he
the keys of death and hell to

Chorus

tri - umph ev - er-more:
took his_ seat a - bove.   lift   up your heart, lift   up   your voice:
Je - sus_ now   are given.

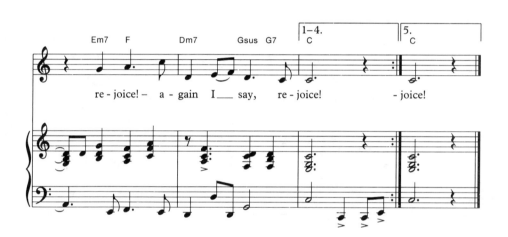

re - joice! - a - gain I__ say,   re - joice!   - joice!

4   He sits at God's right hand,
    till all his foes submit
    and bow to his command
    and fall beneath his feet.
        lift up your heart . . .

5   Rejoice in glorious hope!
    Jesus the judge shall come
    and take his servants up
    to their eternal home:
        we soon shall hear the archangel's voice:
        the trumpet sounds – rejoice, rejoice!

246   Remember, remember

REMEMBER, REMEMBER   Irregular

From Psalm 25
Words of chorus and music: Paul Inwood

23

Gentle syncopation ♩ = 98

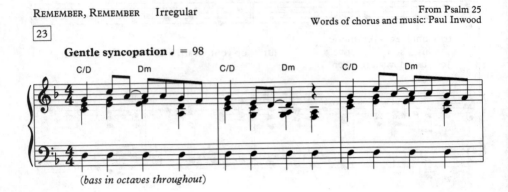

(bass in octaves throughout)

Chorus

ALL   Re - mem-ber, re-mem-ber your mer-cy, Lord;   re -

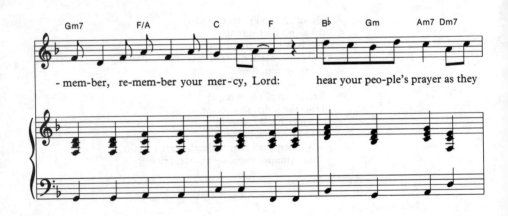

- mem-ber, re-mem-ber your mer-cy, Lord: hear your peo-ple's prayer as they

last time **to Coda** ⊕

Eb   Am   Bbmaj7   F   Gmaj7   Bb

call to you; re - mem-ber, re-mem-ber your mer - cy, Lord.

Verse 1 Dm   Dm/C   Bbmaj7   Gm7

SOLO 1 Lord, make me know your ways, Lord, teach me your

Fmaj7   Dm7/F   G   Em7

paths; make me walk in your truth, and

A   A/F   Bbmaj7   Gm7   C   Am7   **D.C.**

teach me, for you are God my sav - iour.

247 Restore, O Lord

RESTORE, O LORD   10 12 10 13

Words and music: Graham Kendrick
and Christopher Rolinson
Music arranged David Peacock

1&4 Re - store, O Lord, the hon - our of your
(2) - store, O Lord, in all the earth your
(3) us, O Lord, where we are hard and

hon - our of your name works of sov - ereign

name in works of sov - ereign power;_____ come
fame, and in our time re - vive_____ the
cold, in your re - fin - er's fire;_____ come

power; shake the earth a - gain

shake the earth a - gain that all may
Church that bears your name; and in your
pu - ri - fy the gold: though suff - ering

248 Revive your church, O Lord

CARLISLE   6 6 8 6 (SM)

Words: Albert Midlane
in this version Jubilate Hymns
Music: Charles Lockhart
arranged Roger Mayor

make   your peo-ple   hear!   - lone!
your   al - migh-ty   breath.
set   our love a -   flame.

4   Revive your church, O Lord,
    give us a thirst for you,
    a hunger for the bread of life
    our spirits to renew.

5   Revive your church, O Lord,
    and let your power be shown;
    the gifts and graces shall be ours,
    the glory yours alone!

Instrumental obligato

249 Ride on, ride on in majesty

WINCHESTER NEW   8 8 8 8 (LM)

12

Words: Henry Milman
in this version Jubilate Hymns
Music: German chorale melody
arranged David Peacock

Unhurried ♩ = 102

1 Ride

on, ride on in ma - jes - ty as all the crowds 'Ho -
(2) on, ride on in ma - jes - ty, in low - ly pomp ride
(3) on, ride on in ma - jes - ty: the an - gel ar - mies

- san - na!' cry; through wav - ing bran - ches
on to die; O Christ, your tri - umph
of the sky look down with sad and

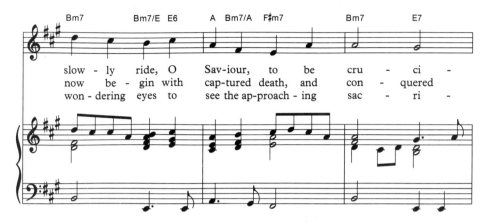

slow - ly ride, O Sav-iour, to be cru - ci -
now be - gin with cap-tured death, and con - quered
won - dering eyes to see the ap-proach - ing sac - ri -

- fied.   2 Ride   reign!
sin!   3 Ride
- fice.   4 Ride

4 Ride on, ride on in majesty,
the last and fiercest foe defy:
the Father on his sapphire throne
awaits his own anointed Son.

5 Ride on, ride on in majesty,
in lowly pomp ride on to die;
bow your meek head to mortal pain,
then take, O God, your power and reign!

250 Rock of ages, cleft for me
(First tune)

PETRA 7 7 7 7 7 7

Words: Augustus Toplady
in this version Jubilate Hymns
Music: Richard Redhead
arranged Roger Mayor

3

Slow, accented ♩ = 76

1 Rock of a - ges,
2 Not the la - bours
3 No-thing in my
4 While I draw this

cleft for me,
of my hands
hand I bring,
fleet - ing breath,

hide me now, my
can ful - fil your
simp - ly to your
when my eye - lids

re - fuge be;
law's de - mands;
cross I cling;
close in death,

let the wa - ter
could my zeal no
nak - ed, come to
when I soar through

250

Rock of ages, cleft for me
(Second tune)

NEW CITY FELLOWSHIP 7 7 7 7 7 7

Words: Augustus Toplady
in this version Jubilate Hymns
Music: James Ward

1 Rock of a - ges, cleft for me, hide me now, my
2 Not the la - bours of my hands can ful - fil your
3 No - thing in my hand I bring, sim - ply to your
4 While I draw this fleet - ing breath, when my eye - lids

re - fuge be; let the wa - ter and the blood
law's de - mands; could my zeal no res - pite know,
cross I cling; na - ked, come to you for dress,
close in death, when I soar through realms un - known,

from your wound - ed side which flowed, be for sin the
could my tears for ev - er flow, all for sin could
help - less, look to you for grace; stained by sin, to
bow be - fore the judge - ment throne: hide me then, my

dou - ble cure –   cleanse   me from   its   guilt   and___
not a - tone: you   must save and   you   a -
you I   cry: 'Wash   me, Sav - iour,   or   I___
re - fuge be,   Rock   of   a - ges,   cleft   for___

power.
- lone.
die!'
me.

Instrumental obligato

251 Safe in the shadow of the Lord

CREATOR GOD   8 6 8 6 (CM)

Words: from Psalm 91
Timothy Dudley-Smith
Music: Norman Warren
arranged Roger Mayor

alternative accompaniment for verses 3 and 5

1 Safe in the sha - dow of the Lord, be -
2 My hope is set on God a - lone though
3 From fears and phan - toms of the night, from

- neath his hand_ and power,_ I
Sa - tan spreads his snare;_ I
foes a - bout_ my way,_ I

trust in him,___ I trust in
trust in him,___ I trust in
trust in him,___ I trust in

him,___ my fort - ress and___ my
him___ to keep___ me in___ his
him___ by dark - ness as___ by

1–5.
tower.
care.
day.

6.
mine.___

4 B
His holy angels keep my feet
secure from every stone;
  I trust in him,
  I trust in him,
and unafraid go on.

5 ALL
Strong in the everlasting name,
and in my Father's care,
  I trust in him,
  I trust in him,
who hears and answers prayer.

6 Safe in the shadow of the Lord,
  possessed by love divine,
    I trust in him,
    I trust in him,
  and meet his love with mine.

The congregation may divide at A and B

252   See, amid the winter snow

HUMILITY   7 7 7 7 and refrain

Words: Edward Caswall
in this version Jubilate Hymns
Music: John Goss
arranged Christopher Norton

1 See, a-mid the win-ter snow, born for us on earth be-low; see, the gen-tle Lamb ap-pears,

2 Low with-in a man-ger lies he who built the star-ry skies; he who, throned in height sub-lime,

3 Say, you hum-ble shep-herds, say what your joy-ful news to-day? Tell us why you left your sheep

Chorus

pro - mised from e - ter - nal years.
reigns a - bove the che - ru - bim. Hail, O ev - er-
on the lone - ly moun - tain steep.

- bless - èd morn: hail, re-demp-tion's hap - py dawn!

Sing through all Je - ru - sa-lem: 'Christ is born in Beth-le-hem!'

4 B
'As we watched at dead of night,
all around us shone a light;
angels singing Peace on earth
told us of a Saviour's birth.'
　Hail, O ever-blessèd morn . . .

5 Sacred infant, king most dear,
what a tender love was here,
thus to come from highest bliss
down to such a world as this!
　Hail, O ever-blessèd morn . . .

6 Holy Saviour, born on earth,
teach us by your lowly birth;
grant that we may ever be
taught by such humility.
　Hail, O ever-blessèd morn . . .

The congregation may divide at A and B

253   See him lying on a bed of straw

CALYPSO CAROL   Irregular

Words and music: Michael Perry
Music arranged Christopher Norton

Calypso style ♩ = 114

1 See him ly - ing on a bed of straw: a
2 Star of sil - ver, sweep a - cross the skies,_
3 An - gels, sing_ a - gain the song you sang,_
4 Mine are rich - es, from your pov - er - ty,___

draugh - ty sta - ble with an o - pen door;_
show where Je - sus in the man - ger lies;_
sing the glo - ry of God's gra - cious plan;_
from your in - no-cence, e - ter - ni - ty;_

Ma - ry cra - dl - ing the babe she bore =   the
shep - herds, swift - ly from your stu - por rise__   to
sing that Beth - le - hem's lit - tle ba - by can_
mine for - give - ness by your death for me,_

254

Shepherds came

QUEM PASTORES LAUDAVERE   8 8 8 7

Words: from the Latin
George Caird
Music: German carol melody
arranged Roger Mayor

1 Shep - herds came, their prai - ses bring - ing,
2 Wise men whom a star had guid - ed
3 Je - sus born the king of hea - ven,

who had heard the an - gels sing - ing:
in - cense, gold and myrrh pro - vi - ded,
Christ to us through Ma - ry giv - en,

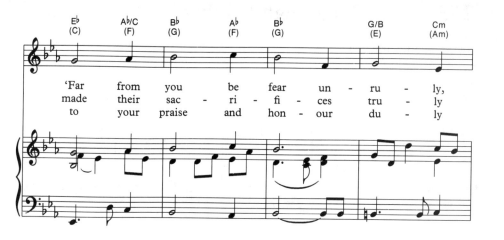

'Far from you be fear un - ru - ly,
made their sac - ri - fi - ces tru - ly
to your praise and hon - our du - ly

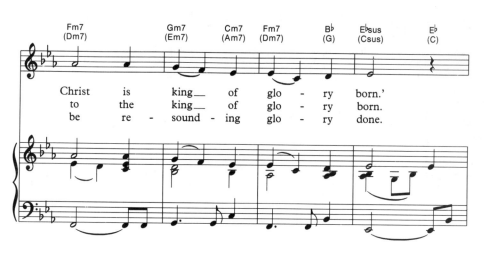

Christ is king __ of glo - ry born.'
to the king __ of glo - ry born.
be re - sound - ing glo - ry done.

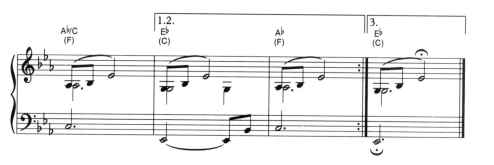

255   Silent night! Holy night!

STILLE NACHT   Irregular

Words: after Joseph Möhr
John Young
Music: Franz Gruber
arranged Roger Mayor

1 Si - lent night!   Ho - ly night!   All is
2 Si - lent night!   Ho - ly night!   Shep - herds
3 Si - lent night!   Ho - ly night!   Son of

calm,   all is bright   round the vir - gin
quail   at the sight,   glo - ry streams from
God,   love's pure light: ra - diant beams your

256 Sing of the Lord's goodness

SING OF THE LORD'S GOODNESS
12 7 7 7 and refrain

Words and music: Ernest Sands
Music arranged Paul Inwood
Descant: Christopher Walker

Lively jazz 'feel' ♩ = 140

Intro (1st time only)

1 Sing of the Lord's good-ness, Fa-ther of all wis-dom,
2 Pow-er he has wield-ed, hon-our is his gar-ment,
3 Cour-age in our dark-ness, com-fort in our sor-row —
4 Praise him with your sing-ing, praise him with the trum-pet,

come to him and bless his name._____ Mer-cy he has shown us,
ri-sen from the snares of death._____ His word he has spo-ken,
Spi-rit of our God most high!_____ Sol-ace for the wea-ry,
praise God with the lute and harp._____ Praise him with the cym-bals,

Descant

You peo-ple

his love is for ev-er, faith-ful to the end of days._____
one bread he has bro-ken, new life he now gives to all._____
par-don for the sin-ner, splen-dour of the liv-ing God!_____
praise him with your danc-ing, praise God till the end of days._____

Another rhythm for the
keyboard accompaniment:

etc.

257 Sing praise to the Lord

LAUDATE DOMINUM   10 10 11 11

9

Words: from Psalms 148, 150
Henry Baker
in this version Jubilate Hymns
Music: C Hubert Parry
arranged Roger Mayor

258   Soldiers of Christ, arise

FROM STRENGTH TO STRENGTH
6 6 8 6 D (DSM)

Words: Charles Wesley
Music: Edward Naylor
arranged Roger Mayor

With urgency ♩ = 120

1 Sol - diers of Christ, a - rise and put your ar - mour on; strong in the strength which God sup - plies through his e - ter - nal Son. Strong in the

2 Stand then in his great might, with all his strength en - dued; and take, to arm you for the fight, the wea - pons of our God. To keep your

3 From strength to strength go on: wres - tle and fight and pray; tread all the powers of dark - ness down and win the well - fought day: Till, hav - ing

Lord   of   hosts, and   in his   migh - ty
ar - mour   bright at - tend with con - stant
all   things   done and   all your   con - flicts

power;   who in the strength of   Je - sus   trusts is   more than
care,   still walk-ing   in   your   cap-tain's   sight and   keep-ing
past,   you o - ver - come through Christ a - lone and   stand com -

con - quer - or.
watch_____ with prayer.
- plete_____ at   last.

Obligato for B♭ instrument

259   Songs of praise the angels sang

WHARFEDALE   7 7 7 7

Words: James Montgomery
Music: Christopher Norton

1 Songs of praise the an - gels sang,
2 Songs of praise an-nounced the dawn
3 Heaven and earth must pass a - way —

heaven with al - le - lu - ias rang_
when the Prince of peace was born;
songs of praise shall crown that day!_

when cre - a - tion
songs of praise a -
God will make new

was be - gun;_
- rose when he _
heavens and earth —

when God spoke, and it was done.
cap - tive led cap - ti - vi - ty._
songs of praise shall greet their birth!

4 And must we alone be dumb
   till that glorious kingdom come?
   No! the church delights to raise
   psalms and hymns and song of praise.

5 Saints below, with heart and voice
   still in songs of praise rejoice;
   learning here by faith and love
   songs of praise to sing above.

6 Hymns of glory, songs of praise,
   Father, now to you we raise;
   Saviour, Jesus, risen Lord,
   with the Spirit be adored.

Instrumental obligato

Melody part for B♭ instruments

260 Speak, Lord, in the stillness

QUIETUDE 6 5 6 5

Words: Emily Crawford
in this version Jubilate Hymns
Music: Harold Green
arranged David Peacock

3

Unhurried ♩ = 80

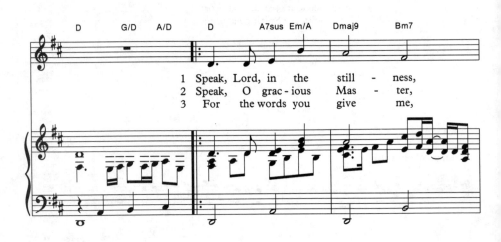

1 Speak, Lord, in the still - ness,
2 Speak, O grac - ious Mas - ter,
3 For the words you give me,

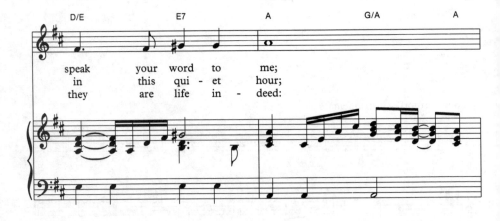

speak your word to me;
in this qui - et hour;
they are life in - deed:

May also be sung to the tune LISTEN TO MY PRAYER (157)

help me now to lis - ten
let me see your face, Lord,
liv - ing Bread from hea - ven,

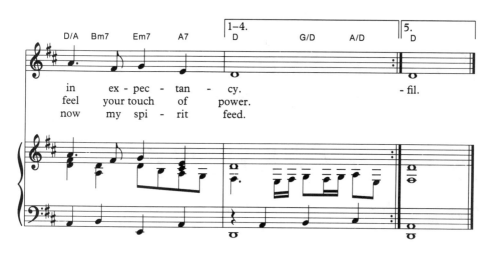

in ex - pec - tan - cy. - fil.
feel your touch of power.
now my spi - rit feed.

4 Speak, your servant listens –
I await your word;
let me know your presence,
let your voice be heard!

5 Fill me with the knowledge
of your glorious will;
all your own good pleasure
in my life fulfil.

261   Spirit divine, inspire our prayers

PICKERING   8 6 8 6 (CM)

Words: Andrew Reed
in this version Jubilate Hymns
Music: Christopher Norton

1 Spi - rit di -

- vine,   in - spire our   prayers, and make our_   hearts   your
(2) light;   re - veal our   need,   our hid - den_   fail - ings
(3) fire,   and cleanse our   hearts with pu - ri - fy - ing

home;   de - scend with   all   your gra - cious   powers =   O
show,   and lead us   in   those paths of   life____   in
flame;   let our whole life   an of - fering   be____   to

Music arrangement: © 1993 HarperCollinsReligious

Words: © in this version Jubilate Hymns

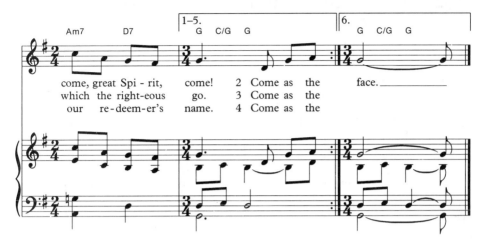

come, great Spi - rit, come! 2 Come as the face._____
which the right-eous go. 3 Come as the
our re-deem-er's name. 4 Come as the

4 Come as the dew and gently bless
this consecrated hour;
may barren souls rejoice to know
your life-creating power.

5 Come as the dove, and spread your wings,
the wings of peaceful love;
and let your church on earth become
blessed as the church above.

6 Come as the wind with rushing sound
and pentecostal grace,
that all the world with joy may see
the glory of your face.

Instrumental obligato

262   See the feast our God prepares

DARTMEET   7 7 7 7

Words: from Isaiah 25
Christopher Idle
Music: David Peacock

3

Relaxed and flowing ♩ = 86

1 See the feast our God pre-pares; all who hun-ger, come to
(2) sud-den-ly re-moves pri-soners' shame and mour-ners'
(3) tears are wiped a-way, now for ev-er death un-
(4) God! With joy ac-claim all the glo-ries of our

dine! Je-sus with his peo-ple shares rich-est
grief; here the wan-derers whom he loves find their
-done; he who rose on Eas-ter Day ends our
king. Christ the Lord! We love his name: ev-ery

1–3.
food and fin-est wine.   2 Here he tongue, his prai-ses sing!
rest and their re-lief.   3 Now our
dark-ness like the sun.   4 Christ our

4.

263   Spirit of faith, by faith be mine

LITTLE STANMORE   8 8 8 6

Words: Timothy Dudley-Smith
Music: John Barnard

1 Spi-rit of faith, by faith be mine;
2 Come to our hearts and there re-main;

Spi-rit of truth, in wis-dom shine;
Spi-rit of life, our life sus-tain;

Spi-rit of ho-li-ness di-vine,
Spi-rit of grace and glo-ry, reign!

Spi-rit of Je-sus,   come!
Spi-rit of Je-sus,   come!

264   Spirit of God most high

LITTLE CORNARD   6 6 6 6 8 8

Words: David Mowbray
Music: Martin Shaw
arranged Christopher Norton

18

1 Spi - rit of God most high,
2 Wind of God's Spi - rit, blow!
3 Fire of God's Spi - rit, melt
4 Spi - rit of Christ our Lord,

Lord of all power and might;   source of our Eas - ter joy,
in - to the val - ley sweep,   bring - ing dry bones to life,
ev - ery un - bend - ing heart;   your peo - ple's love re - new
send us to do your will;   no - thing need hold us back

265   Such love

SUCH LOVE   8 8 8 5

Words and music: Graham Kendrick
Music arranged David Peacock

11

1 Such love, pure as the whit-est snow,
(2) love, still - ing my rest-less-ness,
(3) love springs from e - ter - ni - ty,

such love weeps for the shame I know,
such love, fill - ing my emp-ti-ness,
such love, stream-ing through his - to - ry,

such love,_____ pay-ing the
such love,_____ show-ing me
such love,_____ foun-tain of

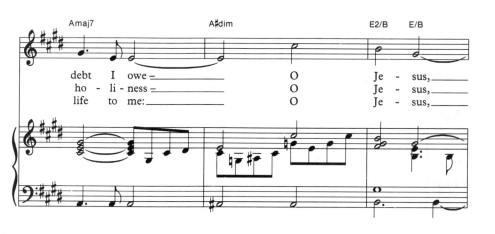

debt I owe =_____ O Je - sus,_____
ho - li - ness =_____ O Je - sus,_____
life to me:_____ O Je - sus,_____

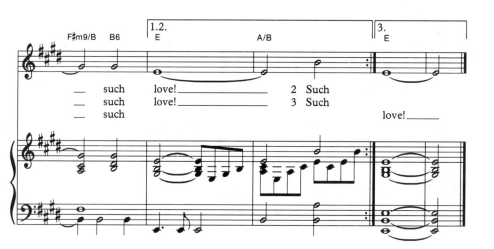

such love!_____ 2 Such
such love!_____ 3 Such
such love!_____

266
Take my life and let it be

HOFFMAN   7 7 7 7

Words: Frances Havergal
in this version Jubilate Hymns
Music: Roger Mayor

3

Thoughtfully ♩ = 78

1 Take my life and let it be
2 Take my hands, and let them move
3 Take my voice, and let me sing

all you pur - pose, Lord, for me; con - se - crate my
at the im - pulse of your love; take my feet, and
al - ways, on - ly, for my King; take my lips, let

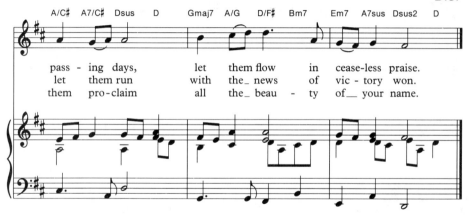

pass - ing days,   let   them flow   in   cease-less praise.
let   them run   with   the_ news   of   vic - tory   won.
them   pro-claim   all   the_ beau - ty   of_ your name.

4   Take my wealth – all I possess,
     make me rich in faithfulness;
     take my mind that I may use
     every power as you shall choose.

5   Take my motives and my will,
     all your purpose to fulfil;
     take my heart – it is your own,
     it shall be your royal throne.

6   Take my love – my Lord, I pour
     at your feet its treasure-store;
     take myself, and I will be
     yours for all eternity.

Instrumental obligato

267   Tell all the world of Jesus

THORNBURY   7 6 7 6 D

Words: James Seddon
Music: Basil Harwood
arranged Christopher Norton

268

Tell out, my soul

GO FORTH   10 10 10 10

Words: from Luke 1
Timothy Dudley-Smith
Music: Michael Baughen
arranged Christopher Norton

12

1 Tell   out, my   soul,   the great-ness of the Lord!
2 Tell   out, my   soul,   the great-ness of his name!
3 Tell   out, my   soul,   the great-ness of his might!
4 Tell   out, my   soul,   the glo - ries of his word!

un - num-bered bless - ings give   my   spi - rit
make   known his might,   the deeds his   arm   has
powers   and do - min - ions lay their glo - ry
firm   is his pro - mise, and his mer - cy

269 The day you gave us

St Clement   9 8 9 8

Words: John Ellerton
in this version Jubilate Hymns
Music: Clement Scholefield
arranged Roger Mayor

1 The day you gave us, Lord, is end - ed, the dark - ness falls at your be - hest; to
2 We thank you that your church, un - sleep - ing while earth rolls on - ward in - to light, through
3 As to each con - ti - nent and is - land the dawn pro - claims a - no - ther day, the

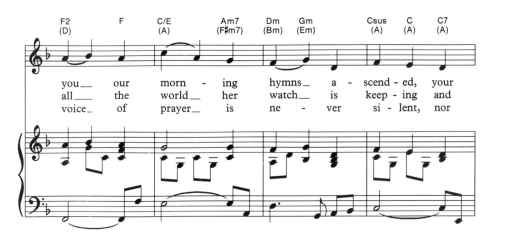

you— our morn - ing hymns— a - scend - ed, your
all— the world— her watch— is keep - ing and
voice— of prayer— is ne - ver si - lent, nor

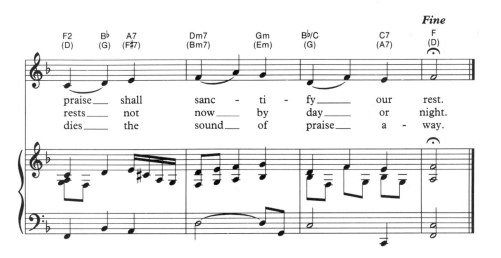

Fine

praise— shall sanc - ti - fy— our rest.
rests— not now— by day— or night.
dies— the sound— of praise— a - way.

4 The sun that bids us rest is waking
  your church beneath the western sky;
  fresh voices hour by hour are making
  your mighty deeds resound on high.

5 So be it, Lord: your throne shall never,
  like earth's proud empires, pass away;
  your kingdom stands, and grows for ever,
  till all your works your rule obey.

270

The earth was dark

LIGHTS TO THE WORLD   8 8 8 8 D (DLM)

Words and music: John Daniels
and Phil Johnson
Music arranged Christopher Norton

7

Spirited ♩ = 88

1 The earth was dark un - til you spoke –
2 In Christ you gave your gift of life
3 Where there is fear may we bring joy,
4 O burn in us, that we may burn

then all was light and all was peace; yet still, O God, so
to save us from the depths of night: O come and set our
and heal-ing to a world of pain: Lord, build your king - dom
with love that tri - umphs in des - pair; and touch our lives with

ma - ny__ wait to see the flame of love re - leased.
spi - rits__ free and draw us to your per - fect light!
through our__ lives till Je - sus walks this earth a - gain.
such a__ fire that souls may search and find you there.

Chorus

Lights to the world! O Light di - vine, kin - dle in us a migh - ty__ flame, till ev-ery heart, con - sumed by love shall__ rise to__ praise your ho - ly name!

271   The first nowell

THE FIRST NOWELL   Irregular

Words: unknown
in this version Word & Music
Music: English traditional melody
arranged David Peacock

Medium tempo ♩ = 106

1 The first now - ell the an - gel did
2 The wise men from a coun - try
3 At Beth - le - hem they en - tered
4 Then let us all with one ac -

say, was to Beth - le - hem's shep - herds in fields as they
far looked up and saw a guid - ing
in, on bend - ed knee they wor - shipped
- cord sing prai - ses to our hea - ven - ly

lay; in fields where they lay keep - ing their
star; they tra - velled on by night and
him; they of - fered there in his pre -
Lord; for Christ has our sal - va - tion

sheep on a cold win-ter's night that was___ so deep:
day to___ reach the place where Je - sus lay:
- sence their gold___ and myrrh and fran - kin - cense:
wrought and___ with___ his blood our life___ has bought:

Chorus

Now - ell,___ now - ell, now - ell, now - ell,

born is the king___ of Is - ra - el!

272 The hands of Christ
(First tune)

SITLEY 8 8 8 8 4

Words: Michael Perry
Music: Christopher Rolinson

Sensitively and with expression ♩ = 94

Capo 3(D)

1 The hands   of Christ,___   the car - ing hands,___   they_
2 The king - ly Christ,___   the sav - iour-king,___   they_
3 Too late   for life,____   in death   too late____   they_
4 To him   be praise,___   all praise   to him____   who_

nailed   them   to   a   cross   of   wood;_____   the
hailed   him   with   a   cru - el   crown;_____   the
tried   to   maim him with   a   spear;_____   for
died   up - on   the   cross   of   pain;_____   whose

272   The hands of Christ
(Second tune)

BEATRICE   8 8 8 8 4

Words and music: Michael Perry
arranged David Peacock

6

With a gentle lilt ♩. = 60

1 The hands of Christ, the
2 The king - ly Christ, the
3 Too late for life, in
4 To him be praise, all

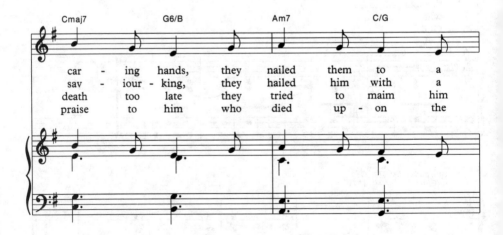

car - ing hands, they nailed them to a
sav - iour - king, they hailed him with a
death too late they tried to maim him
praise to him who died up - on the

cross of wood; the feet that climbed the des - ert road and
cru - el crown; the lips that spoke the truth a - lone, that
with a spear; for sac - ri - lege they could not bear – the
cross of pain; whose ag - on - ies were not in vain – for

brought the news of peace with God, they
made the way to hea - ven known, they
sab - bath comes, so they must tear the
Christ the Lord is risen a - gain and

pierced them through._____
mocked with wine._____
heart from God._____
brings us   joy!_____

273   The head that once was crowned

 St Magnus   8 6 8 6 (CM)

Words: Thomas Kelly
Music: Jeremiah Clarke
arranged Christopher Norton

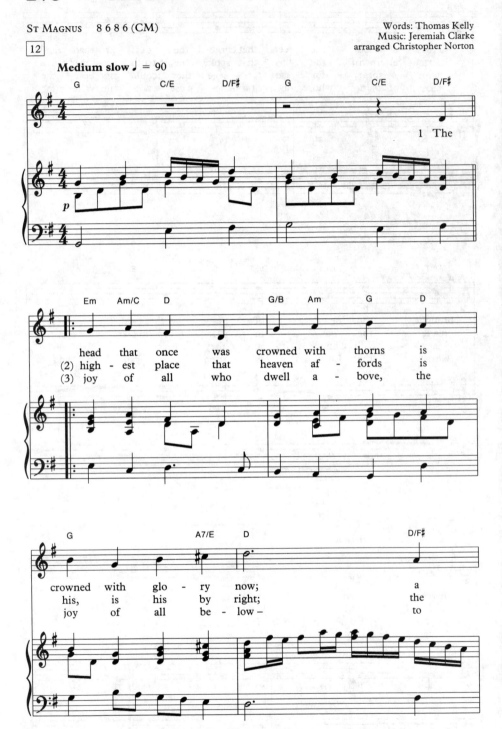

royal diadem adorns the
King of kings and Lord of lords and
whom he demonstrates his love and

mighty victor's brow.
heaven's eternal light.
grants his name to know:

2 The
3 The
4 To

4 To them the cross with all its shame,
with all its grace is given;
their name, an everlasting name,
their joy, the joy of heaven.

5 They suffer with their Lord below,
they reign with him above;
their profit and their joy to know
the mystery of his love.

6 The cross he bore is life and health,
though shame and death to him;
his people's hope, his people's wealth,
their everlasting theme.

274   The king of love my shepherd is

DOMINUS REGIT ME   8 7 8 7

Words: from Psalm 23
Henry Baker
in this version Jubilee Hymns
Music: John Dykes
arranged Christopher Norton

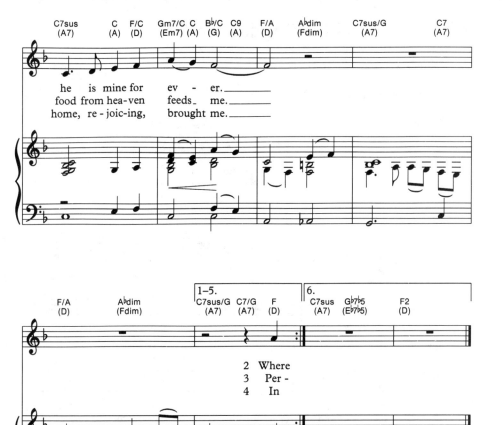

he is mine for ev - er.
food from hea-ven feeds me.
home, re - joic-ing, brought me.

2 Where
3 Per -
4 In

4 In death's dark vale I fear no ill
  with you, dear Lord, beside me;
  your rod and staff my comfort still,
  your cross before to guide me.

5 You spread a banquet in my sight
  of love beyond all knowing;
  and oh the wonder and delight
  from your pure chalice flowing!

6 And so through all the length of days
  your goodness fails me never:
  Good Shepherd, may I sing your praise
  within your house for ever!

275

The kingdom of God

THE KINGDOM OF GOD   10 10 11 11

Words: Bryn Rees
Music: Paul Bateman
arranged Christopher Norton

1 The king-dom of God
2 The king-dom of God
3 The king-dom of God
4 God's king-dom is come,

is jus - tice and joy;
is mer - cy and grace;
is chal - lenge and choice:
the gift and the goal;

for Je - sus re -
the cap-tives are
be - lieve the good
in Je - sus be -

- stores
freed,
news,
- gun,

what sin would des - troy.
the sin - ners find place,
re - pent and re - joice!
in hea - ven made whole.

May also be sung to the tune HANOVER (230)

276

The Lord is king

CHURCH TRIUMPHANT   8 8 8 8 (LM)

Words: Josiah Conder
Music: James Elliott
arranged David Peacock

Medium tempo ♩ = 104

1 The Lord is king! Lift up your voice, O_____ earth, and__ all you heavens, re-joice! From world to world the song shall ring: 'The Lord om - ni - po - tent is king!'

2 The Lord is king! Who then shall dare re - sist his__ will, dis - trust his care or quar - rel with his wise de - crees, or doubt his roy - al pro - mi - ses?

3 The Lord is king! Child of the dust, the judge of__ all the earth is just; ho - ly and true are all his ways – let ev - ery crea - ture sing his praise!

4 God reigns! He reigns with glory crowned:
let Christians make a joyful sound!
And Christ is seated at his side:
the man of love, the crucified.

5 Come, make your needs, your burdens known:
he will present them at the throne;
and angel hosts are waiting there
his messages of love to bear.

6 One Lord one kingdom all secures:
he reigns, and life and death are yours;
through earth and heaven one song shall ring:
'The Lord omnipotent is king!'

For an alternative arrangement of this tune, see no. 133

277   The will of God to mark my way

UNLESS THE LORD   8 6 8 6 (CM)

23

Words: from Psalm 119
Timothy Dudley-Smith
Music: Christopher Norton

278　The Lord my shepherd

THE LORD MY SHEPHERD　　8 6 8 6 (DCM)

Words: from Psalm 23
Christopher Idle
Music: Merla Watson
arranged Roger Mayor

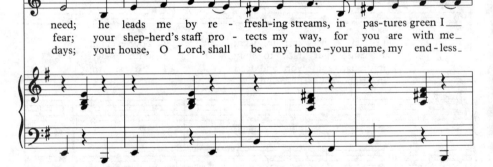

May also be sung to the tune CRIMOND (279)

feed. 2 The Lord re-vives my___ fail-ing strength, he
there. 4 While all my e - ne - mies look on you
praise. 6 To Fa-ther, Son and___ Spi-rit, praise! to

makes my joy com - plete;___ and in right paths, for___
spread a ro - yal___ feast;___ you fill my cup, a -
God whom we a - dore,___ be wor-ship, glo - ry,___

his name's sake, he guides my fal-tering feet.
-noint my head, and treat me as your guest.
power and love, both now and ev - er - - more!

1.2.

3.

ff

279 The Lord's my shepherd

CRIMOND   8 6 8 6 (CM)

Words: from Psalm 23
William Whittingham and others
Music: Jessie Irvine
arranged Christopher Norton

1 The Lord's my shepherd: I'll not want; he makes me down to
(2) soul he doth restore a - gain, and me to walk doth
(3) though I walk through death's dark vale, yet will I fear no

4 My table thou hast furnishèd
  in presence of my foes;
  my head with oil thou dost anoint
  and my cup overflows.

5 Goodness and mercy all my life
  shall surely follow me;
  and in God's house for evermore
  my dwelling-place shall be.

280   The Son of God proclaim

PURE IN HEART   6 6 8 6 (SM)

Words: Basil Bridge
Music: Christopher Norton

12

1 The Son of God pro - claim!
2 He, God's cre - a - tive Word,
3 The Lord of life and death
4 We take this cup in hope,

the Lord of time and space,   the
the chur - ch's Lord and head,   here
with won - dering praise we sing;   we
for he who glad - ly bore   the

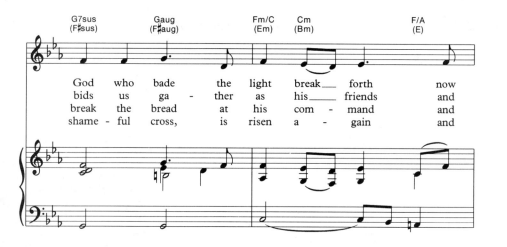

God who bade the light break__ forth now
bids us ga - ther as his__ friends and
break the bread at his com - mand and
shame - ful cross, is risen a - gain and

shines in Je - sus' face.
share his wine and bread.
name him God and king.
reigns for e - ver-more.

Instrumental obligato

281

The strife is past

VICTORY   8 8 8 4

9

Words: from the Latin
Francis Pott
in this version Jubilate Hymns
Music: Giovanni Pierluigi da Palestrina
and William Monk
arranged Christopher Norton

1 The strife is past, the bat - tle done;
2 Death's migh - tiest powers have done— their worst;
3 On the third day he rose— a - gain,
4 Lord o - ver death, our wound - ed king,

now is the vic - tor's tri - umph
and Je - sus has his foes dis-
glo - rious in ma - jes - ty— to
save us from Sa - tan's dead - ly

282   The trumpets sound

THE FEAST IS READY   8 8 8 8 and refrain

Words and music: Graham Kendrick
Music arranged Christopher Norton

Fiesta style ♩ = 160

1 The trum - pets sound, the an - gels sing,
2 Ta - bles are la - den with___ good things:
3 The hun - gry heart he sa - tis - fies,

the feast is rea - dy to___ be - gin; the gates of
O taste the peace and joy___ he brings! He'll fill your
of - fers the poor his pa - ra - dise. Now hear all

1st time to verse 2
2nd and 3rd times to chorus

heaven are o - pen wide, and Je - sus wel - comes you___ in - side.
heart with love___ di - vine, he'll turn your wa - ter in - to wine.
heaven and earth ap - plaud the a - maz - ing good - ness of___ the Lord!

283   The victory of our God is won

WATERSIDE   8 6 8 6 D (DCM)

Words: Christopher Idle
Music: Christopher Norton

Confidently ♩ = 74

1 The victory of our
(2) all be-liev - ers
(3) Christ-ians of these
(4) glo - ry to the

God is won and all cre - a - tion___ sings! Four
in the Lord com - bine in per - fect___ praise: the
lat - ter years shall not be miss - ing___ there: the
Lamb who died and res-cued us by___ blood, the

liv - ing crea - tures round the throne ac - claim the King of
pa - tri-archs who know their God, with saints of an - cient
pas-tors and the pi - on - eers who wres-tled with des -
Sav-iour who was cru - ci - fied to bring the world to

284

There is a green hill far away
(First tune)

HORSLEY 8 6 8 6 (CM)

Words: Cecil Alexander
Music: William Horsley
arranged Roger Mayor

1 There is a green hill
2 We may not know, we
3 He died that we might

far a - way out - side a ci - ty wall, where
can - not tell what pains he had to bear, but
be for - given, he died to make us good; that

our dear Lord was cru - ci - fied, who
we be - lieve it was for us he
we might go at last to heaven, saved

died to save us all.
hung and suf - fered there.
by his pre - cious blood.

you.

4 There was no other good enough
to pay the price of sin;
he, only, could unlock the gate
of heaven – and let us in.

5 Lord Jesus, dearly you have loved;
and we must love you too,
and trust in your redeeming blood
and learn to follow you.

284

There is a green hill far away
(Second tune)

BESSELSLEIGH   8 6 8 6 (CM)

Words: Cecil Alexander
Music: Paul Herrington
arranged David Peacock

3

With feeling ♩ = 100

1 There is   a   green hill   far   a - way___
2 We may   not   know, we   can - not tell___
3 He died   that   we might   be   for - given,

___ out - side   a   ci - ty
___ what pains   he   had   to
___ he died   to   make   us

wall,_____ where our dear Lord was cru - ci -
bear,_____ but we be - lieve it was for
good;_____ that we might go at last to

- fied,_____ who died to save us
us_____ he hung and suf - fered
heaven,_____ saved by his pre - cious

all._____ you._____
there._____
blood._____

4 There was no other good enough
   to pay the price of sin;
   he, only, could unlock the gate
   of heaven – and let us in.

5 Lord Jesus, dearly you have loved;
   and we must love you too,
   and trust in your redeeming blood
   and learn to follow you.

285   There is a Redeemer

Words and music: Melody Green
Music arranged David Peacock

THERE IS A REDEEMER   Irregular

286　There is no moment of my life

GERONTIUS　8 6 8 6 (CM)

Words: from Psalm 139
Brian Foley
Music: John Dykes
arranged Roger Mayor

9

1 There is no mo - ment of my life,
2 Be - fore I speak, my words are
3 If I should close my eyes to
4 He knew my days be - fore all

life, no place where I may
known, and all that I de -
him, he comes to give me
days, be - fore I came to

go,   no ac - tion which God
- cide.   To come or go: God
sight;   if   I should go   where
be;   he keeps me, loves me,

does __ not see, no thought he does not
knows my choice, and makes him - self my
all __ is dark, he makes my dark - ness
in __ my ways – no lo - ver such as

know.   he.
guide.
light.

287
These are the facts

ICOM   10 10 11 10

Words: from 1 Corinthians 15
Michael Saward
Music: Christopher Rolinson

Simply but with expression ♩ = 96

1 These are the facts as we have re-ceived them,
2 These are the facts as we have re-ceived them:
3 These are the facts as we have re-ceived them:

these are the truths that the Christ - ian be-lieves,
Christ had ful-filled what the scrip - tures fore-told,
we, with our sav - iour, have died on the cross;

this is the ba - sis of all of our preach - ing:
A - dam's whole fam - ily in death had been sleep - ing,
now, hav - ing ris - en, our Je - sus lives in us,

4 These are the facts as we have received them:
   we shall be changed in the blink of an eye,
   trumpets shall sound as we face life immortal,
   this is the victory, this is the victory,
   this is the victory, through Jesus our Lord.

5 These are the facts as we have received them:
   these are the truths that the Christian believes,
   this is the basis of all of our preaching:
   Christ died for sinners, Christ died for sinners,
   Christ died for sinners, and rose from the tomb.

288 They who stand in awe of God

THEY WHO STAND   7 7 7 7 D

Words: from Psalm 112
Michael Saward
Music: Alistair Goudie

1

Joyfully ♩ = 136

1 They who stand in awe___ of God___ are hap - py, Hal - le - lu - jah, they whose joy___ is in___ his word___ are hap - py; hal - le - lu - jah,

2 In the dark - ness, they___ re - main bright - shi - ning – Hal - le - lu - jah, gen - erous, mer - ci - ful,___ and just,___ bright - shi - ning; hal - le - lu - jah,

3 Trou - ble can - not fright - en them, they trust___ God, Hal - le - lu - jah, they can con - quer ev - ery fear,___ they trust___ God; hal - le - lu - jah,

289   This Child

THIS CHILD   9 10 10 5 and refrain

Words and music: Graham Kendrick
Music arranged Christopher Norton

1 This Child,   sec - ret - ly comes__ in the night: oh this
(2) Child,   ris - ing on us___ like the sun: oh this
(3) Child,   rais - ing the hum - ble and poor: oh this

Child,   hid - ing a hea - ven - ly light, oh this Child,   com - ing to us__
Child,   giv - en to light__ ev - ery-one, oh this Child,   guid - ing our feet__
Child,   mak - ing the proud ones to fall; oh this Child,   fill - ing the hun -

__ like a stran - ger,   this hea - ven - ly Child.   This
__ on the path - way   to peace__ on earth.
- gry with good things,   this hea - ven - ly Child.

290 This earth belongs to God

TRUMPET VOLUNTARY   6 9 6 8 9 9 8 6

Words: from Psalm 24
Christopher Idle
Music: Jeremiah Clark
arranged Christopher Norton

March style ♩ = 128

1 This earth be - longs to God, the
2 Lift high your heads, you gates, rise
3 Lift high your heads, you gates, and
4 All glo - ry be to God the

world, its wealth, and all its peo - ple; he formed the
up, you ev - er - last - ing doors, as here now the
fling wide o - pen the an - cient doors, for here comes the
Fa - ther, Son and Ho - ly Spi - rit; from a - ges

The congregation may divide at A (e.g. Men) and B (e.g. Women)

291   This is the day the Lord has made

PILGRIM'S JOY   8 6 8 6 (CM)

Words: Isaac Watts
Music: Christopher Norton

23

1 This is the day the Lord has made, he
(2) day he rose and left the dead, and
(3) -san - na to the anoin - ted king,_ to

calls the hours his own: __ let heaven re - joice, let
Sa - tan's em - pire fell;__ to - day the saints his
Da - vid's ho - ly Son!__ Help us, O Lord; de -

292 Through all the changing scenes

WILTSHIRE 8 6 8 6 (CM)

Words: from Psalm 34
Nahum Tate and Nicholas Brady
in this version Jubilate Hymns
Music: George Smart
arranged Christopher Norton

4 O taste his goodness, prove his love!
Experience will decide
how blessed they are, and only they,
who in his truth confide.

5 Fear him, you saints, and you will then
have nothing else to fear;
his service shall be your delight,
your needs shall be his care.

6 To Father, Son and Spirit, praise!
To God whom we adore
be worship, glory, power and love,
both now and evermore!

293   To God be the glory

Words: Frances van Alstyne
Music: William Doane
arranged Roger Mayor

To God Be The Glory
11 11 11 11 and refrain

24 **With vigour** ♩ = 110

1 To God be the glo - ry! Great things he has done: so loved he the world that he gave us his Son who yield - ed his life an a - tone-ment for

2 O per - fect re - demp - tion, the pur-chase of blood! To ev - ery be - liev - er the pro-mise of God: the vil - est of-fend-er who tru - ly be -

3 Great things he has taught us, great things he has done, and great our re - joic - ing through Je - sus the Son: but pur - er and high-er and great - er will

294

To him we come

LIVING LORD   9 8 8 8 8 3

4

Words: James Seddon
Music: Patrick Appleford
arranged Noël Tredinnick

1 To him we come —
2 In him we live —
3 For him we go —

come — Je - sus Christ our Lord, God's own
live — Christ our strength and stay, life and
go — sol - diers of the cross, count - ing

liv - ing Word, his dear Son:
truth and way, friend di - vine:
all things loss him to know;

in him there is no east or west,
his power can break the chains of sin,
go-ing to ev - ery land and race,

in him all na - tions
still all life's storms with -
preach-ing to all re -

shall be blessed;
- out, with - in,
- deem - ing grace,

to all he of - fers peace and rest —
help us the dai - ly fight to win —
build-ing his church in ev - ery place —

lov - ing Lord!
liv - ing Lord!
con - quering Lord!

Lord!

4 With him we serve –
   his the work we share
   with saints everywhere,
   near and far;
   one in the task which faith requires,
   one in the zeal which never tires,
   one in the hope his love inspires –
      coming Lord!

5 Onward we go –
   faithful, bold, and true,
   called his will to do
   day by day
   till, at the last, with joy we'll see
   Jesus, in glorious majesty;
   live with him through eternity –
      reigning Lord!

295   We believe in God Almighty

ANSDELL   8 7 8 7 8 7

3

Words: David Mowbray
Music: Bob Fraser
arranged Christopher Norton

Thoughtfully ♩ = 98

1 We be-lieve   in God   Al - migh-ty,
2 We be-lieve   in Christ the   Sav-iour,
3 We be-lieve   in God   the   Spi - rit,

mak-er of   the earth and sky;   all   we   see   and
Son of God   and Son of Man;   born of Ma - ry,
pre-sent in   our lives to-day;   speak-ing through   the

296   We believe in God the Father

WE BELIEVE   8 7 8 7 D and refrain

Words and music: Graham Kendrick
Music arranged Roger Mayor

With strength ♩ = 120

1 We be-lieve in God the Fa-ther, ma-ker of the u-ni-verse,
2 We be-lieve he sends his Spi-rit on his church with gifts of power;

and in Christ his Son our sav-iour, come to us by vir-gin birth.
God, his word of truth af-firm-ing, sends us to the na-tions now.

We be-lieve he died to save us, bore our sins, was cru-ci-fied;
He will come a-gain in glo-ry, judge the liv-ing and the dead:

then from death he rose vic-to-rious, a-scen-ded to the
ev-ery knee shall bow be-fore him, then must ev-ery

297 We break this bread

WE BREAK THIS BREAD Irregular

Words: from *The Alternative Service Book 1980*
Music: Christopher Rolinson
arranged David Peacock

The congregation may divide at A and B

we are one bo-dy,_____ be-cause we all__ share, we

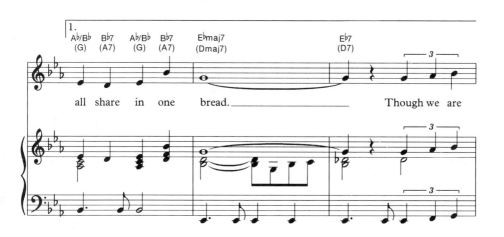

all share in one bread._____ Though we are

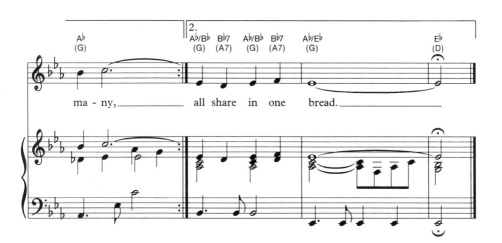

ma - ny,_____ all share in one bread._____

298   We come as guests invited

CRÜGER   7 6 7 6 D

3

Words: Timothy Dudley-Smith
Music: Johann Crüger
arranged Christopher Norton

1 We come as guests invited when Jesus bids us dine, his friends on earth united to

(2) eat and drink, receiving from Christ the grace we need, and in our hearts believing on

(3) bread is ours for sharing, one single fruitful vine, our felowship declaring re-

299   We give God thanks

NEWINNTON   8 8 8 8 (LM)

Words: Michael Perry
Music: Colin Avery

1 We give God thanks for those who
(2) prayer for all who
(3) - cate our skills and
(4) touch of heal - ing

knew the touch of Je - sus' heal-ing love; they trust - ed
go re - ly - ing on his grace and power, to help the
time to those who suf - fer where we live, to bring such
grace lives on__ with - in our will - ing care; by thought and

300
We have a gospel

FULDA   8 8 8 8 (LM)

Words: Edward Burns
Music: William Gardiner
arranged Christopher Norton

1 We have a gospel to proclaim,
good news for all throughout the

2 Tell of his birth at Bethlehem,
not in a royal house or

3 Tell of his death at Calvary,
hated by those he came to

4 Tell of that glorious Easter morn:
  empty the tomb, for he was free!
  He broke the power of death and hell
  that we might share his victory.

5 Tell of his reign at God's right hand,
  by all creation glorified;
  he sends his Spirit on his church
  to live for him, the Lamb who died.

6 Now we rejoice to name him king:
  Jesus is Lord of all the earth;
  this gospel-message we proclaim:
  we sing his glory, tell his worth.

301

We love the place, O God

QUAM DILECTA   6 6 6 6

3

Words: William Bullock
and Henry Baker
in this version Jubilate Hymns
Music: Henry Jenner
arranged David Peacock

1 We love the place, O God,
in which your hon-our dwells:
the joy of your a-bode,
all

(2) love the house of prayer:
for where Christ's peo-ple meet,
our ris-en Lord is there
to

(3) love the word of life,
the word that tells of peace,
of com-fort in the strife
and

4   We love the cleansing sign
     of life through Christ our Lord,
     where with the name divine
     we seal the child of God.

5   We love the holy feast
     where, nourished with this food,
     by faith we feed on Christ,
     his body and his blood.

6   We love to sing below
     of mercies freely given,
     but O, we long to know
     the triumph-song of heaven.

7   Lord Jesus, give us grace
     on earth to love you more,
     in heaven to see your face
     and with your saints adore.

302   We plough the fields, and scatter

WIR PFLÜGEN   7 6 7 6 D and refrain

Words: after Matthias Claudius
Jane Campbell
Music: Johann Schulz
arranged Christopher Norton

(2) on - ly is the ma - ker of all things near and
(3) thank you, then, our Fa - ther, for all things bright and

plough the fields, and scat - ter the good seed on the

land; but it is fed and wa - tered by God's al - migh - ty
far; he paints the way-side flo - wer, he lights the eve - ning
good; the seed-time and the har - vest, our life, our health, our

Music arrangement: © 1993 HarperCollins*Religious*

Chorus

All good gifts a - round us are sent from heaven a - bove: then

thank the Lord, O thank the Lord for all_____ his love.

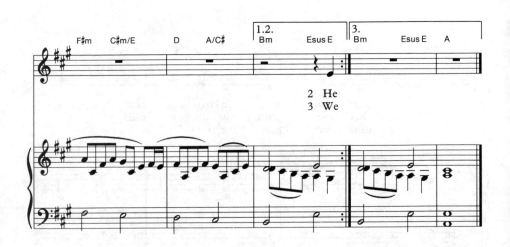

2 He
3 We

303

We trust in you

FINLANDIA 11 10 11 10 11 10

Words: Edith Cherry
in this version Jubilate Hymns
Music: Jean Sibelius
arranged Roger Mayor

1 We trust in you, our shield and our de-
2 We trust in you, O Cap-tain of sal-
3 We go in faith, our own great weak-ness
4 We trust in you, our shield and our de-

-fend-er; we do not fight a-
-va-tion! in your dear name, all
feel-ing, and need-ing more each
-fend-er: yours is the bat - tle—

304   We worship God in harmony

AULD LANG SYNE   8 6 8 6 D

Words: Michael Baughen
Music: Scottish traditional melody
arranged David Peacock

1 We worship God in harmony with hearts in full accord;
we share one Spirit, hope and faith, one Father and one

(2) children now of God by grace – our new life has begun,
where male and female, Greek and Jew, both bound and free are

(3) live as those whom Christ has called to love with Christ-like mind
that looks towards each other's needs, forbearing, patient,

(4) day we'll see him face to face, to him we'll bow the knee;
we'll never say goodbye again – the best is yet to

305   What a friend we have in Jesus

CONVERSE   8 7 8 7 D

Words: Joseph Scriven
Music: Charles Converse
arranged David Peacock

1

Slow blues ♩ = 68

1 What a friend we have in Je - sus
2 Have we tri - als and temp - ta - tions
3 Are we weak and hea - vy - la - den,

all our sins and griefs to bear;
is there trou - ble a - ny - where?
bur - dened with a load of care?

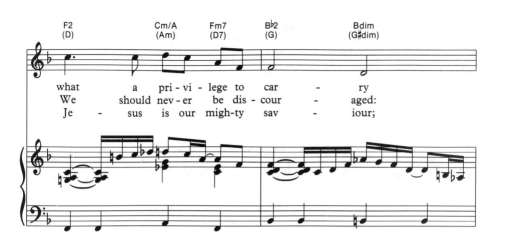

what   a   pri - vi - lege to   car -   ry
We   should nev - er be dis - cour -   aged:
Je -   sus is our migh-ty sav -   iour;

ev - ery-thing to God in prayer!   O   what peace we of - ten
take it to the Lord in prayer.   Can we find a friend so
he will lis-ten to our prayer.   Do your friends des-pise, for -

for - feit,   O what need-less pain we bear,
faith - ful   who will all our sor-rows share?
- sake   you? Take it   to the Lord in prayer:

F2   Cm6/A   F7   B♭2   Bdim
(D)   (Am)   (D7)   (G)   (G♯dim)

all   be - cause we   do not car -   ry
Je -   sus knows our ev - ery weak - ness –
in   his arms he will en - fold   you

1.2.

F2   C/D   Gm7   C7   F   Am/D
(D)   (A)   (Em)   (A7)   (D)   (F♯m)

ev -   ery-thing to God in prayer.
take   it to the Lord in prayer.
and   his love will shield you

3.

Gm   B♭/C   C7♭9 F   F2♭5
(Em)   (G)   (A7) (D)

there.

rall.

306   When all your mercies

ALL YOUR MERCIES   8 6 8 6 (CM)

Words: Joseph Addison
in this version Jubilate Hymns
Music: Christopher Norton

4   In health and sickness, joy and pain,
    your goodness I'll pursue;
    and after death, in distant worlds,
    the glorious theme renew.

5   Throughout eternity, O Lord,
    a joyful song I'll raise;
    but all eternity's too short
    to utter all your praise!

307   When I survey the wondrous cross

ROCKINGHAM   8 8 8 8 (LM)

Words: Isaac Watts
Music: adapted by Edward Miller
arranged Roger Mayor

1 When

(1) I___ sur - vey the won - drous cross on
(2) - bid___ it, Lord, that I should boast save
(3) from___ his head, his hands, his feet, sor -
(4) the___ whole realm of na - ture mine, that

which the prince of glo - ry died,___ my
in the cross of Christ my God:___ the
- row and love flow min - gled down: when
were an offer - ing far___ too small; love

When the king shall come again

TEMPUS ADEST FLORIDUM   7 6 7 6 D

Words: from Isaiah 35
Christopher Idle
Music: English traditional melody
arranged David Peacock

16

With a swing ♩ = 126

1 When the king shall
2 In the de - sert
3 Strength-en fee - ble
4 There God's high-way

come a - gain   all his power re - veal - ing,
trees take root   fresh from his cre - a - tion;
hands and knees,   faint-ing hearts be cheer - ful!
shall be seen   where no roar-ing li - on,

splen-dour shall an - nounce his reign,   life and joy and
plants and flowers and sweet - est fruit   join the ce - le -
God who comes for such as these   seeks and saves the
no - thing e - vil or un - clean   walks the road to

309 When things began to happen

ICH REDE   7 6 7 6 D

Words: from John 1
Michael Saward
Music: Paul Bischoff
arranged David Peacock

310   When you prayed beneath the trees

KELVINGROVE   13 13 14 13

Words: Christopher Idle
Music: Scottish traditional melody
arranged David Peacock

6

Unhurried ♩. = 62

1 When you prayed be - neath the trees, it was for
2 When their tri - umph looked com - plete, it was for
3 When you stum - bled up the road, you walked for
4 When you spoke with king - ly power, it was for

me, O Lord;___ when you cried up - on your
me, O Lord,___ when it seemed like your de -
me, O Lord,___ when you took your dead - ly
me, O Lord,___ in that dread and des - tined

311   While shepherds watched

WINCHESTER OLD   8 6 8 6 (CM)

Words: Nahum Tate
Music: from Thomas Este's 'Psalmes'
arranged David Peacock

shep - herds watched their flocks by night all seat - ed on the
(2) not,' said he — for migh - ty dread had seized their trou - bled
(3) you in Beth - le - hem this day is born of Da - vid's

ground, the an - gel of the Lord came down and
mind – 'Good news of great - est joy I bring to
line a sav - iour, who is Christ the Lord. And

Music arrangement: © David Peacock / Jubilate Hymns

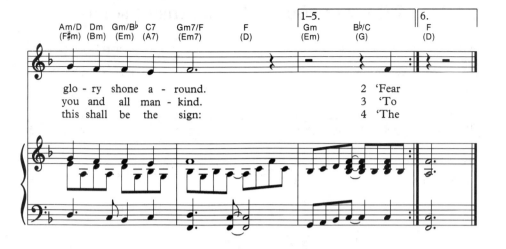

glo - ry shone a - round.
you and all man - kind.
this shall be the sign:

2 'Fear
3 'To
4 'The

4 'The heavenly babe you there shall find
to human view displayed,
all simply wrapped in swaddling clothes
and in a manger laid.'

5 Thus spoke the seraph, and forthwith
appeared a shining throng
of angels praising God, who thus
addressed their joyful song:

6 'All glory be to God on high,
and to the earth be peace!
Goodwill henceforth from highest heaven
begin and never cease.'

Melody part for B♭ instruments

312   Who can sound the depths of sorrow

WHO CAN SOUND   8 7 8 7 8 7 5 5 4

From Psalms 12 and 82
Words and music: Graham Kendrick
arranged Christopher Norton

light that we've ex-tin-guished has brought dark-ness to our land:
truth a-gain shine on us, let your ho-ly fear de-scend:
are a God of jus-tice, and your judge-ment sure-ly comes:

up-on our na-tion, up-on our na-tion have
up-on our na-tion, up-on our na-tion have
up-on our na-tion, up-on our na-tion have

mer-cy Lord! 2 We have Lord!_____
mer-cy Lord! A 3 Who can
mer-cy Lord! B 4 Who will

4 B
  Who will stand against the violence?
  Who will comfort those who mourn?
  In an age of cruel rejection,
  who will build for love a home?
  ALL
  Come and shake us into action,
  come and melt our hearts of stone:
    upon your people, upon your people,
    have mercy Lord!

5 Who can sound the depths of mercy
  in the Father heart of God?
  For there is a Man of sorrows
  who for sinners shed his blood.
  He can heal the wounds of nations,
  he can wash the guilty clean:
    because of Jesus, because of Jesus
    have mercy Lord!

The congregation may divide at A and B

313   You holy angels bright

DARWALL'S 148TH   6 6 6 6 8 8

Words: Richard Baxter
in this version Jubilate Hymns
Music: John Darwall
arranged Roger Mayor

1 You
2 You
3 You
4 So

ho - ly an - gels bright   who wait at God's right
faith - ful souls at rest,   who ran this earth - ly
saints who serve be - low,   a - dore your heaven - ly
take, my soul, your part;   tri - umph in God a -

hand,   or through the realms of light fly at your
race,   and now from sin re - leased be - hold the
King,   and as you on - ward go your joy - ful
- bove,   and with a well - tuned heart sing out your

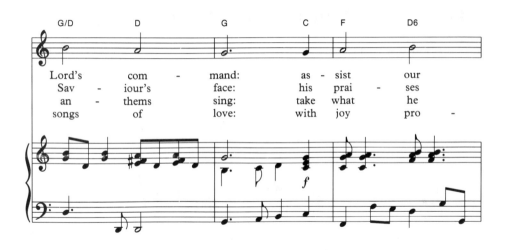

Lord's com - mand: as - sist our
Sav - iour's face: his prai - ses
an - thems sing: take what he
songs of love: with joy pro -

song, or else the theme too high will seem for
sound and all u - nite in sweet de - light to
gives and praise him still through good and ill, who
- claim through all your days in cease - less praise his

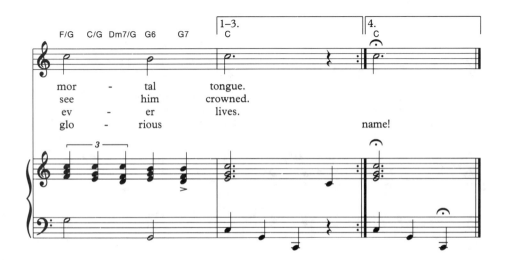

mor - tal tongue.
see him crowned.
ev - er lives.
glo - rious name!

314   You servants of God

LAUDATE DOMINUM   10 10 11 11

Words: Charles Wesley
Music: C Hubert Parry
arranged Roger Mayor

315 Your hand, O God, has guided

THORNBURY 7 6 7 6 D

Words: Edward Plumptre
Music: Basil Harwood
arranged Christopher Norton

1 Your hand, O God, has guid - ed your flock, from age to age;
your faith - ful - ness is writ - ten on his - to - ry's ev - ery page.
They knew your per - fect

(2) her - alds brought the gos - pel to great - est as to least;
they sum - moned us to has - ten and share the great king's feast.
And this was all their

(3) ma - ny days of dark - ness, through ma - ny scenes of strife,
the faith - ful few fought brave - ly to guard the na - tion's life.
Their gos - pel of re -

Music: © Executors of the late Dr Basil Harwood.
Published by permission

4 And we, shall we be faithless?
   Shall hearts fail, hands hang down?
   Shall we evade the conflict
   and throw away the crown?
   Not so! In God's deep counsels
   some better thing is stored;
   we will maintain, unflinching,
      one church, one faith, one Lord.

5 Your mercy will not fail us
   nor leave your work undone;
   with your right hand to help us,
   the victory shall be won.
   And then by earth and heaven
   your name shall be adored;
   and this shall be their anthem:
      One church, one faith, one Lord.

316 Yours be the glory

Maccabaeus 10 11 11 11 and refrain

Words: after Edmund Budry
Richard Hoyle
in this version Jubilee Hymns
Music: adapted from George Handel
arranged Christopher Norton

1 Yours be the glo - ry! ri - sen, con-quering Son;
2 See! Je - sus meets us, ri - sen_ from the tomb,
3 No more we doubt you, glo - rious prince of life:

end - less_ is the vic - tory o - ver death you won;
lov - ing - ly he greets us, scat - ters fear and gloom;
what is__ life with - out you? aid us in our strife;

The traditional version of this text may be found in the words edition

Drum Kit Patterns

13 
Gospel

14 
8 beat D

15 

16 
8 beat E

17 

Rock ballad B

18 

19 
Waltz C

20 

Waltz D

21 
8 beat E

22 

Waltz D

23 
Tango

24 

Jazz waltz

25 

Scripture Index

Genesis
1.	All things bright and beautiful – 11
1.1	At the name of Jesus – 22
1.1	I believe in God the Father – 131
1.1	My God, how wonderful you are – 200
1.1	My Lord of light who made the worlds – 203
1.3	God, whose almighty word – 100
1.3	He who created light – 115
1.3	Morning has broken like the first morning – 198
1.3	Songs of praise the angels sang – 259
1.3	The Earth was dark until you spoke – 270
1.12	We plough the fields, and scatter – 302
2.3	This is the day the Lord has made – 291
2.7	Breathe on me, breath of God – 36
2.7	O Breath of life, come sweeping through us – 214
3.15	Jesus! the name high over all – 159
5.22	Like a mighty river flowing – 179
9.16	O love that will not let me go – 227
22.8	New every morning is the love – 208
22.8	See, amid the winter snow – 252
24.45	Like a mighty river flowing – 179
32.30	Here, O my Lord, I see you face to face – 120
35.19	O little town of Bethlehem – 222

Exodus
3.6	Holy, holy, holy, Lord God almighty – 122
6.7	God whose love we cannot measure – 101
12.3	No weight of gold or silver – 209
13.21	Guide me, O my great Redeemer – 104
14.22	Lead us, heavenly Father, lead us – 167
16.10	Be still – 26
16.31	Dear Lord and Father of mankind – 71
19.6	Church of God, elect and glorious – 54
19.18	Let us love and sing and wonder – 171
19.20	O come, O come, Emmanuel – 216
20.11	This is the day the Lord has made – 291
23.16	Come, you thankful people, come – 65
23.16	For the fruits of his creation – 82
24.6	O for a heart to praise my God – 217
24.16	Let us love and sing and wonder – 171
33.21	Rock of ages, cleft for me – 250
35.2	This is the day the Lord has made – 291

Leviticus
6.4	We plough the fields, and scatter – 302
7.2	Glory be to Jesus – 88
7.2	O for a heart to praise my God – 217
14.13	Glory in the highest – 89
14.24	Glory in the highest – 89
23.22	For the fruits of his creation – 82
26.12	God whose love we cannot measure – 101

Numbers
6.12	Glory in the highest – 89
6.14	Hail the day that sees him rise – 106
11.9	Dear Lord and Father of mankind – 71
20.8	Rock of ages, cleft for me – 250
33.48	Guide me, O my great Redeemer – 104

Deuteronomy
4.11	O Lord, the clouds are gathering – 224
4.22	Guide me, O my great Redeemer – 104
8.15	Rock of ages, cleft for me – 250
11.31	Guide me, O my great Redeemer – 104
26.2	We plough the fields, and scatter – 302
28.2	Praise God from whom all blessings flow – 235
29.5	Guide me, O my great Redeemer – 104
32.4	God is our fortress and our rock – 96
33.27	What a friend we have in Jesus – 305
33.29	We trust in you, our shield and our defender – 303

Joshua
2.24	Rejoice, rejoice! Christ is in you – 244
6.2	Rejoice, rejoice! Christ is in you – 244

Judges
7.15	In heavenly armour we'll enter the land – 140

1 Samuel
1.13	Like a mighty river flowing – 179
2.2	Rock of ages, cleft for me – 250
3.	Speak, Lord, in the stillness – 260
20.42	Like a mighty river flowing – 179
23.18	Like a mighty river flowing – 179

2 Samuel
7.27	We love the place, O God – 301
22.3	God is our fortress and our rock – 96
22.3	We trust in you, our shield and our defender – 303
22.12	O Lord, the clouds are gathering – 224

1 Kings
8.	Almighty God, our heavenly Father – 14
8.30	We love the place, O God – 301
8.66	Praise God from whom all blessings flow – 235
18.45	O Lord, the clouds are gathering – 224
19.11	Be still – 26
19.12	Dear Lord and Father of mankind – 71
19.12	Lord, you sometimes speak in wonders – 184

1 Chronicles
16.29	O for a heart to praise my God – 217
16.29	O worship the Lord in the beauty of holiness – 231
16.29	You holy angels bright – 313
16.31	Rejoice, the Lord is King – 245
16.42	Songs of praise the angels sang – 259
23.30	The day you gave us, Lord, is ended – 269
29.12	Lord, you need no house – 183

2 Chronicles
6.21	We love the place, O God – 301
20.21	O worship the Lord in the beauty of holiness – 231
26.	Almighty God, our heavenly Father – 14
35.11	Glory be to Jesus – 88
35.11	O for a heart to praise my God – 217

Ezra
10.1	We love the place, O God – 301

Nehemiah

9.5   You holy angels bright – 313
9.11   How firm a foundation, you people of God – 125
9.12   Guide me, O my great Redeemer – 104
9.15   Guide me, O my great Redeemer – 104
9.19   O Jesus, I have promised – 221
12.46   Songs of praise the angels sang – 259

Job

10.9   Rejoice, rejoice! Christ is in you – 244
13.15   O God beyond all praising – 219
19.25   I know that my redeemer lives – 133
29.4   Like a mighty river flowing – 179
33.4   Breathe on me, breath of God – 36
33.4   O Breath of life, come sweeping through us – 214
35.5   Like a mighty river flowing – 179
36.31   We plough the fields, and scatter – 302
37.6   We plough the fields, and scatter – 302
37.12   We plough the fields, and scatter – 302
38.7   O little town of Bethlehem – 222

Psalms

5.   Lord, as I wake I turn to you – 174
5.3   Angel voices ever singing – 18
5.3   Holy, holy, holy, Lord God almighty – 122
8.4   Not the grandeur of the mountains – 210
9.7   The Lord is king! Lift up your voice – 276
10.16   The Lord is king! Lift up your voice – 276
10.17   Angel voices ever singing – 18
12.   Who can sound the depths of sorrow – 312
13.   How long, O Lord, – 128
16.2   Lord, you need no house – 183
16.11   Lead us, heavenly Father, lead us – 167
17.15   Speak, Lord, in the stillness – 260
18.   I love you, O Lord, you alone – 134
18.   O worship the King all glorious above – 230
18.2   God is our fortress and our rock – 96
18.2   We trust in you, our shield and our defender – 303
18.4   Jesus, lover of my soul – 154
18.9   O Lord, the clouds are gathering – 224
18.31   God is our fortress and our rock – 96
18.46   Rock of ages, cleft for me – 250
19.1   Christ whose glory fills the skies – 51
19.1   O little town of Bethlehem – 222
20.5   The victory of our God is won – 283
20.7   We trust in you, our shield and our defender – 303
22.   O Lord my God, – 223
22.28   The Lord is king! Lift up your voice – 276
23.   Because the Lord is my shepherd – 27
23.   The king of love my shepherd is – 274
23.   The Lord my shepherd rules my life – 278
23.   The Lord's my shepherd: I'll not want – 279
23.2   In heavenly love abiding – 141
23.3   O worship the Lord in the beauty of holiness – 231
23.4   In heavenly love abiding – 141
24.   This earth belongs to God – 290
24.7   God of gods, we sound his praise – 98
24.7   King of glory, king of peace – 165
25.   Remember, remember your mercy, Lord – 246
25.6   Restore, O Lord – 247
27.5   Rock of ages, cleft for me – 250
27.7   What a friend we have in Jesus – 305

28.7   We plough the fields, and scatter – 302
28.7   We trust in you, our shield and our defender – 303
29.2   O for a heart to praise my God – 217
29.2   O worship the Lord in the beauty of holiness – 231
30.5   O worship the Lord in the beauty of holiness – 231
31.3   How sweet the name of Jesus sounds – 129
31.3   Rock of ages, cleft for me – 250
31.4   Lord, be my vision, supreme in my heart – 175
34.   Through all the changing scenes of life – 292
34.1   Love divine, all loves excelling – 188
36.   Immortal, invisible, God only wise, – 137
36.7   Jesus, lover of my soul – 154
36.7   Not the grandeur of the mountains – 210
36.8   See the feast our God prepares – 262
36.9   Such love, pure as the whitest snow – 265
37.4   Born of the water – 33
37.6   All shall be well – 10
37.7   Be still – 26
40.9   Take my life and let it be – 266
41.4   Almighty God, our heavenly Father – 14
42.   Just as a lost and thirsty deer – 163
42.1   As water to the thirsty – 20
42.2   As water to the thirsty – 20
42.2   My Lord, I did not choose you – 202
42.4   We plough the fields, and scatter – 302
42.8   Lord, be my vision, supreme in my heart – 175
46.   God is our strength and refuge – 95
46.10   Be still – 26
47.5   Christ in majesty ascending – 40
50.1   Jesus shall reign where'er the sun – 156
51.2   My Lord, what love is this – 205
51.4   Almighty God, our heavenly Father – 14
51.10   O Breath of life, come sweeping through us – 214
51.15   All things bright and beautiful – 11
55.17   What a friend we have in Jesus – 305
57.1   Jesus, lover of my soul – 154
59.16   Holy, holy, holy, Lord God almighty – 122
59.16   Lord, be my vision, supreme in my heart – 175
60.4   In heavenly armour we'll enter the land – 140
60.12   The victory of our God is won – 283
61.1   What a friend we have in Jesus – 305
61.3   Lord, be my vision, supreme in my heart – 175
62.6   Rock of ages, cleft for me – 250
62.11   God has spoken – by his prophets – 94
63.1   As water to the thirsty – 20
63.1   My Lord, I did not choose you – 202
63.5   Songs of praise the angels sang – 259
63.5   See the feast our God prepares – 262
63.7   Jesus, lover of my soul – 154
64.1   What a friend we have in Jesus – 305
66.   Praise our God with shouts of joy – 238
67.   God of mercy, God of grace, – 97
67.   Let the people praise you, O God – 169
68.   What a friend we have in Jesus – 305
69.20   I cannot tell why he whom angels worship – 135
69.34   All creatures of our God and King – 5
69.34   Holy, holy, holy, Lord God almighty – 122
71.3   Lord, be my vision, supreme in my heart – 175

77.19	How firm a foundation, you people of God – 125
77.19	O Jesus, I have promised – 221
77.20	Your hand, O God, has guided – 315
78.20	Rock of ages, cleft for me – 250
78.24	Dear Lord and Father of mankind – 71
78.35	God is our fortress and our rock – 96
78.52	Guide me, O my great Redeemer – 104
78.52	Your hand, O God, has guided – 315
79.13	Your hand, O God, has guided – 315
80.18	O Breath of life, come sweeping through us – 214
82.	Who can sound the depths of sorrow – 312
84.4	Love divine, all loves excelling – 188
84.10	We love the place, O God – 301
85.6	O Breath of life, come sweeping through us – 214
86.	Hear me, O Lord, and respond to my prayer – 116
86.15	Not the grandeur of the mountains – 210
87.7	Praise God from whom all blessings flow – 235
88.1	Lord, be my vision, supreme in my heart – 175
88.13	Holy, holy, holy, Lord God almighty – 122
89.26	Rock of ages, cleft for me – 250
89.28	I am trusting you, Lord Jesus – 130
90.	O God, our help in ages past – 220
90.	O Lord, the refuge of each generation – 225
91.	From fears and phantoms of the night – 251
93.1	Clothed in kingly majesty – 55
93.1	The Lord is king! Lift up your voice – 276
94.22	God is our fortress and our rock – 96
95.	Let us sing to the god of salvation – 172
95.2	Songs of praise the angels sang – 259
95.7	How sure the Scriptures are – 127
95.7	Tell all the world of Jesus – 267
95.7	Your hand, O God, has guided – 315
96.9	O for a heart to praise my God – 217
96.9	O worship the Lord in the beauty of holiness – 231
96.10	The Lord is king! Lift up your voice – 276
97.1	Rejoice, the Lord is King – 245
97.1	The day you gave us, Lord, is ended – 269
97.1	The Lord is king! Lift up your voice – 276
98.6	Blow upon the trumpet – 31
99.1	The Lord is king! Lift up your voice – 276
100.	All people that on earth do dwell – 9
100.	Bring to the Lord a glad new song – 37
100.3	Your hand, O God, has guided – 315
102.1	What a friend we have in Jesus – 305
103.	Praise my soul, the king of heaven – 237
103.	Praise to the Lord, the almighty – 242
103.13	We plough the fields, and scatter – 302
103.17	Loved with everlasting love – 190
103.20	You holy angels bright – 313
103.22	Holy, holy, holy, Lord God almighty – 122
103.29	All creatures of our God and King – 5
104.30	O Breath of life, come sweeping through us – 214
105.40	Guide me, O my great Redeemer – 104
107.9	As water to the thirsty – 20
107.9	My Lord, I did not choose you – 202
110.1	Rejoice, the Lord is King – 245
110.7	It came upon the midnight clear – 143
111.8	Not the grandeur of the mountains – 210
112.	They who stand in awe of God are happy – 288
113.3	From the sun's rising unto the sun's setting – 86
114.7	Be still – 26
114.8	Rock of ages, cleft for me – 250
118.3	Not the grandeur of the mountains – 210
119.36	How can we sing with joy to God – 124
119.105	Come down, O Love divine – 61
119.105	Lord, your word shall guide us – 187
119.105	O love that will not let me go – 227
119.114	We trust in you, our shield and our defender – 303
119.129	The will of God to mark my way – 277
119.165	Like a mighty river flowing – 179
119.165	Not the grandeur of the mountains – 210
119.170	What a friend we have in Jesus – 305
121.1	Like a mighty river flowing – 179
126.6	We plough the fields, and scatter – 302
130.	From deep despair to you I call – 81
130.2	What a friend we have in Jesus – 305
130.5	O God beyond all praising – 219
132.9	My hope is built on nothing less – 201
133.1	Spirit of God most high – 264
136.26	Not the grandeur of the mountains – 210
139.	There is no moment of my life – 286
139.23	Lord, the light of your love is shining – 182
141.1	What a friend we have in Jesus – 305
141.2	The day you gave us, Lord, is ended – 269
143.6	As water to the thirsty – 20
143.6	My Lord, I did not choose you – 202
143.10	How good is the God we adore – 126
143.10	O Jesus, I have promised – 221
144.1	Rock of ages, cleft for me – 250
145.2	Tell all the world of Jesus – 267
145.7	Sing of the Lord's goodness – 256
145.7	When all your mercies, O my God – 306
145.10	All creatures of our God and King – 5
145.21	Holy, holy, holy, Lord God almighty – 122
146.10	The Lord is king! Lift up your voice – 276
147.	Fill your hearts with joy and gladness – 77
147.3	No weight of gold or silver – 209
147.8	Like a mighty river flowing – 179
148.	Praise him, praise him, praise him – 236
148.	Praise the Lord of heaven – 239
148.	Praise the Lord, you heavens, adore him – 240
148.5	Bless the Lord, created things – 28
148.5	Holy, holy, holy, Lord God almighty – 122
148.7	All creatures of our God and King – 5
149.	Bring to the Lord a glad new song – 37
149.	Sing of the Lord's goodness – 256
149.4	Angel voices ever singing – 18
150.	Sing of the Lord's goodness – 256
150.	Sing praise to the Lord – 257
150.6	All creatures of our God and King – 5
150.6	Holy, holy, holy, Lord God almighty – 122
150.6	Jesus Christ the Lord is born – 147

Proverbs

| 30.8 | We plough the fields, and scatter – 302 |
| 30.11 | Now thank we all our God – 213 |

Ecclesiastes

| 11.6 | We plough the fields, and scatter – 302 |
| 12.2 | O Lord, the clouds are gathering – 224 |

Song of Songs

1.3	How sweet the name of Jesus sounds – 129
4.15	Jesus, lover of my soul – 154
6.3	How sweet the name of Jesus sounds – 129

8.6   Revive your church, O Lord – 248

Isaiah
1.18   My Lord, what love is this – 205
2.4   O Lord, the clouds are gathering – 224
6.2   My God, how wonderful you are – 200
6.3   God of gods, we sound his praise – 98
6.3   Holy, holy, holy, Lord God almighty – 122
6.3   In awe and wonder, Lord our God – 138
6.7   Take my life and let it be – 266
6.8   O Lord, who came from realms above – 226
7.14   A child is born for us today – 1
7.14   Had he not loved us – 105
7.14   Hark! the herald angels sing – 108
7.14   Lord, you were rich beyond all splendour – 185
7.14   O come, all ye faithful – 215
7.14   O come, O come, Emmanuel – 216
7.14   O little town of Bethlehem – 222
7.14   O Trinity, O Trinity – 229
8.8   Hark! the herald angels sing – 108
9.2   A child is born for us today – 1
9.2   Christ whose glory fills the skies – 51
9.2   God whose love we cannot measure – 101
9.2   O come, O come, Emmanuel – 216
9.2   O Spirit of the living God – 228
9.6   A child is born for us today – 1
9.6   Come and hear the joyful singing – 56
9.6   Hark! the herald angels sing – 108
9.6   It came upon the midnight clear – 143
9.6   Songs of praise the angels sang – 259
9.7   Hail to the Lord's anointed – 107
11.1   O come, O come, Emmanuel – 216
11.10   In heavenly armour we'll enter the land – 140
12.   God brings us comfort where his anger burned – 92
13.7   Your hand, O God, has guided – 315
17.10   Rock of ages, cleft for me – 250
22.22   O come, O come, Emmanuel – 216
25.   See the feast our God prepares – 262
25.7   Darkness like a shroud – 70
25.9   We trust in you, our shield and our defender – 303
26.3   Like a mighty river flowing – 179
26.3   Loved with everlasting love – 190
26.3   Not the grandeur of the mountains – 210
26.4   Rock of ages, cleft for me – 250
28.16   How firm a foundation, you people of God – 125
29.18   Lord, I was blind; I could not see – 177
30.23   We plough the fields, and scatter – 302
30.27   O Spirit of the living God – 228
32.2   Jesus, lover of my soul – 154
32.2   Rock of ages, cleft for me – 250
32.15   Born in song – 32
33.2   O Lord, the clouds are gathering – 224
33.11   I believe in God the Father – 131
33.11   Lord of the church, we pray for our renewing – 180
33.11   Spirit divine, inspire our prayers – 261
34.4   Loved with everlasting love – 190
34.8   Jesus! the name high over all – 159
35.   Joy to the world! The Lord has come – 161
35.   When the king shall come again – 308
35.5   Lord, I was blind; I could not see – 177
40.11   How sweet the name of Jesus sounds – 129
40.20   Lord, you need no house – 183

41.1   God rest you merry, gentlemen – 99
41.4   God has spoken – by his prophets – 94
41.10   How firm a foundation, you people of God – 125
42.5   I believe in God the Father – 131
42.5   O Breath of life, come sweeping through us – 214
42.16   O Jesus, I have promised – 221
42.16   O love that will not let me go – 227
42.18   Lord, I was blind; I could not see – 177
43.2   How firm a foundation, you people of God, – 125
44.5   O for a heart to praise my God – 217
44.6   Christ upon the mountain peak – 52
44.6   God has spoken – by his prophets – 94
44.8   God is our fortress and our rock – 96
44.8   Rock of ages, cleft for me – 250
44.10   Lord, you need no house – 183
44.22   No weight of gold or silver – 209
45.6   Jesus shall reign where'er the sun – 156
48.12   Christ upon the mountain peak – 52
48.18   Like a mighty river flowing – 179
48.21   Rock of ages, cleft for me – 250
49.7   All my heart this night rejoices – 8
51.13   Songs of praise the angels sang – 259
52.7   Take my life and let it be – 266
52.14   Lord, I was blind; I could not see – 177
53.   He was pierced for our transgressions – 114
53.   No weight of gold or silver – 209
53.2   Lord, I was blind; I could not see – 177
53.3   Man of sorrows! what a name – 195
53.5   Come and see, come and see – 58
53.7   I cannot tell why he whom angels worship – 135
53.7   Led like a lamb to the slaughter – 168
53.9   My song is love unknown – 206
53.11   Christ triumphant, ever reigning – 50
53.11   From heaven you came, helpless Babe – 85
53.12   Broken for me, broken for you – 38
53.12   I come with joy to meet my Lord – 132
54.8   Loved with everlasting love – 190
55.10   We plough the fields, and scatter – 302
55.11   I am trusting you, Lord Jesus – 130
56.7   We love the place, O God – 301
59.2   How can we sing with joy to God – 124
59.19   Jesus shall reign where'er the sun – 156
60.1   Darkness like a shroud – 70
60.3   All my heart this night rejoices – 8
60.3   Angels from the realms of glory – 19
60.19   O little town of Bethlehem – 222
61.1   Hail to the Lord's anointed – 107
61.10   Here, O my Lord, I see you face to face – 120
61.10   My hope is built on nothing less – 201
63.12   How firm a foundation, you people of God – 125
66.12   Like a mighty river flowing – 179
66.72   Lord, the light of your love is shining – 182

Jeremiah
2.2   Guide me, O my great Redeemer – 104
2.13   Lord of the church, we pray for our renewing – 180
2.13   Such love, pure as the whitest snow – 265
6.1   Blow upon the trumpet – 31
14.20   Almighty God, our heavenly Father – 14
15.16   Lord, I was blind; I could not see – 177

17.13 Lord of the church, we pray for our renewing – 180
17.13 Such love, pure as the whitest snow – 265
30.10 How firm a foundation, you people of God – 125
30.17 We give God thanks for those who knew – 299
31.3 Loved with everlasting love – 190
31.9 O Jesus, I have promised – 221
46.27 How firm a foundation, you people of God – 125

Lamentations
3.23 Great is your faithfulness, O God my Father – 103
3.23 New every morning is the love – 208
3.41 O God beyond all praising – 219

Ezekiel
10.4 Be still – 26
17.6 Rock of ages, cleft for me – 250
34.26 Hail to the Lord's anointed – 107
36.28 God whose love we cannot measure – 101
37.4 Spirit of God most high – 264
37.9 Breathe on me, breath of God – 36
37.9 O Breath of life, come sweeping through us – 214
37.10 Rejoice, rejoice! Christ is in you – 244
38.15 Rejoice, rejoice! Christ is in you – 244
47.12 Guide me, O my great Redeemer – 104
47.12 Jesus, lover of my soul – 154

Daniel
4.37 Shepherds came, their praises bringing – 254
7.9 Such love, pure as the whitest snow – 265
9.8 Almighty God, our heavenly Father – 14
9.19 O Lord, the clouds are gathering – 224

Hosea
11.1 When all your mercies, O my God – 306
14.8 Praise God from whom all blessings flow – 235

Joel
2.1 Blow upon the trumpet – 31
2.2 O Lord, the clouds are gathering – 224
2.13 How can we sing with joy to God – 124
2.15 Blow upon the trumpet – 31
2.32 In awe and wonder, Lord our God – 138
3.18 Jesus, lover of my soul – 154

Amos
5.24 O Lord, the clouds are gathering – 224
7.2 O Lord, the clouds are gathering – 224

Micah
5.2 O little town of Bethlehem – 222
5.4 How sweet the name of Jesus sounds – 129
7.8 God whose love we cannot measure – 101

Habakkuk
3.17 God is our fortress and our rock – 96

Zephaniah
3.16 Your hand, O God, has guided – 315

Zechariah
2.13 Be still – 26

8.12 Praise God from whom all blessings flow – 235
8.12 We plough the fields, and scatter – 302
8.22 Angels from the realms of glory – 19
9.9 Ride on, ride on in majesty – 249
9.14 Blow upon the trumpet – 31
10.3 How sweet the name of Jesus sounds – 129
12.10 Spirit of faith, by faith be mind – 263
14.8 Lord of the church, we pray for our renewing – 180
14.8 Such love, pure as the whitest snow – 265

Malachi
3.2 Restore, O Lord – 247
4.2 All shall be well – 10
4.2 Christ whose glory fills the skies – 51
4.2 God, whose almighty word – 100
4.2 Hark! the herald angels sing – 108
4.2 Judge eternal, throned in splendour – 162

Matthew
1. Holy child, how still you lie – 121
1.16 I cannot tell why he whom angels worship – 135
1.18 O come, all ye faithful – 215
1.21 How sweet the name of Jesus sounds – 129
1.21 O for a thousand tongues to sing – 218
1.23 A child is born for us today – 1
1.23 Had he not loved us – 105
1.23 Hark! the herald angels sing – 108
1.23 Lord, you were rich beyond all splendour – 185
1.23 O come, all ye faithful – 215
1.23 O come, O come, Emmanuel – 216
1.23 O little town of Bethlehem – 222
1.23 O Trinity, O Trinity – 229
1.35 Dear Lord and Father of mankind – 71
2. Mary came with meekness – 193
2.1 Angels from the realms of glory – 19
2.1 Jesus Christ the Lord is born – 147
2.1 The first nowell the angel did say – 271
2.1 We have a gospel to proclaim – 300
2.2 As with gladness men of old – 21
2.6 O little town of Bethlehem – 222
2.9 As with gladness men of old – 21
2.11 Come and sing the Christmas story – 58
2.11 Hail to the Lord's anointed – 107
2.11 Holy child, how still you lie – 121
2.11 O worship the Lord in the beauty of holiness – 231
2.11 See him lying on a bed of straw – 253
2.11 Shepherds came, their praises bringing – 254
2.18 Jesus Christ the Lord is born – 147
2.23 I cannot tell why he whom angels worship – 135
3.11 I believe in God the Father – 131
3.11 Lord of the church, we pray for our renewing – 180
3.11 My Lord of light who made the worlds – 203
3.11 O Lord, who came from realms above – 226
3.11 Spirit divine, inspire our prayers – 261
3.16 God, whose almighty word – 100
3.16 Like the murmur of the dove's song – 173
3.16 Spirit divine, inspire our prayers – 261
4.1 Lead us, heavenly Father, lead us – 167
4.16 Christ whose glory fills the skies – 51
4.16 O Spirit of the living God – 228

4.19 Dear Lord and Father of mankind – 71
4.19 From heaven you came, helpless Babe – 85
4.23 God, whose almighty word – 100
5.8 Blessed are the pure in heart – 30
5.9 Make me a channel of your peace – 192
5.9 Put peace into each other's hands – 243
5.12 Christ is surely coming – 46
5.14 The Earth was dark until you spoke – 270
5.15 Christ is the king! O friends rejoice – 47
5.15 Make me a channel of your peace – 192
5.24 I come with joy to meet my Lord – 132
5.24 Spirit of God most high – 264
5.24 We plough the fields, and scatter – 302
6.9 Father God in heaven, Lord most high – 73
6.9 Father in heaven – 74
6.10 For the bread which you have broken – 80
6.11 We plough the fields, and scatter – 302
6.12 'Forgive our sins as we forgive' – 83
6.12 Make me a channel of your peace – 192
6.13 O Jesus, I have promised – 221
7.11 We plough the fields, and scatter – 302
7.14 As with gladness men of old – 21
7.16 O Trinity, O Trinity – 229
7.24 Rock of ages, cleft for me – 250
8.3 Heal me, hands of Jesus – 113
8.3 We give God thanks for those who knew – 299
8.20 My song is love unknown – 206
8.22 From heaven you came, helpless Babe – 85
8.26 I cannot tell why he whom angels worship – 135
8.26 Jesus, lover of my soul – 154
8.27 We plough the fields, and scatter – 302
9.9 From heaven you came, helpless Babe – 85
9.20 We give God thanks for those who knew – 299
9.35 We believe in God Almighty – 295
9.38 Come, you thankful people, come – 65
9.38 For the fruits of his creation – 82
10.16 Put peace into each other's hands – 243
10.34 In silent pain the eternal Son – 142
10.38 Praise to the Holiest in the height – 241
11.5 He gave his life in selfless love – 109
11.5 Lord, I was blind; I could not see – 177
11.5 O for a thousand tongues to sing – 218
11.19 We come as guests invited – 298
11.28 How sweet the name of Jesus sounds – 129
11.28 I cannot tell why he whom angels worship – 135
11.28 Just as I am, without one plea – 164
11.28 What a friend we have in Jesus – 305
12.23 Hail to the Lord's anointed – 107
13.24 He gave his life in selfless love – 109
13.25 Come, you thankful people, come – 65
13.30 From the sun's rising unto the sun's setting – 86
13.31 The day you gave us, Lord, is ended – 269
13.31 The kingdom of God is justice and joy – 275
13.44 Lord, your word shall guide us – 187
13.46 Like a mighty river flowing – 179
13.54 We believe in God Almighty – 295
14.19 Break now the bread of life – 35
14.33 The Son of God proclaim – 280
15.13 Lord, I was blind; I could not see – 177
15.30 He who created light – 115
15.31 My song is love unknown – 206
15.31 O for a thousand tongues to sing – 218

15.31 We give God thanks for those who knew – 299
15.36 Break now the bread of life – 35
16.6 There is a Redeemer – 285
16.21 The strife is past, the battle done – 281
16.23 Spirit of God most high – 264
16.24 Praise to the Holiest in the height – 241
16.27 Christ is surely coming – 46
17. Christ upon the mountain peak – 52
17.2 Lord, the light of your love is shining – 182
17.7 Heal me, hands of Jesus – 113
17.7 We give God thanks for those who knew – 299
17.20 Rejoice, rejoice! Christ is in you – 244
18.21 'Forgive our sins as we forgive' – 83
18.32 Such love, pure as the whitest snow – 265
19.3 Heal me, hands of Jesus – 113
19.21 In heavenly love abiding – 141
19.21 Lord, be my vision, supreme in my heart – 175
19.22 Take my life and let it be – 266
19.26 Rejoice, rejoice! Christ is in you – 244
20.19 Come and see, come and see – 58
20.19 The strife is past, the battle done – 281
20.19 This is the day the Lord has made – 291
20.30 Hail to the Lord's anointed – 107
20.34 We give God thanks for those who knew – 299
21.5 Ride on, ride on in majesty – 249
21.8 All glory, praise and honour – 6
21.9 Hail to the Lord's anointed – 107
21.9 Let trumpets sound – 170
21.9 My song is love unknown – 206
21.9 Ride on, ride on in majesty – 249
21.9 This is the day the Lord has made – 291
21.11 I cannot tell why he whom angels worship – 135
21.13 We love the place, O God – 301
21.14 He who created light – 115
21.14 My song is love unknown – 206
21.14 O for a thousand tongues to sing – 218
21.16 All glory, praise and honour – 6
22.2 The kingdom of God is justice and joy – 275
22.3 See the feast our God prepares – 262
22.4 See the feast our God prepares – 262
22.4 The trumpets sound, the angels sing – 282
22.41 Rejoice, the Lord is King – 245
22.42 Hail to the Lord's anointed – 107
23.11 Come and see, come and see – 58
24.14 We have a gospel to proclaim – 300
24.29 Christ is ascending! let creation sing – 42
24.29 Loved with everlasting love – 190
24.30 I cannot tell why he whom angels worship – 135
24.30 Jesus comes with clouds descending – 149
24.31 Jesus the saviour comes – 160
24.31 My hope is built on nothing less – 201
25.1 Christ is the king! O friends rejoice – 47
25.10 Here, O my Lord, I see you face to face – 120
25.31 Tell all the world of Jesus – 267
26.15 Christ is the world's Light, he and none other – 48
26.19 Love is his word, love is his way – 189
26.24 Jesus is king, and we will extol him – 151
26.26 Bread of the world in mercy broken – 34
26.26 Broken for me, broken for you – 38
26.26 For the bread which you have broken – 80

26.26 Love is his word, love is his way – 189
26.26 'Peace be with you all,' we sing – 234
26.26 The Son of God proclaim – 280
26.29 He gave his life in selfless love – 109
26.29 Here, O my Lord, I see you face to face – 120
26.36 When you prayed beneath the trees – 310
26.47 When you prayed beneath the trees – 310
26.63 I cannot tell why he whom angels worship – 135
26.63 When you prayed beneath the trees – 310
27.3 Christ is the world's Light, he and none other – 48
27.9 Christ is the world's Light, he and none other – 48
27.9 My Lord of light who made the worlds – 203
27.9 No weight of gold or silver – 209
27.17 My Lord, what love is this – 205
27.21 My song is love unknown – 206
27.23 My song is love unknown – 206
27.23 When you prayed beneath the trees – 310
27.26 He gave his life in selfless love – 109
27.29 It is a thing most wonderful – 144
27.29 The hands of Christ, the caring hands – 272
27.29 When I survey the wondrous cross – 307
27.31 Lord Jesus Christ, you have come to us – 178
27.33 There is a green hill far away – 284
27.35 I believe in God the Father – 131
27.35 In silent pain the eternal Son – 142
27.35 The hands of Christ, the caring hands – 272
27.36 My Lord, what love is this – 205
27.45 When you prayed beneath the trees – 310
27.48 The hands of Christ, the caring hands – 272
27.54 The Son of God proclaim – 280
27.60 Lord, you need no house – 183
27.66 All creation join to say – 4
28.1 Comes Mary to the grave – 66
28.1 Led like a lamb to the slaughter – 168
28.6 Christ is risen – 45
28.6 Christ the Lord is risen again – 49
28.6 Jesus Christ is risen today – 146
28.6 Led like a lamb to the slaughter – 168
28.6 The hands of Christ, the caring hands – 272
28.19 From the sun's rising unto the sun's setting – 86
28.19 Go forth and tell! O church of God, awake – 90
28.19 I believe in God the Father – 131
28.19 Lord, your church on earth is seeking – 186
28.19 O Spirit of the living God – 228
28.38 Praise to the Holiest in the height – 241

Mark

1.1 The Son of God proclaim – 280
1.9 I cannot tell why he whom angels worship – 135
1.10 God, whose almighty word – 100
1.10 Like the murmur of the dove's song – 173
1.10 Spirit divine, inspire our prayers – 261
1.13 Lead us, heavenly Father, lead us – 167
1.15 The kingdom of God is justice and joy – 275
1.17 Dear Lord and Father of mankind – 71
1.17 From heaven you came, helpless Babe – 85

1.24 There is a Redeemer – 285
1.41 Heal me, hands of Jesus – 113
1.41 We give God thanks for those who knew – 299
2.19 Here, O my Lord, I see you face to face – 120
3.11 The Son of God proclaim – 280
4.21 Christ is the king! O friends rejoice – 47
4.21 Make me a channel of your peace – 192
4.39 Jesus, lover of my soul – 154
4.41 We plough the fields, and scatter – 302
5.27 Heal me, hands of Jesus – 113
5.27 We give God thanks for those who knew – 299
6.29 Lord, you need no house – 183
6.41 Break now the bread of life – 35
6.56 We give God thanks for those who knew – 299
7.33 We give God thanks for those who knew – 299
7.37 Lord, I was blind; I could not see – 177
7.37 O for a thousand tongues to sing – 218
8.22 We give God thanks for those who knew – 299
8.23 Heal me, hands of Jesus – 113
8.29 There is a Redeemer – 285
8.34 Praise to the Holiest in the height – 241
9.36 What a friend we have in Jesus – 305
9.49 How firm a foundation, you people of God – 125
10.21 In heavenly love abiding – 141
10.21 Lord, be my vision, supreme in my heart – 175
10.22 Take my life and let it be – 266
10.27 Rejoice, rejoice! Christ is in you – 244
11.8 All glory, praise and honour – 6
11.9 Let trumpets sound – 170
11.9 My song is love unknown – 206
11.9 Ride on, ride on in majesty – 249
11.9 This is the day the Lord has made – 291
11.25 Forgive our sins as we forgive – 83
11.27 We love the place, O God – 301
12.36 Rejoice, the Lord is King – 245
13.24 Christ is ascending! let creation sing – 42
13.25 Loved with everlasting love – 190
13.26 I cannot tell why he whom angels worship – 135
13.26 Jesus comes with clouds descending – 149
14.12 Christ the Lord is risen again – 49
14.16 Love is his word, love is his way – 189
14.22 Bread of the world in mercy broken – 34
14.22 Broken for me, broken for you – 38
14.22 For the bread which you have broken – 80
14.22 Love is his word, love is his way – 189
14.22 'Peace be with you all,' we sing – 234
14.22 The Son of God proclaim – 280
14.25 He gave his life in selfless love – 109
14.25 Here, O my Lord, I see you face to face – 120
14.34 Praise to the Holiest in the height – 241
14.36 He gave his life in selfless love – 109
14.36 When you prayed beneath the trees – 310
14.43 When you prayed beneath the trees – 310
14.50 In silent pain the eternal Son – 142
14.55 He stood before the court – 112
15.59 He stood before the court – 112
14.61 I cannot tell why he whom angels worship – 135
14.61 When you prayed beneath the trees – 310
14.62 Jesus comes with clouds descending – 149

14.62 Jesus is king, and we will extol him – 151
14.62 Led like a lamb to the slaughter – 168
15.13 My song is love unknown – 206
15.14 The hands of Christ, the caring hands – 272
15.14 When you prayed beneath the trees – 310
15.17 A purple robe, a crown of thorn – 2
15.17 Come and see, come and see – 58
15.17 Come and see, come and see – 58
15.17 It is a thing most wonderful – 144
15.17 My Lord of light who made the worlds – 203
15.17 The hands of Christ, the caring hands – 272
15.17 When I survey the wondrous cross – 307
15.19 The Son of God proclaim – 280
15.20 Lord Jesus Christ, you have come to us – 178
15.21 When you prayed beneath the trees – 310
15.22 There is a green hill far away – 284
15.24 He gave his life in selfless love – 109
15.24 I believe in God the Father – 131
15.24 In silent pain the eternal Son – 142
15.31 Come and see, come and see – 58
15.33 When you prayed beneath the trees – 310
15.36 The hands of Christ, the caring hands – 272
15.37 It is a thing most wonderful – 144
15.37 When you prayed beneath the trees – 310
16.1   Comes Mary to the grave – 66
16.1   Led like a lamb to the slaughter – 168
16.3   All creation join to say – 4
16.6   Christ is risen – 45
16.6   Christ the Lord is risen again – 49
16.6   Jesus Christ is risen today – 146
16.6   Led like a lamb to the slaughter – 168
16.6   The hands of Christ, the caring hands – 272
16.15 Born in song – 32
16.15 Christ the Lord is risen again – 49
16.15 Go forth and tell! O church of God, awake – 90
16.15 Tell all the world of Jesus – 267
16.15 To him we come – 294
16.15 We have a gospel to proclaim – 300
16.19 Glory in the highest – 89
16.19 Jesus is king, and we will extol him – 151
16.19 Once in royal David's city – 232

Luke
1.27   Silent night! Holy night – 255
1.31   O for a thousand tongues to sing – 218
1.32   Tell all the world of Jesus – 267
1.35   The Son of God proclaim – 280
1.35   There is a Redeemer – 285
1.37   Rejoice, rejoice! Christ is in you – 244
1.46   Glad music fills the Christmas sky – 87
1.46   Mary sang a song, a song of love – 194
1.46   Tell out, my soul, the greatness of the Lord – 268
1.52   This Child, secretly comes in the night – 289
1.68   Come, O long-expected Jesus – 57
1.78   All shall be well – 10
1.78   I am trusting you, Lord Jesus – 130
1.79   Christ whose glory fills the skies – 51
1.79   God whose love we cannot measure – 101
1.79   O Jesus, I have promised – 221
1.79   This Child, secretly comes in the night – 289

2.   Holy child, how still you lie – 121
2.   Jesus Christ the Lord is born – 147
2.   Jesus, good above all other – 150
2.   While shepherds watched their flocks – 311
2.2   All creation join to say – 4
2.4   Hail to the Lord's anointed – 107
2.4   Once in royal David's city – 232
2.7   Child in the manger, infant of Mary – 39
2.7   God rest you merry, gentlemen – 99
2.7   Holy child, how still you lie – 121
2.7   I cannot tell why he whom angels worship – 135
2.7   Jesus, saviour, holy child, sleep tonight – 155
2.7   Lord, the light of your love is shining – 182
2.7   Mary came with meekness – 193
2.7   O little town of Bethlehem – 222
2.7   Once in royal David's city – 232
2.7   See, amid the winter snow – 252
2.7   See him lying on a bed of straw – 253
2.8   Angels from the realms of glory – 19
2.8   Silent night! Holy night – 255
2.8   The first nowell the angel did say – 271
2.9   Angels from the realms of glory – 19
2.9   Darkness like a shroud – 70
2.9   God rest you merry, gentlemen – 99
2.9   Hark! the herald angels sing – 108
2.10   Christians, awake, salute the happy morn – 53
2.10   It came upon the midnight clear – 143
2.11   All my heart this night rejoices – 8
2.11   Angels from the realms of glory – 19
2.11   Come and hear the joyful singing – 56
2.11   Good Christians all, rejoice – 102
2.13   All my heart this night rejoices – 8
2.13   Come and sing the Christmas story – 60
2.14   Christ is the world's Light, he and none other – 48
2.14   Glad music fills the Christmas sky – 87
2.14   Glory in the highest – 89
2.14   Jesus, saviour, holy child, sleep tonight – 155
2.14   O come, all ye faithful – 215
2.15   Mary came with meekness – 193
2.15   O come, all ye faithful – 215
2.15   See, amid the winter snow – 252
2.16   Away in a manger, no crib for a bed – 24
2.16   Christians, awake, salute the happy morn – 53
2.16   Come and hear the joyful singing – 56
2.16   Glad music fills the Christmas sky – 87
2.16   God rest you merry, gentlemen – 99
2.16   Lord, the light of your love is shining – 182
2.16   See him lying on a bed of straw – 253
2.16   Shepherds came, their praises bringing – 254
2.16   Silent night! Holy night – 255
2.19   Glad music fills the Christmas sky – 87
2.29   Holy child, how still you lie – 121
2.29   Now at last – 211
2.29   'Peace be with you all,' we sing – 234
2.32   Come, O long-expected Jesus – 57
2.32   The Earth was dark until you spoke – 270
2.34   This Child, secretly comes in the night – 289
2.51   I cannot tell why he whom angels worship – 135

3.16   I believe in God the Father – 131
3.16   Lord of the church, we pray for our renewing – 180
3.16   My Lord of light who made the worlds – 203
3.16   O Lord, who came from realms above – 226
3.16   Spirit divine, inspire our prayers – 261
3.22   God, whose almighty word – 100
3.22   Like the murmur of the dove's song – 173
3.22   Spirit divine, inspire our prayers – 261
4.2   Lead us, heavenly Father, lead us – 167
4.14   Almighty God, we thank you for feeding us – 15
4.15   We believe in God Almighty – 295
4.18   Hail to the Lord's anointed – 107
4.18   Let trumpets sound – 170
4.18   O for a thousand tongues to sing – 218
4.18   The kingdom of God is justice and joy – 275
4.18   We give God thanks for those who knew – 299
4.34   There is a Redeemer – 285
4.40   Heal me, hands of Jesus – 113
4.41   The Son of God proclaim – 280
4.41   There is a Redeemer – 285
5.13   Heal me, hands of Jesus – 113
5.13   We give God thanks for those who knew – 299
5.34   Here, O my Lord, I see you face to face – 120
5.72   From heaven you came, helpless Babe – 85
6.6   We believe in God Almighty – 295
6.19   God, whose almighty word – 100
6.37   Make me a channel of your peace – 192
6.48   Rock of ages, cleft for me – 250
7.22   He gave his life in selfless love – 109
7.22   Lord, I was blind; I could not see – 177
7.22   My song is love unknown – 206
7.34   We come as guests invited – 298
7.42   Such love, pure as the whitest snow – 265
7.47   Like a mighty river flowing – 179
7.50   'Peace be with you all,' we sing – 234
8.16   Christ is the king! O friends rejoice – 47
8.16   Make me a channel of your peace – 192
8.24   I cannot tell why he whom angels worship – 135
8.24   Jesus, lover of my soul – 154
8.44   We give God thanks for those who knew – 299
9.   Christ upon the mountain peak – 52
9.16   Break now the bread of life – 35
9.20   There is a Redeemer – 285
9.22   The strife is past, the battle done – 281
9.23   Praise to the Holiest in the height – 241
9.58   My song is love unknown – 206
9.59   From heaven you came, helpless Babe – 85
9.60   I come with joy to meet my Lord – 132
10.2   Come, you thankful people, come – 65
10.2   For the fruits of his creation – 82
10.34 We give God thanks for those who knew – 299
11.2   Father God in heaven, Lord most high – 73
11.2   Father in heaven – 74
11.2   For the bread which you have broken – 80
11.3   We plough the fields, and scatter – 302
11.4   'Forgive our sins as we forgive' – 83
11.4   O Jesus, I have promised – 221
11.13 We plough the fields, and scatter – 302

11.33 Christ is the king! O friends rejoice – 47
11.33 Make me a channel of your peace – 192
12.27 We plough the fields, and scatter – 302
12.29 In heavenly love abiding – 141
12.33 In heavenly love abiding – 141
12.34 Lord, be my vision, supreme in my heart – 175
12.35 Christ is the king! O friends rejoice – 47
13.12 Freedom and life are ours – 84
13.22 The hands of Christ, the caring hands – 272
14.1   The kingdom of God is justice and joy – 275
14.17 See the feast our God prepares – 262
14.17 The trumpets sound, the angels sing – 282
14.27 Praise to the Holiest in the height – 241
15.18 Almighty God, our heavenly Father – 14
15.21 Almighty God, our heavenly Father – 14
15.23 See the feast our God prepares – 262
17.4   'Forgive our sins as we forgive' – 83
17.5   Help us to help each other, Lord – 118
18.19 He stood before the court – 112
18.22 From heaven you came, helpless Babe – 85
18.22 In heavenly love abiding – 141
18.22 Lord, be my vision, supreme in my heart – 175
18.25 Take my life and let it be – 266
18.27 Rejoice, rejoice! Christ is in you – 244
18.33 The strife is past, the battle done – 281
18.38 Hail to the Lord's anointed – 107
18.42 Break now the bread of life – 35
19.10 He gave his life in selfless love – 109
19.10 Holy child, how still you lie – 121
19.38 Glory in the highest – 89
19.38 We have a gospel to proclaim – 300
19.46 We love the place, O God – 301
20.41 Hail to the Lord's anointed – 107
20.43 Rejoice, the Lord is King – 245
21.27 Be still – 26
21.27 I cannot tell why he whom angels worship – 135
21.28 In heavenly armour we'll enter the land – 140
22.7   Christ the Lord is risen again – 49
22.15 Love is his word, love is his way – 189
22.18 He gave his life in selfless love – 109
22.18 Here, O my Lord, I see you face to face – 120
22.19 Bread of the world in mercy broken – 34
22.19 Broken for me, broken for you – 38
22.19 Father in heaven – 74
22.19 For the bread which you have broken – 80
22.19 Lord Jesus Christ, you have come to us – 178
22.19 Love is his word, love is his way – 189
22.19 'Peace be with you all,' we sing – 234
22.19 The Son of God proclaim – 280
22.20 My Lord, what love is this – 205
22.30 He gave his life in selfless love – 109
22.30 Here, O my Lord, I see you face to face – 120
22.40 O Jesus, I have promised – 221
22.42 From heaven you came, helpless Babe – 85
22.42 He gave his life in selfless love – 109
22.44 Praise to the Holiest in the height – 241
22.44 When you prayed beneath the trees – 310
22.51 Heal me, hands of Jesus – 113
22.52 When you prayed beneath the trees – 310
22.53 When you prayed beneath the trees – 310
22.66 He stood before the court – 112

22.69	Glory in the highest – 89
22.69	Jesus is king, and we will extol him – 151
22.69	Led like a lamb to the slaughter – 168
22.69	Once in royal David's city – 232
23.11	Come and see, come and see – 58
23.21	My song is love unknown – 206
23.21	When you prayed beneath the trees – 310
23.26	When you prayed beneath the trees – 310
23.33	He gave his life in selfless love – 109
23.33	I believe in God the Father – 131
23.33	In silent pain the eternal Son – 142
23.33	The hands of Christ, the caring hands – 272
23.34	Meekness and majesty – 197
23.36	The hands of Christ, the caring hands – 272
23.44	When you prayed beneath the trees – 310
23.46	It is a thing most wonderful – 144
23.46	When you prayed beneath the trees – 310
23.49	My Lord, what love is this – 205
23.53	Lord, you need no house – 183
24.6	Christ is risen – 45
24.6	Christ the Lord is risen again – 49
24.6	Jesus Christ is risen today – 146
24.6	Led like a lamb to the slaughter – 168
24.6	Lord of the cross of shame – 181
24.6	The hands of Christ, the caring hands – 272
24.7	The strife is past, the battle done – 281
24.23	Christ is alive! let Christians sing – 41
24.23	Jesus lives! Your terrors now – 153
24.29	Abide with me, fast falls the eventide – 3
24.30	For the bread which you have broken – 80
24.30	'Peace be with you all,' we sing – 234
24.34	Christ is risen – 45
24.34	Christ the Lord is risen again – 49
24.34	Jesus Christ is risen today – 146
24.34	Led like a lamb to the slaughter – 168
24.36	Jesus, stand among us – 157
24.36	'Peace be with you all,' we sing – 234
24.39	From heaven you came, helpless Babe – 85
24.40	Crown him with many crowns – 69
24.46	The strife is past, the battle done – 281
24.46	This is the day the Lord has made – 291

John

1.	When things began to happen – 309
1.1	God has spoken – by his prophets – 94
1.3	Alleluia! Raise the anthem – 12
1.3	My God, how wonderful you are – 200
1.3	The Son of God proclaim – 280
1.4	Speak, Lord, in the stillness – 260
1.4	Such love, pure as the whitest snow – 265
1.5	God whose love we cannot measure – 101
1.9	Christ is the world's Light – 48
1.11	Child in the manger, infant of Mary – 39
1.11	My song is love unknown – 206
1.14	Alleluia! Raise the anthem – 12
1.14	Christ triumphant, ever reigning – 50
1.14	Jesus is king, and we will extol him – 151
1.14	This is the day the Lord has made – 291
1.14	We have a gospel to proclaim – 300
1.18	Holy, holy, holy, Lord God almighty – 122
1.18	You servants of God, your master proclaim – 314
1.29	Christ the Lord is risen again – 49
1.29	Glory be to Jesus – 88
1.29	Glory in the highest – 89
1.29	Hail the day that sees him rise – 106
1.29	Jesus! the name high over all – 159

1.29	My Lord, what love is this – 205
1.29	No weight of gold or silver – 209
1.29	See, amid the winter snow – 252
1.29	There is a Redeemer – 285
1.32	God, whose almighty word – 100
1.32	Like the murmur of the dove's song – 173
1.32	Spirit divine, inspire our prayers – 261
1.36	Christ the Lord is risen again – 49
1.36	Glory be to Jesus – 88
1.36	Jesus! the name high over all – 159
1.36	No weight of gold or silver – 209
1.36	See, amid the winter snow – 252
1.36	There is a Redeemer – 285
1.41	There is a Redeemer – 285
1.43	From heaven you came, helpless Babe – 85
1.45	I cannot tell why he whom angels worship – 135
1.49	The first nowell the angel did say – 271
1.49	The Son of God proclaim – 280
2.	Jesus, come! for we invite you – 148
2.9	The trumpets sound, the angels sing – 282
2.23	Love is his word, love is his way – 189
2.23	O for a thousand tongues to sing – 218
3.3	Hark! the herald angels sing – 108
3.5	Born of the water – 33
3.7	Hark! the herald angels sing – 108
3.8	Born of the water – 33
3.8	I believe in God the Father – 131
3.8	Lord of the church, we pray for our renewing – 180
3.14	Man of sorrows! what a name – 195
3.14	When you prayed beneath the trees – 310
3.16	Christ is the world's Light, he and none other – 48
3.16	For God so loved the world – 78
3.16	It is a thing most wonderful – 144
3.16	See him lying on a bed of straw – 253
3.16	To God be the glory – 293
3.29	Here, O my Lord, I see you face to face – 120
3.36	Christ is the world's Light, he and none other – 48
4.10	Jesus, lover of my soul – 154
4.10	Lord of the church, we pray for our renewing – 180
4.10	Such love, pure as the whitest snow – 265
4.14	Jesus, lover of my soul – 154
4.42	Christians, awake, salute the happy morn – 53
4.42	I cannot tell why he whom angels worship – 135
4.46	The trumpets sound, the angels sing – 282
5.24	He who created light – 115
5.26	Such love, pure as the whitest snow – 265
5.29	Hail the day that sees him rise – 106
6.27	We come as guests invited – 298
6.32	Alleluia, sing to Jesus – 13
6.33	Guide me, O my great Redeemer – 104
6.33	Here, O my Lord, I see you face to face – 120
6.35	Break now the bread of life – 35
6.35	Come, let us worship Christ – 63
6.35	We come as guests invited – 298
6.40	Christ is the world's Light, he and none other – 48
6.41	Alleluia, sing to Jesus – 13
6.48	Break now the bread of life – 35
6.48	Come, let us worship Christ – 63
6.48	We come as guests invited – 298
6.49	Dear Lord and Father of mankind – 71

6.50 Alleluia, sing to Jesus – 13
6.51 Guide me, O my great Redeemer – 104
6.51 Jesus, the joy of loving hearts – 158
6.51 Speak, Lord, in the stillness – 260
6.53 Almighty God, we thank you for feeding us – 15
6.53 Glory be to Jesus – 88
6.53 We love the place, O God – 301
6.54 We come as guests invited – 298
6.58 Alleluia, sing to Jesus – 13
6.58 Dear Lord and Father of mankind – 71
6.68 Creator of the earth and skies – 67
6.69 There is a Redeemer – 285
7.38 Lord of the church, we pray for our renewing – 180
7.38 Such love, pure as the whitest snow – 265
7.42 Once in royal David's city – 232
8.12 Christ is the world's Light, he and none other – 48
8.12 Come and sing the Christmas story – 60
8.12 Come, let us worship Christ – 63
8.12 Come, light of the world – 64
8.12 Darkness like a shroud – 70
8.28 When you prayed beneath the trees – 310
8.32 Freedom and life are ours – 84
8.36 Freedom and life are ours – 84
9.2 He healed the darkness of my mind – 110
9.5 Christ is the world's Light, he and none other – 48
9.5 Come, let us worship Christ – 63
9.5 Come, light of the world – 64
9.5 Darkness like a shroud – 70
9.5 The Earth was dark until you spoke – 270
9.6 Break now the bread of life – 35
9.25 Amazing grace – how sweet the sound – 16
9.25 He healed the darkness of my mind – 110
9.25 Lord, I was blind; I could not see – 177
9.25 One thing I know, that Christ has healed me – 233
9.39 Rejoice, the Lord is King – 245
10.10 Christ is the world's Light, he and none other – 48
10.10 Jesus Christ gives life and gladness – 145
10.11 How sweet the name of Jesus sounds – 129
11.20 Jesus, good above all other – 150
11.27 The Son of God proclaim – 280
11.27 There is a Redeemer – 285
11.35 It is a thing most wonderful – 144
11.43 He who created light – 115
12.13 All glory, praise and honour – 6
12.13 Let trumpets sound – 170
12.13 My song is love unknown – 206
12.13 Ride on, ride on in majesty – 249
12.13 The first nowell the angel did say – 271
12.13 This is the day the Lord has made – 291
12.13 We have a gospel to proclaim – 300
12.15 Ride on, ride on in majesty – 249
12.31 God is our fortress and our rock – 96
12.32 When you prayed beneath the trees – 310
12.46 Christ is the world's Light, he and none other – 48
12.46 God whose love we cannot measure – 101
13.5 Jesus, Jesus, fill us with your love – 152
13.5 Meekness and majesty – 197
13.15 Blessed are the pure in heart – 30
14.2 I know that my redeemer lives – 133
14.2 We trust in you, our shield and our defender – 303
14.6 Christ is the world's Light, he and none other – 48

14.6 Christ the Lord is risen again – 49
14.6 The hands of Christ, the caring hands – 272
14.6 To God be the glory – 293
14.17 Spirit of faith, by faith be mind – 263
14.18 Alleluia, sing to Jesus – 13
14.26 Come down, O Love divine – 61
14.27 Christ is the world's Light, he and none other – 48
14.30 God is our fortress and our rock – 96
15.5 We come as guests invited – 298
15.13 My song is love unknown – 206
15.13 Tell all the world of Jesus – 267
15.14 The Son of God proclaim – 280
15.14 What a friend we have in Jesus – 305
15.15 We come as guests invited – 298
15.26 Christ in majesty ascending – 40
15.26 Come down, O Love divine – 61
15.26 Creator Spirit, come, inspire – 68
15.26 Spirit of faith, by faith be mind – 263
15.26 There is a Redeemer – 285
16.7 My Lord of light who made the worlds – 203
16.11 God is our fortress and our rock – 96
16.13 Creator Spirit, come, inspire – 68
16.13 Spirit of faith, by faith be mind – 263
16.13 There is a Redeemer – 285
16.33 Tell all the world of Jesus – 267
17.11 Christ is made the sure foundation – 44
17.23 Spirit of God most high – 264
17.24 Christ is made the sure foundation – 44
18.14 Jesus, good above all other – 150
19.2 My Lord of light who made the worlds – 203
19.2 The hands of Christ, the caring hands – 272
19.2 When I survey the wondrous cross – 307
19.5 Come and see, come and see – 58
19.5 It is a thing most wonderful – 144
19.6 My song is love unknown – 206
19.9 He was pierced for our transgressions – 114
19.17 Come and see, come and see – 58
19.17 There is a green hill far away – 284
19.18 He gave his life in selfless love – 109
19.18 I believe in God the Father – 131
19.18 The hands of Christ, the caring hands – 272
19.29 The hands of Christ, the caring hands – 272
19.30 God of gods, we sound his praise – 98
19.30 He gave his life in selfless love – 109
19.30 It is a thing most wonderful – 144
19.34 The hands of Christ, the caring hands – 272
19.34 When I survey the wondrous cross – 307
19.41 My song is love unknown – 206
19.42 Lord, you need no house – 183
20.1 Comes Mary to the grave – 66
20.6 Yours be the glory! risen, conquering Son – 316
20.11 Led like a lamb to the slaughter – 168
20.16 Comes Mary to the grave – 66
20.16 O for a thousand tongues to sing – 218
20.16 Yours be the glory! risen, conquering Son – 316
20.17 Christ is going to the Father – 43
20.19 Christ is the world's Light, he and none other – 48
20.19 Jesus, stand among us – 157

20.19 'Peace be with you all,' we sing – 234
20.20 Crown him with many crowns – 69
20.22 Jesus, stand among us – 157
20.25 Christ is risen – 45
20.25 From heaven you came, helpless Babe – 85
20.25 In silent pain the eternal Son – 142
20.25 It is a thing most wonderful – 144
20.25 The hands of Christ, the caring hands – 272
20.25 When you prayed beneath the trees – 310
20.26 Jesus, stand among us – 157
20.26 'Peace be with you all,' we sing – 234
20.29 Yours be the glory! risen, conquering Son – 316
20.31 No weight of gold or silver – 209
20.31 O for a thousand tongues to sing – 218
20.31 The Son of God proclaim – 280
21.19 From heaven you came, helpless Babe – 85
21.23 God of gods, we sound his praise – 98

Acts
1.3 Christ is alive! let Christians sing – 41
1.4 Christ is ascending! let creation sing – 42
1.9 Alleluia, sing to Jesus – 13
1.9 Christ in majesty ascending – 40
1.9 Christ is ascending! let creation sing – 42
1.9 Christ is going to the Father – 43
1.9 Hail the day that sees him rise – 106
1.11 Christ is ascending! let creation sing – 42
1.11 Christ is surely coming – 46
2.3 O Spirit of the living God – 228
2.3 Spirit divine, inspire our prayers – 261
2.4 Lord of the church, we pray for our renewing – 180
2.20 Christ is ascending! let creation sing – 42
2.21 In awe and wonder, Lord our God – 138
2.23 When you prayed beneath the trees – 310
2.24 Low in the grave he lay – 191
2.26 I believe in God the Father – 131
2.27 There is a Redeemer – 285
2.28 Spirit divine, inspire our prayers – 261
2.30 Tell all the world of Jesus – 267
2.32 Comes Mary to the grave – 66
2.33 Glory in the highest – 89
2.33 Once in royal David's city – 232
2.35 Rejoice, the Lord is King – 245
2.36 Go forth and tell! O church of God, awake – 90
2.36 We believe in God Almighty – 295
2.36 We believe in God the Father – 296
2.38 O for a thousand tongues to sing – 218
3.6 O for a thousand tongues to sing – 218
3.16 O for a thousand tongues to sing – 218
3.18 Child in the manger, infant of Mary – 39
3.19 How can we sing with joy to God – 124
4.2 Jesus Christ is risen today – 146
4.10 Comes Mary to the grave – 66
4.10 O for a thousand tongues to sing – 218
4.12 In awe and wonder, Lord our God – 138
4.18 O for a thousand tongues to sing – 218
4.31 Lord of the church, we pray for our renewing – 180
5.30 Comes Mary to the grave – 66
5.30 When you prayed beneath the trees – 310
5.31 Low in the grave he lay – 191
5.31 Once in royal David's city – 232
5.42 There is a Redeemer – 285
6.7 God is our fortress and our rock – 96
7.55 Once in royal David's city – 232
7.56 Glory in the highest – 89

7.59 Jesus, lover of my soul – 154
8.12 How sweet the name of Jesus sounds – 129
8.12 You servants of God, your master proclaim – 314
8.32 He was pierced for our transgressions – 114
8.32 I cannot tell why he whom angels worship – 135
9.20 The Son of God proclaim – 280
9.27 You servants of God, your master proclaim – 314
9.31 We believe in God the Father – 296
10.36 We believe in God the Father – 296
10.39 When you prayed beneath the trees – 310
10.40 Comes Mary to the grave – 66
10.40 Low in the grave he lay – 191
10.40 The strife is past, the battle done – 281
10.48 How sweet the name of Jesus sounds – 129
12.7 And can it be that I should gain – 17
12.7 Jesus shall reign where'er the sun – 156
12.7 Jesus! the name high over all – 159
12.24 God is our fortress and our rock – 96
13.29 Lord, the light of your love is shining – 182
13.30 Low in the grave he lay – 191
13.35 There is a Redeemer – 285
13.37 Comes Mary to the grave – 66
13.47 The Earth was dark until you spoke – 270
13.48 He who created light – 115
13.52 Lord of the church, we pray for our renewing – 180
15.11 Amazing grace – how sweet the sound – 16
16.7 Spirit of faith, by faith be mind – 263
16.25 The day you gave us, Lord, is ended – 269
16.26 Lord, I was blind; I could not see – 177
17.23 There is a Redeemer – 285
19.5 How sweet the name of Jesus sounds – 129
19.17 How sweet the name of Jesus sounds – 129
19.17 O for a thousand tongues to sing – 218
20.11 'Peace be with you all,' we sing – 234
20.28 The first nowell the angel did say – 271
20.28 There is a green hill far away – 284
21.13 How sweet the name of Jesus sounds – 129
22.16 My Lord, what love is this – 205
26.18 God whose love we cannot measure – 101
26.18 Holy child, how still you lie – 121
26.20 How can we sing with joy to God – 124
27.35 'Peace be with you all,' we sing – 234

Romans
1.4 Spirit of faith, by faith be mind – 263
1.4 The Son of God proclaim – 280
1.17 My hope is built on nothing less – 201
1.17 There is a green hill far away – 284
1.20 I believe in God the Father – 131
1.25 Jesus shall reign where'er the sun – 156
2.16 Rejoice, the Lord is King – 245
2.16 We believe in God the Father – 296
3.21 There is a green hill far away – 284
3.24 And can it be that I should gain – 17
3.24 King of glory, king of peace – 165
3.25 Alleluia! Raise the anthem – 12
3.25 And can it be that I should gain – 17
3.25 There is a green hill far away – 284
4.11 And can it be that I should gain – 17
5.1 Christ is the world's Light, he and none other – 48
5.5 Born in song – 32
5.5 In heavenly love abiding – 141
5.5 Lead us, heavenly Father, lead us – 167

5.5   Lord Jesus Christ, you have come to us – 178

5.5   Lord of the cross of shame – 181

5.5   Love divine, all loves excelling – 188

5.5   May the mind of Christ my saviour – 199

5.6   And can it be that I should gain – 17

5.8   In awe and wonder, Lord our God – 138

5.8   Jesus lives! Your terrors now – 153

5.9   I am trusting you, Lord Jesus – 130

5.9   King of glory, king of peace – 165

5.9   The victory of our God is won – 283

5.10   O Spirit of the living God – 228

5.10   Spirit of God most high – 264

5.17   And can it be that I should gain – 17

5.17   Jesus Christ the Lord is born – 147

6.4   Baptised in water – 25

6.4   Born of the water – 33

6.4   Jesus Christ the Lord is born – 147

6.5   He stood before the court – 112

6.6   I believe in God the Father – 131

6.6   Lord, for the years – 176

6.9   The strife is past, the battle done – 281

6.10   He gave his life in selfless love – 109

6.18   Freedom and life are ours – 84

6.23   Christ is the world's Light, he and none other – 48

7.25   The strife is past, the battle done – 281

8.   He lives in us, the Christ of God – 111

8.1   And can it be that I should gain – 17

8.2   Freedom and life are ours – 84

8.2   Spirit of faith, by faith be mind – 263

8.3   He stood before the court – 112

8.6   Take my life and let it be – 266

8.10   Rejoice, rejoice! Christ is in you – 244

8.15   We worship God in harmony – 304

8.17   Born of the water – 33

8.17   The head that once was crowned with thorns – 273

8.25   Help us to help each other, Lord – 118

8.25   In heavenly love abiding – 141

8.29   New every morning is the love – 208

8.34   Glory in the highest – 89

8.34   Hail the day that sees him rise – 106

8.34   Jesus is king, and we will extol him – 151

8.34   Jesus lives! Your terrors now – 153

8.34   Once in royal David's city – 232

8.35   Had he not loved us – 105

8.35   In heavenly love abiding – 141

8.35   It is a thing most wonderful – 144

8.35   Loved with everlasting love – 190

8.35   O love that will not let me go – 227

8.37   Soldiers of Christ, arise – 258

8.37   Yours be the glory! risen, conquering Son – 316

8.38   The strife is past, the battle done -- 281

8.39   O for a heart to praise my God – 217

10.9   Comes Mary to the grave – 66

10.9   Low in the grave he lay – 191

10.9   Name of all majesty – 207

10.9   O Spirit of the living God – 228

10.9   We have a gospel to proclaim – 300

10.12   To him we come – 294

10.15   Take my life and let it be – 266

11.8   O Spirit of the living God – 228

11.9   Spirit of God most high – 264

11.33   Lord, be my vision, supreme in my heart – 175

11.33   See him lying on a bed of straw – 253

11.36   The kingdom of God is justice and joy – 275

11.36   Jesus shall reign where'er the sun – 156

12.1   Almighty God, we thank you for feeding us – 15

12.1   Take my life and let it be – 266

12.1   When I survey the wondrous cross – 307

12.2   King of glory, king of peace – 165

12.2   O Breath of life, come sweeping through us – 214

12.2   O Lord, who came from realms above – 226

12.2   Take my life and let it be – 266

12.10   From heaven you came, helpless Babe – 85

12.11   To him we come – 294

12.15   Make me a channel of your peace – 192

13.11   Spirit of God most high – 264

13.14   Dear Lord and Father of mankind – 71

14.19   Make me a channel of your peace – 192

15.2   Help us to help each other, Lord – 118

15.6   Christ is the king! O friends rejoice; – 47

15.13   In heavenly love abiding – 141

15.17   O come, all ye faithful – 215

15.19   Almighty God, we thank you for feeding us – 15

15.33   'Peace be with you all,' we sing – 234

16.27   O come, all ye faithful – 215

1 Corinthians

1.8   Jesus the saviour comes – 160

1.10   Take my life and let it be – 266

1.21   See him lying on a bed of straw – 253

2.2   I believe in God the Father – 131

2.2   When I survey the wondrous cross – 307

2.8   The hands of Christ, the caring hands – 272

2.16   May the mind of Christ my saviour – 199

3.7   We plough the fields, and scatter – 302

3.8   Christ is surely coming – 46

3.11   Jesus Christ gives life and gladness – 145

5.7   Christ the Lord is risen again – 49

6.11   How sweet the name of Jesus sounds – 129

6.11   My Lord, what love is this – 205

6.14   Comes Mary to the grave – 66

6.20   There is a green hill far away – 284

7.23   There is a green hill far away – 284

8.6   Glory in the highest – 89

8.9   See, amid the winter snow – 252

9.24   Fight the good fight with all your might – 75

9.24   You holy angels bright – 313

10.4   Rock of ages, cleft for me – 250

10.10   Bread of the world in mercy broken – 34

10.10   I come with joy to meet my Lord – 132

10.16   He gave his life in selfless love – 109

10.16   No weight of gold or silver – 209

10.16   'Peace be with you all,' we sing – 234

10.16   Put peace into each other's hands – 243

10.17   I come with joy to meet my Lord – 132

10.17   Sing of the Lord's goodness – 256

10.17   We break this bread – 297

10.17   We come as guests invited – 298

11.18   I come with joy to meet my Lord – 132

11.24   Broken for me, broken for you – 38

11.24   Father in heaven – 74

11.24   Lord Jesus Christ, you have come to us – 178

11.24   Love is his word, love is his way – 189

11.24   The Son of God proclaim – 280

11.25   For the bread which you have broken – 80

11.25   We come as guests invited – 298

11.26   I come with joy to meet my Lord – 132

12.3   Name of all majesty – 207
12.3   O Spirit of the living God – 228
12.3   We have a gospel to proclaim – 300
12.9   We give God thanks for those who knew – 299
12.12   Born in song – 32
12.25   I come with joy to meet my Lord – 132
13.   Holy Spirit, gracious guest – 123
13.12   Hail the day that sees him rise – 106
13.12   It is a thing most wonderful – 144
13.12   Lord, the light of your love is shining – 182
13.12   My God, how wonderful you are – 200
13.13   Songs of praise the angels sang – 259
14.12   We believe in God the Father – 296
14.15   Take my life and let it be – 266
15.   If Christ had not been raised from death – 136
15.   These are the facts as we have received them – 287
15.2   Hark! the herald angels sing – 108
15.3   And can it be that I should gain – 17
15.4   The strife is past, the battle done – 281
15.24   Name of all majesty – 207
15.25   Rejoice, the Lord is King – 245
15.32   My hope is built on nothing less – 201
15.47   Praise to the Holiest in the height – 241
15.52   Come, let us worship Christ – 63
15.54   Name of all majesty – 207
15.54   Yours be the glory! risen, conquering Son – 316
15.55   All creation join to say – 4
15.55   Christ is risen – 45
15.55   I know that my redeemer lives – 133
15.55   Jesus lives! Your terrors now – 153
15.55   Low in the grave he lay – 191
15.55   Ride on, ride on in majesty – 249
15.55   The strife is past, the battle done – 281
15.55   Yours be the glory! risen, conquering Son – 316
15.57   The victory of our God is won – 283
16.2   We give God thanks for those who knew – 299
16.19   Blessed are the pure in heart – 30

2 Corinthians
1.10   In heavenly love abiding – 141
1.20   God has spoken – by his prophets – 94
1.21   Now let us learn of Christ – 212
1.22   Father in heaven – 74
1.22   I believe in God the Father – 131
1.22   We come as guests invited – 298
3.15   Lord, the light of your love is shining – 182
3.18   Love divine, all loves excelling – 188
4.4   Meekness and majesty – 197
4.4   O come, all ye faithful – 215
4.6   God whose love we cannot measure – 101
4.6   Silent night! Holy night – 255
4.6   Spirit divine, inspire our prayers – 261
4.13   Spirit of faith, by faith be mind – 263
5.7   No weight of gold or silver – 209
5.14   In awe and wonder, Lord our God – 138
5.14   It is a thing most wonderful – 144
5.17   Love divine, all loves excelling – 188
5.17   We worship God in harmony – 304
5.18   Spirit of God most high – 264
5.19   O Spirit of the living God – 228
5.21   He gave his life in selfless love – 109

5.21   My Lord of light who made the worlds – 203
5.21   My song is love unknown – 206
6.3   Spirit of God most high – 264
8.9   For God so loved the world – 78
8.9   Jesus, saviour, holy child, sleep tonight – 155
8.9   Lord, you were rich beyond all splendour – 185
8.9   My Lord, you wore no royal crown – 204
8.9   Once in royal David's city – 232
8.9   See him lying on a bed of straw – 253
11.31   O for a thousand tongues to sing – 218
12.9   One thing I know, that Christ has healed me – 233
13.13   May the grace of Christ our saviour – 196

Galatians
1.1   Comes Mary to the grave – 66
1.1   Low in the grave he lay – 191
2.6   To him we come – 294
2.20   I am trusting you, Lord Jesus – 130
2.20   Lord, for the years – 176
2.20   No weight of gold or silver – 209
3.1   When I survey the wondrous cross – 307
3.8   To him we come – 294
3.13   When I survey the wondrous cross – 307
3.13   When you prayed beneath the trees – 310
3.14   I believe in God the Father – 131
3.19   Born of the water – 33
3.24   King of glory, king of peace – 165
3.27   And can it be that I should gain – 17
3.28   To him we come – 294
4.6   I believe in God the Father – 131
5.1   Now let us learn of Christ – 212
5.7   Fight the good fight with all your might – 75
5.13   Freedom and life are ours – 84
5.22   O Trinity, O Trinity – 229
5.24   Lord, for the years – 176
6.2   Help us to help each other, Lord – 118
6.14   In the cross of Christ I glory – 139
6.14   When I survey the wondrous cross – 307
6.15   Love divine, all loves excelling – 188
6.15   No weight of gold or silver – 209
6.15   We worship God in harmony – 304

Ephesians
1.4   My Lord, I did not choose you – 202
1.5   We worship God in harmony – 304
1.6   Holy child, how still you lie – 121
1.7   See him lying on a bed of straw – 253
1.11   See him lying on a bed of straw – 253
1.13   Father in heaven – 74
1.13   Freedom and life are ours – 84
1.13   We come as guests invited – 298
1.18   In heavenly love abiding – 141
1.18   Lord, be my vision, supreme in my heart – 175
1.20   Low in the grave he lay – 191
1.22   Lord of the church, we pray for our renewing – 180
1.22   The Son of God proclaim – 280
2.4   How good is the God we adore – 126
2.5   Amazing grace – how sweet the sound – 16
2.6   Comes Mary to the grave – 66
2.7   How sweet the name of Jesus sounds – 129
2.8   Amazing grace – how sweet the sound – 16
2.8   My hope is built on nothing less – 201
2.13   No weight of gold or silver – 209

2.16 O Spirit of the living God – 228
2.17 Christ is the world's Light, he and none other – 48
2.20 Christ is made the sure foundation – 44
3.3 See him lying on a bed of straw – 253
3.4 Now let us learn of Christ – 212
3.8 Lord, be my vision, supreme in my heart – 175
3.17 How firm a foundation, you people of God – 125
3.18 Had he not loved us – 105
3.18 It is a thing most wonderful – 144
3.18 Just as I am, without one plea – 164
3.19 Come down, O Love divine – 61
3.19 God whose love we cannot measure – 101
3.19 How good is the God we adore – 126
3.19 Lord, you were rich beyond all splendour – 185
3.19 Not the grandeur of the mountains – 210
3.19 Tell all the world of Jesus – 267
3.21 Restore, O Lord – 247
3.21 Revive your church, O Lord – 248
4.2 Put peace into each other's hands – 243
4.5 Glory in the highest – 89
4.5 One thing I know, that Christ has healed me – 233
4.5 We worship God in harmony – 304
4.5 Your hand, O God, has guided – 315
4.8 Christ in majesty ascending – 40
4.8 God of gods, we sound his praise – 98
4.8 My Lord of light who made the worlds – 203
4.8 Revive your church, O Lord – 248
4.11 Revive your church, O Lord – 248
4.15 Help us to help each other, Lord – 118
4.15 Now let us learn of Christ – 212
4.20 Now let us learn of Christ – 212
4.24 And can it be that I should gain – 17
4.28 Take my life and let it be – 266
4.29 Help us to help each other, Lord – 118
4.30 Baptised in water – 25
4.30 Born of the water – 33
4.30 I believe in God the Father – 131
4.32 'Forgive our sins as we forgive' – 83
4.32 Make me a channel of your peace – 192
5.2 Now let us learn of Christ – 212
5.2 There is a green hill far away – 284
5.8 God whose love we cannot measure – 101
5.19 Born in song – 32
5.20 How sweet the name of Jesus sounds – 129
5.20 When all your mercies, O my God – 306
5.21 We worship God in harmony – 304
5.23 Lord of the church, we pray for our renewing – 180
5.25 I come with joy to meet my Lord – 132
5.27 Jesus the saviour comes – 160
6.6 Jesus, Jesus, fill us with your love – 152
6.8 Christ is surely coming – 46
6.10 We trust in you, our shield and our defender – 303
6.12 Holy child, how still you lie – 121
6.12 Soldiers of Christ, arise – 258
6.12 To him we come – 294
6.13 Lord, be my vision, supreme in my heart – 175
6.13 Now let us learn of Christ – 212
6.17 Darkness like a shroud – 70
6.18 Like the murmur of the dove's song – 173
6.18 The day you gave us, Lord, is ended – 269
6.18 The Lord is king! Lift up your voice – 276
6.18 We give God thanks for those who knew – 299

Philippians
1.19 Spirit of faith, by faith be mind – 263
1.21 Lord, for the years – 176
1.23 Jesus lives! Your terrors now – 153
1.26 Jesus, the joy of loving hearts – 158
2. At the name of Jesus – 22
2. Before the heaven and earth – 29
2. My Lord, you wore no royal crown – 204
2.1 We have a gospel to proclaim – 300
2.2 May the mind of Christ my saviour – 199
2.2 We worship God in harmony – 304
2.3 How can we sing with joy to God – 124
2.7 And can it be that I should gain – 17
2.7 Christ triumphant, ever reigning – 50
2.7 For God so loved the world – 78
2.7 From heaven you came, helpless Babe – 85
2.7 Jesus Christ gives life and gladness – 145
2.7 Lord, you were rich beyond all splendour – 185
2.8 Holy child, how still you lie – 121
2.8 Meekness and majesty – 197
2.8 The kingdom of God is justice and joy – 275
2.9 Christ the Lord is risen again – 49
2.9 Jesus! the name high over all – 159
2.9 The head that once was crowned with thorns – 273
2.9 We believe in God the Father – 296
2.10 All hail the power of Jesus' name – 7
2.10 Christ is risen – 45
2.10 O for a thousand tongues to sing – 218
2.10 You servants of God, your master proclaim – 314
2.11 Holy child, how still you lie – 121
2.11 Name of all majesty – 207
2.11 O Spirit of the living God – 228
2.16 Lord, for the years – 176
2.16 Speak, Lord, in the stillness – 260
2.16 We love the place, O God – 301
3.13 One thing I know, that Christ has healed me – 233
3.14 Fight the good fight with all your might – 75
3.14 You holy angels bright – 313
4.5 Put peace into each other's hands – 243
4.6 The Lord is king! Lift up your voice – 276
4.6 We plough the fields, and scatter – 302
4.6 What a friend we have in Jesus – 305
4.7 Heal me, hands of Jesus – 113
4.7 In the cross of Christ I glory – 139
4.7 Like a mighty river flowing – 179
4.7 May the mind of Christ my saviour – 199
4.13 Go forth and tell! O church of God, awake – 90

Colossians
1.5 In heavenly love abiding – 141
1.11 We trust in you, our shield and our defender – 303
1.15 O come, all ye faithful – 215
1.16 At the name of Jesus – 22
1.16 I believe in God the Father – 131
1.16 My God, how wonderful you are – 200
1.16 See, amid the winter snow – 252
1.18 Lord of the church, we pray for our renewing – 180
1.19 Hark! the herald angels sing – 108

1.20   Glory be to Jesus – 88
1.20   O Spirit of the living God – 228
1.22   I come with joy to meet my Lord – 132
1.22   Jesus the saviour comes – 160
1.22   Spirit of God most high – 264
1.23   How firm a foundation, you people of God – 12
1.27   Rejoice, rejoice! Christ is in you – 244
1.27   See him lying on a bed of straw – 253
1.29   Now let us learn of Christ – 212
2.12   Comes Mary to the grave – 66
2.14   Such love, pure as the whitest snow – 265
2.14   When I survey the wondrous cross – 307
2.14   When you prayed beneath the trees – 310
2.15   Holy child, how still you lie – 121
2.15   Name of all majesty – 207
3.1   In heavenly love abiding – 141
3.1   Jesus lives! Your terrors now – 153
3.1   Lord of the cross of shame – 181
3.13   'Forgive our sins as we forgive' – 83
3.13   Make me a channel of your peace – 192
3.14   Come down, O Love divine – 61
3.14   Spirit of God most high – 264
3.15   Heal me, hands of Jesus – 113
3.15   When all your mercies, O my God – 306
3.16   Born in song – 32
3.16   May the mind of Christ my saviour – 199
3.17   How sweet the name of Jesus sounds – 129
3.24   From heaven you came, helpless Babe – 85
4.3   We give God thanks for those who knew – 299

1 Thessalonians
2.19   In heavenly love abiding – 141
3.12   We love the place, O God – 301
4.14   All creation join to say – 4
4.16   Come, let us worship Christ – 63
4.16   Hail the day that sees him rise – 106
4.16   Jesus the saviour comes – 160
4.16   Man of sorrows! what a name – 195
4.16   My hope is built on nothing less – 201
4.16   Rejoice, the Lord is King – 245
5.10   From heaven you came, helpless Babe – 85
5.10   Jesus lives! Your terrors now – 153
5.11   Help us to help each other, Lord – 118
5.19   I believe in God the Father – 131
5.19   Lord of the church, we pray for our renewing – 180
5.19   My Lord of light who made the worlds – 203
5.19   O Lord, who came from realms above – 226
5.19   Spirit divine, inspire our prayers – 261
5.25   We give God thanks for those who knew – 299

2 Thessalonians
1.12   How sweet the name of Jesus sounds – 129
1.12   O come, all ye faithful – 215
2.13   My Lord, I did not choose you – 202
2.16   There is a green hill far away – 284
3.1   We give God thanks for those who knew – 299

1 Timothy
1.2   We believe in God Almighty – 295
1.7   Immortal, invisible, God only wise, – 137
1.12   Go forth and tell! O church of God, awake – 90

1.14   Lord Jesus Christ, you have come to us – 178
2.1   The Lord is king! Lift up your voice – 276
2.8   Take my life and let it be – 266
3.3   Put peace into each other's hands – 243
4.4   I believe in God the Father – 131
4.6   We come as guests invited – 298
4.6   We love the place, O God – 301
5.10   Meekness and majesty – 197
6.12   You holy angels bright – 313
6.15   Christ the Lord is risen again – 49
6.15   Judge eternal, throned in splendour – 162
6.15   The head that once was crowned with thorns – 273
6.15   The victory of our God is won – 283
6.16   Alleluia! Raise the anthem – 12
6.17   Immortal, invisible, God only wise, – 137
6.17   Lord, be my vision, supreme in my heart – 175

2 Timothy
1.5   Now thank we all our God – 213
1.7   Almighty God, we thank you for feeding us – 15
1.10   Jesus Christ the Lord is born – 147
1.10   Name of all majesty – 207
2.3   To him we come – 294
2.12   Jesus lives! Your terrors now – 153
2.12   The head that once was crowned with thorns – 273
2.24   Dear Lord and Father of mankind – 71
3.15   Lord, your word shall guide us – 187
3.16   Lord, for the years – 176
3.16   Lord, you sometimes speak in wonders – 184
4.1   We believe in God the Father – 296
4.7   Fight the good fight with all your might – 75
4.7   Soldiers of Christ, arise – 258
4.7   You holy angels bright – 313
4.8   Rejoice, the Lord is King – 245
4.17   Go forth and tell! O church of God, awake – 90

Titus
1.2   In heavenly love abiding – 141
2.13   God is our fortress and our rock – 96
3.2   Put peace into each other's hands – 243
3.5   O Breath of life, come sweeping through us – 214
3.7   King of glory, king of peace – 165
3.7   See him lying on a bed of straw – 253

Hebrews
1.1   God has spoken – by his prophets – 94
1.1   It came upon the midnight clear – 143
1.2   I believe in God the Father – 131
1.2   Lord, you sometimes speak in wonders – 184
1.3   Hark! the herald angels sing – 108
1.3   Jesus is king, and we will extol him – 151
1.3   Meekness and majesty – 197
1.3   O come, all ye faithful – 215
1.3   Once in royal David's city – 232
1.3   Rejoice, the Lord is King – 245
1.3   See, amid the winter snow – 252
1.4   We believe in God the Father – 296
1.8   Alleluia, sing to Jesus – 13
1.10   Alleluia! Raise the anthem – 12
1.10   At the name of Jesus – 22

1.11	The day you gave us, Lord, is ended – 269
1.13	Rejoice, the Lord is King – 245
4.12	Darkness like a shroud – 70
4.12	God is our fortress and our rock – 96
4.12	How sure the Scriptures are – 127
4.15	Holy child, how still you lie – 121
4.15	Lead us, heavenly Father, lead us – 167
4.15	What a friend we have in Jesus – 305
5.2	Holy child, how still you lie – 121
5.2	Lead us, heavenly Father, lead us – 167
5.2	Once in royal David's city – 232
5.8	Meekness and majesty – 197
5.10	O Trinity, O Trinity – 229
5.12	Break now the bread of life – 35
6.6	Lord of the cross of shame – 181
6.19	In heavenly love abiding – 141
6.19	Jesus is king, and we will extol him – 151
6.19	My hope is built on nothing less – 201
6.20	Glory be to Jesus – 88
7.1	Christ triumphant, ever reigning – 50
7.2	King of glory, king of peace – 165
7.25	Hail the day that sees him rise – 106
7.25	I know that my redeemer lives – 133
7.25	Jesus is king, and we will extol him – 151
7.27	He gave his life in selfless love – 109
7.27	Jesus Christ is risen today – 146
8.1	Rejoice, the Lord is King – 245
9.12	He gave his life in selfless love – 109
9.12	The first nowell the angel did say – 271
9.13	Glory be to Jesus – 88
9.14	Heal me, hands of Jesus – 113
9.14	Here, O my Lord, I see you face to face – 120
9.14	No weight of gold or silver – 209
9.15	Freedom and life are ours – 84
9.19	O for a heart to praise my God – 217
9.21	O for a heart to praise my God – 217
9.22	Baptised in water – 25
9.22	Heal me, hands of Jesus – 113
9.24	Christ the Lord is risen again – 49
9.28	My Lord, what love is this – 205
10.12	Glory in the highest – 89
10.12	Jesus is king, and we will extol him – 151
10.12	My Lord, what love is this – 205
10.13	Rejoice, the Lord is King – 245
10.22	Heal me, hands of Jesus – 113
10.22	In silent pain the eternal Son – 142
10.22	O Jesus, I have promised – 221
10.22	Spirit divine, inspire our prayers – 261
10.22	The Lord is king! Lift up your voice – 276
10.29	Spirit of faith, by faith be mind – 263
11.5	Like a mighty river flowing – 179
11.28	O for a heart to praise my God – 217
12.1	Fight the good fight with all your might – 75
12.1	You holy angels bright – 313
12.2	Glory in the highest – 89
12.2	He gave his life in selfless love – 109
12.2	Jesus Christ is risen today – 146
12.2	Jesus lives! Your terrors now – 153
12.2	Lord of the cross of shame – 181
12.2	May the mind of Christ my saviour – 199
12.2	Such love, pure as the whitest snow – 265
12.2	The head that once was crowned with thorns – 273
12.2	The Son of God proclaim – 280
12.2	When I survey the wondrous cross – 307
12.10	Such love, pure as the whitest snow – 265
12.18	Let us love and sing and wonder – 171
12.24	Glory be to Jesus – 88

12.24	O for a heart to praise my God – 217
12.26	Restore, O Lord – 247
13.8	Christ is the king! O friends rejoice – 47
13.8	I know that my redeemer lives – 133
13.12	Glory be to Jesus – 88
13.13	There is a green hill far away – 284
13.15	For the beauty of the earth – 79
13.15	How sweet the name of Jesus sounds – 129
13.15	O God beyond all praising – 219
13.18	The day you gave us, Lord, is ended – 269
13.18	We give God thanks for those who knew – 299

James

1.6	Just as I am, without one plea – 164
1.12	My Lord of light who made the worlds – 203
1.17	Fight the good fight with all your might – 75
1.17	For the beauty of the earth – 79
1.17	Lord, you need no house – 183
1.17	O God beyond all praising – 219
1.17	Praise God from whom all blessings flow – 235
1.17	We plough the fields, and scatter – 302
1.17	When all your mercies, O my God – 306
3.16	How can we sing with joy to God – 124
3.17	Put peace into each other's hands – 243
3.18	Put peace into each other's hands – 243
4.8	O Jesus, I have promised – 221
4.8	The Lord is king! Lift up your voice – 276
5.3	Lord, be my vision, supreme in my heart – 175
5.9	Rejoice, the Lord is King – 245
5.13	Songs of praise the angels sang – 259

1 Peter

1.2	I am trusting you, Lord Jesus – 130
1.3	In heavenly love abiding – 141
1.6	O love that will not let me go – 227
1.7	How firm a foundation, you people of God – 125
1.7	How sure the Scriptures are – 127
1.7	Restore, O Lord – 247
1.7	The head that once was crowned with thorns – 273
1.8	Jesus, the joy of loving hearts – 158
1.8	To God be the glory – 293
1.12	Glad music fills the Christmas sky – 87
1.12	Ride on, ride on in majesty – 249
1.13	God is our fortress and our rock – 96
1.18	How firm a foundation, you people of God – 125
1.19	Alleluia! Raise the anthem – 12
1.19	Christ the Lord is risen again – 49
1.19	No weight of gold or silver – 209
1.19	O Trinity, O Trinity – 229
1.21	Comes Mary to the grave – 66
1.21	Low in the grave he lay – 191
1.25	Jesus, the joy of loving hearts – 158
2.4	Jesus Christ gives life and gladness – 145
2.5	Christ is made the sure foundation – 44
2.6	Christ is made the sure foundation – 44
2.9	Church of God, elect and glorious – 54
2.16	Freedom and life are ours – 84
2.21	Blessed are the pure in heart – 30
2.24	Christ the Lord is risen again – 49
2.24	He stood before the court – 112
2.24	Jesus Christ gives life and gladness – 145
2.24	No weight of gold or silver – 209

2.24 The hands of Christ, the caring hands – 272
2.24 The head that once was crowned with thorns – 273
2.24 There is a green hill far away – 284
2.24 When I survey the wondrous cross – 307
2.24 When you prayed beneath the trees – 310
3.4 Put peace into each other's hands – 243
3.8 Make me a channel of your peace – 192
3.15 God is our fortress and our rock – 96
3.18 And can it be that I should gain – 17
3.18 Christ is alive! let Christians sing – 41
3.18 He gave his life in selfless love – 109
3.21 We love the place, O God – 301
3.22 Holy child, how still you lie – 121
3.22 Name of all majesty – 207
3.22 Once in royal David's city – 232
4.5 Rejoice, the Lord is King – 245
4.11 Now let us learn of Christ – 212
4.11 The kingdom of God is justice and joy – 275
4.12 How firm a foundation, you people of God – 125
4.14 Spirit of faith, by faith be mind – 263
4.17 The kingdom of God is justice and joy – 275
5.5 Dear Lord and Father of mankind – 71
5.5 We worship God in harmony – 304
5.7 Here, O my Lord, I see you face to face – 120
5.7 I cannot tell why he whom angels worship – 135
5.7 Tell all the world of Jesus – 267
5.7 What a friend we have in Jesus – 305
5.10 Love divine, all loves excelling – 188
5.10 Now let us learn of Christ – 212
5.10 We trust in you, our shield and our defender – 303

2 Peter
1.21 We believe in God Almighty – 295
3.18 Now let us learn of Christ – 212
3.18 O come, all ye faithful – 215

1 John
1.1 He who created light – 115
1.1 Lord, for the years – 176
1.1 Speak, Lord, in the stillness – 260
1.1 We love the place, O God – 301
2.20 There is a Redeemer – 285
3.5 My Lord, what love is this – 205
3.14 Jesus Christ the Lord is born – 147
3.16 I come with joy to meet my Lord – 132
3.23 Now let us learn of Christ – 212
4.2 Jesus Christ gives life and gladness – 145
4.6 Spirit of faith, by faith be mind – 263
4.8 God is love – his the care – 93
4.10 Love divine, all loves excelling – 188
4.10 O God beyond all praising – 219
4.10 There is a green hill far away – 284
4.12 Holy, holy, holy, Lord God almighty – 122
4.12 You servants of God, your master proclaim – 314
4.14 Christians, awake, salute the happy morn – 53
4.14 I cannot tell why he whom angels worship – 135
4.15 The Son of God proclaim – 280
5.11 See him lying on a bed of straw – 253
5.20 The Son of God proclaim – 280

2 John
.2 Not the grandeur of the mountains – 210
.3 We believe in God Almighty – 295
.7 Jesus Christ gives life and gladness – 145

3 John
.14 'Peace be with you all,' we sing – 234

Jude
.24 Jesus the saviour comes – 160
.24 Soldiers of Christ, arise – 258
.25 Name of all majesty – 207

Revelation
1.5 I am trusting you, Lord Jesus – 130
1.5 In heavenly armour we'll enter the land – 140
1.5 Just as I am, without one plea – 164
1.5 Let us love and sing and wonder – 171
1.5 The victory of our God is won – 283
1.6 O come, all ye faithful – 215
1.7 Jesus comes with clouds descending – 149
1.7 Jesus the saviour comes – 160
1.7 Once in royal David's city – 232
1.8 At your feet we fall, mighty risen Lord – 23
1.15 At your feet we fall, mighty risen Lord – 23
1.16 In silent pain the eternal Son – 142
1.17 At your feet we fall, mighty risen Lord – 23
1.17 Christ upon the mountain peak – 52
1.17 God has spoken – by his prophets – 94
1.17 How good is the God we adore – 126
1.18 I believe in God the Father – 131
1.18 Rejoice, the Lord is King – 245
1.20 Christ is the king! O friends rejoice – 47
2.1 In silent pain the eternal Son – 142
2.8 Christ upon the mountain peak – 52
2.8 God has spoken – by his prophets – 94
2.8 How good is the God we adore – 126
2.10 My Lord of light who made the worlds – 203
2.17 Dear Lord and Father of mankind – 71
3.4 The victory of our God is won – 283
3.7 O come, O come, Emmanuel – 216
3.12 O for a heart to praise my God – 217
3.12 We love the place, O God – 301
3.17 Just as I am, without one plea – 164
3.17 Lord, I was blind; I could not see – 177
3.18 How firm a foundation, you people of God – 125
3.18 How sure the Scriptures are – 127
4. Come and see the shining hope – 59
4.2 Ride on, ride on in majesty – 249
4.4 The victory of our God is won – 283
4.6 Holy, holy, holy, Lord God almighty – 122
4.8 Angel voices ever singing – 18
4.8 God of gods, we sound his praise – 98
4.8 Heavenly hosts in ceaseless worship – 117
4.8 Holy, holy, holy, Lord God almighty – 122
4.8 In awe and wonder, Lord our God – 138
4.8 My God, how wonderful you are – 200
4.8 The victory of our God is won – 283
4.9 Alleluia! Raise the anthem – 12
4.9 At your feet we fall, mighty risen Lord – 23
4.10 Crown him with many crowns – 69
4.10 Jesus shall reign where'er the sun – 156
4.10 Love divine, all loves excelling – 188

4.11	Heavenly hosts in ceaseless worship – 117
4.11	I believe in God the Father – 131
4.11	The kingdom of God is justice and joy – 275
5.	Come and see the shining hope – 59
5.6	No weight of gold or silver – 209
5.6	There is a Redeemer – 285
5.8	You servants of God, your master proclaim – 314
5.9	Alleluia, sing to Jesus – 13
5.9	The first nowell the angel did say – 271
5.9	The victory of our God is won – 283
5.9	There is a green hill far away – 284
5.9	To God be the glory – 293
5.11	O for a thousand tongues to sing – 218
5.12	Come let us join our cheerful songs – 62
5.12	Heavenly hosts in ceaseless worship – 117
5.12	Let us love and sing and wonder – 171
5.13	Bless the Lord, created things – 28
5.13	Come let us join our cheerful songs – 62
5.13	Glory in the highest – 89
5.13	Hail the day that sees him rise – 106
5.13	Tell all the world of Jesus – 267
6.2	God is our fortress and our rock – 96
6.10	Joy to the world! The Lord has come – 161
6.10	Judge eternal, throned in splendour – 162
6.11	The victory of our God is won – 283
7.	Here from all nations – 119
7.9	Alleluia, sing to Jesus – 13
7.9	The victory of our God is won – 283
7.12	You servants of God, your master proclaim – 314
7.14	In heavenly armour we'll enter the land – 140
7.14	The victory of our God is won – 283
7.17	Lord of the church, we pray for our renewing – 180
7.17	No weight of gold or silver – 209
7.17	Such love, pure as the whitest snow – 265
9.13	My hope is built on nothing less – 201
9.13	We have a gospel to proclaim – 300
10.6	Alleluia! Raise the anthem – 12
11.11	Breathe on me, breath of God – 36
12.1	Once in royal David's city – 232
12.10	There is a Redeemer – 285
12.11	In heavenly armour we'll enter the land – 140
14.3	Alleluia, sing to Jesus – 13
14.5	Jesus the saviour comes – 160
14.7	We believe in God the Father – 296
14.14	All hail the power of Jesus' name – 7
14.14	Christ triumphant, ever reigning – 50
14.14	The head that once was crowned with thorns – 273
15.2	Holy, holy, holy, Lord God almighty – 122
16.5	There is a Redeemer – 285
17.14	Christ the Lord is risen again – 49
17.14	The head that once was crowned with thorns – 273
17.14	The victory of our God is won – 283
18.14	Lord, be my vision, supreme in my heart – 175
19.6	Jesus is king, and we will extol him – 151
19.6	Judge eternal, throned in splendour – 162
19.7	Here, O my Lord, I see you face to face – 120
19.11	God is our fortress and our rock – 96
19.12	Crown him with many crowns – 69
19.12	Jesus shall reign where'er the sun – 156
19.12	The head that once was crowned with thorns – 273
19.16	Christ the Lord is risen again – 49
19.16	The head that once was crowned with thorns – 273
19.16	The victory of our God is won – 283
19.17	See the feast our God prepares – 262
20.6	Jesus lives! Your terrors now – 153
20.6	The head that once was crowned with thorns – 273
21.1	Loved with everlasting love – 190
21.1	Songs of praise the angels sang – 259
21.2	It came upon the midnight clear – 143
21.4	Come, you thankful people, come – 65
21.4	O love that will not let me go – 227
21.6	Christ is surely coming – 46
21.6	How good is the God we adore – 126
21.14	The victory of our God is won – 283
21.19	Christ is made the sure foundation – 44
21.23	As with gladness men of old – 21
22.1	No weight of gold or silver – 209
22.5	Lord, be my vision, supreme in my heart – 175
22.7	Christ is surely coming – 46
22.13	Christ upon the mountain peak – 52
22.13	God has spoken – by his prophets – 94
22.13	How good is the God we adore – 126
22.16	Christ is surely coming – 46
22.17	Christ is surely coming – 46
22.17	Here, O my Lord, I see you face to face – 120
22.20	Christ is surely coming – 46
22.20	Jesus comes with clouds descending – 149
22.20	Love divine, all loves excelling – 188

Thematic Index

GOD

LORD AND FATHER

Creating and Sustaining

All creatures of our God and king – 5
All hail the power of Jesus' name – 7
All people that on earth do dwell – 9
All things bright and beautiful – 11
Alleluia! Raise the anthem – 12
At the name of Jesus – 22
Bless the Lord – 28
Breathe on me, breath of God – 36
Christ whose glory fills the skies – 51
Clothed in kingly majesty – 55
Come, you thankful people – 65
Creator of the earth and skies – 67
Fill your hearts with joy – 77
For the fruits of his creation – 82
From heaven you came – 85
God has spoken – 94
God is love – 93
God, whose almighty word – 100
God whose love we cannot measure – 101
Great is your faithfulness – 103
He who created light – 115
Heavenly hosts – 117
Holy, holy, holy – 122
I believe in God the Father – 131
Immortal, invisible, God only wise – 137
In awe and wonder, Lord our God – 138
Jesus come! for we invite you – 148
Jesus shall reign where'er the sun – 156
King of the universe – 166
Let us sing – 172
Like a mighty river flowing – 179
Lord be my vision – 175
Love divine, all loves excelling – 188
Morning has broken – 198
My God, how wonderful you are – 200
My Lord of light – 203
Not the grandeur of the mountains – 210
O Lord, the refuge – 225
O worship the king – 230
Praise him, praise him – 236
Praise, my soul – 237
Praise the Lord of heaven – 239
Praise the Lord, you heavens – 240
Praise to the Lord, the almighty – 242
Sing praise to the Lord – 257
Songs of praise the angels sang – 259
The earth was dark – 270
The Lord is king – 276
The Son of God proclaim – 280
We believe in God Almighty – 295
We believe in God the Father – 296
We plough the fields and scatter – 302
When things began to happen – 309

Gracious and Merciful

All people that on earth do dwell – 9
Amazing grace – 16
And can it be – 17
Because the Lord is my shepherd – 27
Christ whose glory fills the skies – 51
Church of God – 54

Come and see the shining hope – 59
Creator of the earth and skies – 67
Creator Spirit, come, inspire – 68
Father in heaven – 74
Fill your hearts with joy – 77
For the fruits of his creation – 82
Forgive our sins as we forgive – 83
From deep despair to you I call – 81
Glory in the highest – 89
Go forth and tell – 90
God brings us comfort (Praise God today) – 92
God is love – 93
God of mercy, God of grace – 97
God whose love we cannot measure – 101
Great is your faithfulness – 103
Hear me, O Lord – 116
Here from all nations – 119
Holy, holy, holy – 122
How good is the God we adore – 126
How long O Lord – 128
I love you, O Lord – 134
In awe and wonder, Lord our God – 138
In the cross of Christ I glory – 139
It is a thing most wonderful – 144
Jesus is king – 151
Jesus, lover of my soul – 154
Jesus, the joy of loving hearts – 158
Jesus! the name high over all – 159
Just as I am – 164
King of glory, king of peace – 165
King of the universe – 166
Let the people praise you – 169
Like a mighty river flowing – 179
Lord, as I wake – 174
Lord, you were rich – 185
Love divine, all loves excelling – 188
Mary sang a song – 194
Meekness and majesty – 197
My God, how wonderful you are – 200
My Lord, I did not choose you – 202
My Lord, what love is this – 205
My song is love unknown – 206
Name of all majesty – 207
New every morning is the love – 208
Not the grandeur of the mountains – 210
Now at last – 211
Now thank we all our God – 213
O for a thousand tongues to sing – 218
O God beyond all praising – 219
O God, our help in ages past – 220
O Lord, the refuge – 225
O love that will not let me go – 227
O worship the king – 230
Praise, my soul – 237
Praise to the Lord, the almighty – 242
Rejoice, rejoice! Christ is in you – 244
Remember, remember your mercy, Lord – 246
Sing of the Lord's goodness – 256
Sing praise to the Lord – 257
Such love – 265
Tell all the world of Jesus – 267
Tell out my soul – 268
The king of love my shepherd is – 274
The kingdom of God – 275
The Lord my shepherd – 278
The Lord's my shepherd – 279

The trumpets sound – 282
There is no moment of my life – 286
This is the day the Lord has made – 291
Through all the changing scenes – 292
To God be the glory – 293
To him we come – 294
We give God thanks – 299
We love the place, O God – 301
We trust in you – 303
What a friend we have in Jesus – 305
When all your mercies, O my God – 306
When things began to happen – 309
Who can sound the depths of sorrow – 312
Your hand, O God, has guided – 315

LORD AND SAVIOUR

Promised and Born

A child is born for us today – 1
All my heart this night rejoices – 8
Angels from the realms of glory – 19
As with gladness – 21
Away in a manger – 24
Child in the manger – 39
Christ is the world's Light – 48
Christians, awake – 53
Come and hear the joyful singing – 56
Come and sing the Christmas story – 60
Come, light of the world – 64
Come, O long-expected Jesus – 57
Darkness like a shroud – 70
From heaven you came – 85
Glad music fills the Christmas sky – 87
Glory in the highest – 89
God has spoken – 94
God rest you merry, gentlemen – 99
Had he not loved us – 105
Hail to the Lord's anointed – 107
Hark! the herald angels sing – 108
Holy child, how still you lie – 121
I cannot tell – 135
It came upon the midnight clear – 143
Jesus Christ gives life – 145
Jesus Christ the Lord is born – 147
Jesus, saviour, holy child – 155
Jesus the saviour comes – 160
Joy to the world – the Lord has come – 161
Let trumpets sound! (Hark, the glad sound) – 170
Lord, you were rich – 185
Mary came with meekness – 193
Mary sang a song – 194
Now at last – 211
O come all ye faithful – 215
O come, O come, Emmanuel – 216
O little town of Bethlehem – 222
O worship the Lord – 231
Once in royal David's city – 232
Praise to the holiest – 241
See amid the winter snow – 252
See him lying on a bed of straw – 253
Shepherds came – 254
Silent night! holy night – 255
Songs of praise the angels sang – 259
Speak Lord, in the stillness – 260
Tell out my soul – 268
The first nowell – 271
This Child – 289
We believe in God the Father – 296
We have a gospel – 300

When things began to happen – 309
While shepherds watched – 311

Growing, Teaching, Serving

All hail the power of Jesus' name – 7
Alleluia! Raise the anthem – 12
Before the heaven and earth – 29
Blessed are the pure in heart – 30
Break now the bread of life – 35
Come let us join our cheerful songs – 62
For God so loved the world – 78
From heaven you came – 85
God is love – 93
He gave his life – 109
He healed the darkness of my mind – 110
He who created light – 115
How sweet the name – 129
Jesus, Jesus, fill us with your love – 152
Jesus! the name high over all – 159
Lead us, heavenly Father – 167
Let us love and sing – 171
Love divine, all loves excelling – 188
Meekness and majesty – 197
My Lord you wore no royal crown – 204
Name of all majesty – 207
O for a thousand tongues to sing – 218
The hands of Christ – 272
We believe in God Almighty – 295

Transfigured

All glory, praise and honour – 6
As water to the thirsty – 20
As with gladness – 21
Blessed are the pure in heart – 30
Christ upon the mountain peak – 52
Come let us join our cheerful songs – 62
Dear Lord and Father – 71
Forgive our sins as we forgive – 83
I cannot tell – 135
Jesus, good above all other – 150
Lord, I was blind – 177
Lord, you sometimes speak in wonders – 184
My Lord, I did not choose you – 202
My Lord you wore no royal crown – 204
Praise, my soul – 237
Praise to the holiest – 241
Ride on, ride on in majesty – 249
Speak Lord, in the stillness – 260
Through all the changing scenes – 292

Suffering and Dying

A purple robe – 2
All glory, praise and honour – 6
And can it be – 17
Before the heaven and earth – 29
Bread of the world – 34
Broken for me – 38
Child in the manger – 39
Christ is alive – 41
Christ is ascending – 42
Christ is going to the Father – 43
Christ is the world's Light – 48
Christ triumphant, ever reigning – 50
Come and see – 58
Come let us join our cheerful songs – 62
Crown him with many crowns – 69
Father in heaven – 74
For God so loved the world – 78
From heaven you came – 85
Glory be to Jesus – 88

Glory in the highest – 89
God brings us comfort (Praise God today) – 92
God of gods, we sound his praises – 98
Had he not loved us – 105
He gave his life – 109
He stood before the court – 112
He was pierced – 114
How sweet the name – 129
I believe in God the Father – 131
I cannot tell – 135
In silent pain the eternal Son – 142
In the cross of Christ I glory – 139
It is a thing most wonderful – 144
Jesus Christ gives life – 145
King of glory, king of peace – 165
Led like a lamb – 168
Let us love and sing – 171
Lord Jesus Christ – 178
Lord of the cross of shame – 181
Lord, you were rich – 185
Man of sorrows – 195
May the mind of Christ my saviour – 196
Meekness and majesty – 197
My Lord of light – 203
My Lord, what love is this – 205
My song is love unknown – 206
Name of all majesty – 207
No weight of gold or silver – 209
O love that will not let me go – 227
Praise to the holiest – 241
Ride on, ride on in majesty – 249
The hands of Christ – 272
The head that once was crowned – 273
There is a green hill – 284
There is a Redeemer – 285
These are the facts – 287
This is the day the Lord has made – 291
To God be the glory – 293
We believe in God Almighty – 295
We believe in God the Father – 296
We have a gospel – 300
When I survey the wondrous cross – 307
When you prayed beneath the trees – 310
Who can sound the depths of sorrow – 312

Risen and Victorious
Abide with me – 3
All creation join to say – 4
All creatures of our God and king – 5
All shall be well – 10
Alleluia! Raise the anthem – 12
At the name of Jesus – 22
At your feet we fall – 23
Baptised in water – 25
Blow upon the trumpet – 31
Born in song – 32
Child in the manger – 39
Christ in majesty ascending – 40
Christ is alive – 41
Christ is going to the Father – 43
Christ is risen – 45
Christ is the king – 47
Christ the Lord is risen again – 49
Christ triumphant, ever reigning – 50
Christ whose glory fills the skies – 51
Come and see – 58
Come and see the shining hope – 59
Come let us worship Christ – 63
Comes Mary to the grave – 66
Crown him with many crowns – 69

Eternal light, shine in my heart – 72
Father in heaven – 74
For God so loved the world – 78
Glory in the highest – 89
God brings us comfort (Praise God today) – 92
God is love – 93
God is our fortress – 96
God of gods, we sound his praises – 98
Good Christians all, rejoice – 102
Had he not loved us – 105
Hail the day that sees him rise – 106
He lives in us – 111
I believe in God the Father – 131
I know that my redeemer lives – 133
I love you, O Lord – 134
If Christ had not been raised – 136
Jesus Christ gives life – 145
Jesus Christ is risen today – 146
Jesus, good above all other – 150
Jesus lives! Your terrors now – 153
Jesus stand among us – 157
Jesus! the name high over all – 159
Jesus the saviour comes – 160
Led like a lamb – 168
Lord Jesus Christ – 178
Lord of the cross of shame – 181
Low in the grave he lay – 191
Name of all majesty – 207
No weight of gold or silver – 209
O Lord my God – 223
O Trinity, O Trinity – 229
See the feast our God prepares – 262
Sing of the Lord's goodness – 256
Spirit of God most high – 264
The hands of Christ – 272
The head that once was crowned – 273
The strife is past – 281
The trumpets sound – 282
These are the facts – 287
This is the day the Lord has made – 291
To him we come – 294
We believe in God Almighty – 295
We believe in God the Father – 296
We have a gospel – 300
When you prayed beneath the trees – 310
Yours be the glory – 316

Ascended and Reigning
All glory, praise and honour – 6
Alleluia, sing to Jesus – 13
At the name of Jesus – 22
Before the heaven and earth – 29
Christ in majesty ascending – 40
Christ is ascending – 42
Christ is going to the Father – 43
Christ is risen – 45
Christ the Lord is risen again – 49
Christ triumphant, ever reigning – 50
Clothed in kingly majesty – 55
Crown him with many crowns – 69
Glory in the highest – 89
God of gods, we sound his praises – 98
Hail the day that sees him rise – 106
Here from all nations – 119
I know that my redeemer lives – 133
If Christ had not been raised – 136
Jesus is king – 151
Led like a lamb – 168
Lord of the church, we pray for our renewing – 180
Man of sorrows – 195

My Lord of light – 203
Praise him, praise him – 236
Rejoice, the Lord is king – 245
The head that once was crowned – 273
The Lord is king – 276
The Son of God proclaim – 280
The victory of our God is won – 283
This earth belongs to God – 290
We believe in God Almighty – 295
We believe in God the Father – 296
We have a gospel – 300
You servants of God – 314
Your hand, O God, has guided – 315

Returning and Triumphant
All hail the power of Jesus' name – 7
At your feet we fall – 23
Blow upon the trumpet – 31
Born in song – 32
Christ is ascending – 42
Christ is surely coming – 46
Christ is the world's Light – 48
Come and see the shining hope – 59
Come let us worship Christ – 63
Come, O long-expected Jesus – 57
Come, you thankful people – 65
Hail to the Lord's anointed – 107
He gave his life – 109
I cannot tell – 135
I come with joy – 132
It came upon the midnight clear – 143
Jesus comes with clouds descending – 149
Jesus shall reign where'er the sun – 156
Jesus the saviour comes – 160
Joy to the world – the Lord has come – 161
Let trumpets sound! (Hark, the glad sound) – 170
Man of sorrows – 195
O come, O come, Emmanuel – 216
O Spirit of the living God – 228
Rejoice, the Lord is king – 245
Tell all the world of Jesus – 267
There is a Redeemer – 285
These are the facts – 287
To God be the glory – 293
To him we come – 294
We believe in God the Father – 296
We worship God in harmony – 304
When the king shall come again – 308

LORD AND SPIRIT

Breath of Life
All people that on earth do dwell – 9
At your feet we fall – 23
Baptised in water – 25
Be still, for the presence of the Lord – 26
Born in song – 32
Born of the water – 33
Break now the bread of life – 35
Breathe on me, breath of God – 36
Christ in majesty ascending – 40
Christ is ascending – 42
Come down, O Love divine – 61
Come, light of the world – 64
Creator Spirit, come, inspire – 68
Eternal light, shine in my heart – 72
Father in heaven – 74
For the fruits of his creation – 82
Freedom and life are ours – 84

God, whose almighty word – 100
He lives in us – 111
Holy Spirit, gracious guest – 123
How good is the God we adore – 126
I believe in God the Father – 131
Jesus stand among us – 157
Lead us, heavenly Father – 167
Let us love and sing – 171
Like the murmur of the dove's song – 173
Lord of the church, we pray for our renewing – 180
Lord, the light of your love – 182
Lord, your church on earth is seeking – 186
Loved with everlasting love – 190
My Lord of light – 203
O Breath of life, come sweeping through us – 214
O Lord, who came from realms above – 226
O Spirit of the living God – 228
O Trinity, O Trinity – 229
Revive your church O Lord – 248
Sing of the Lord's goodness – 256
Spirit divine, inspire our prayers – 261
Spirit of faith, by faith be mine – 263
Spirit of God most high – 264
There is a Redeemer – 285
These are the facts – 287
We believe in God Almighty – 295
We believe in God the Father – 296
We have a gospel – 300
We worship God in harmony – 304

Word of Truth: the Scriptures
Break now the bread of life – 35
Freedom and life are ours – 84
God has spoken – 94
God is our strength and refuge – 95
How firm a foundation – 125
How sure the scriptures are – 127
Let trumpets sound! (Hark, the glad sound) – 170
Lord, for the years – 176
Lord, you sometimes speak in wonders – 184
Lord, your word shall guide us – 187
Speak Lord, in the stillness – 260
These are the facts – 287
They who stand in awe of God – 288
We love the place, O God – 301

THE TRINITY

All creatures of our God and king – 5
All people that on earth do dwell – 9
Alleluia! Raise the anthem – 12
Angel voices ever singing – 18
Baptised in water – 25
Christ is made the sure foundation – 44
Father in heaven – 74
God has spoken – 94
God of gods, we sound his praises – 98
God, whose almighty word – 100
God whose love we cannot measure – 101
He who created light – 115
Holy, holy, holy – 122
I believe in God the Father – 131
Lead us, heavenly Father – 167
May the grace – 196
My Lord of light – 203
Now thank we all our God – 213
O Trinity, O Trinity – 229
Praise God from whom all blessings flow – 235
Songs of praise the angels sang – 259

We believe in God Almighty – 295
We believe in God the Father – 296

GOD'S WORLD

Days and Nights
Abide with me – 3
Christ whose glory fills the skies – 51
Fill now my life – 76
For the beauty of the earth – 79
Great is your faithfulness – 103
Holy, holy, holy – 122
Jesus stand among us – 157
Like a mighty river flowing – 179
Lord, as I wake – 174
Love is his word – 189
Morning has broken – 198
New every morning is the love – 208
O Lord my God – 223
The day you gave us – 269
This is the day the Lord has made – 291

Land, Sea and Harvest
All creatures of our God and king – 5
All things bright and beautiful – 11
Bless the Lord – 28
Christ upon the mountain peak – 52
Clothed in kingly majesty – 55
Come let us join our cheerful songs – 62
Come, you thankful people – 65
Dear Lord and Father – 71
Fill your hearts with joy – 77
For the beauty of the earth – 79
For the fruits of his creation – 82
God of mercy, God of grace – 97
Great is your faithfulness – 103
King of the universe – 166
Loved with everlasting love – 190
Not the grandeur of the mountains – 210
Praise God from whom all blessings flow – 235
Praise him, praise him – 236
Praise the Lord of heaven – 239
Put peace into each other's hands – 243
This earth belongs to God – 290
We plough the fields and scatter – 302

Marriage, Home and Children
Because the Lord is my shepherd – 27
Father God in heaven – 73
For the beauty of the earth – 79
Love divine, all loves excelling – 188
Now thank we all our God – 213
Who can sound the depths of sorrow – 312

Work and Leisure: Art and Science
Angel voices ever singing – 18
Bring to the Lord a glad new song – 37
O for a thousand tongues to sing – 218
Sing of the Lord's goodness – 256
Sing praise to the Lord – 257
Songs of praise the angels sang – 259

Nations, Justice and Peace
Angels from the realms of glory – 19
Bring to the Lord a glad new song – 37
Christ is alive – 41
Christ is surely coming – 46

Christ is the world's Light – 48
Christ upon the mountain peak – 52
Come and see the shining hope – 59
Come, light of the world – 64
Creator of the earth and skies – 67
Crown him with many crowns – 69
Darkness like a shroud – 70
From the sun's rising – 86
God has spoken – 94
God is our strength and refuge – 95
Here from all nations – 119
I cannot tell – 135
Immortal, invisible, God only wise – 137
In silent pain the eternal Son – 142
Joy to the world – the Lord has come – 161
Judge eternal, throned in splendour – 162
King of the universe – 166
Let the people praise you – 169
Lord, for the years – 176
Lord, the light of your love – 182
Make me a channel of your peace – 192
O Lord my God – 223
O Lord, the clouds are gathering – 224
O Spirit of the living God – 228
O Trinity, O Trinity – 229
Praise to the holiest – 241
Put peace into each other's hands – 243
Sing of the Lord's goodness – 256
The kingdom of God – 275
The victory of our God is won – 283
To him we come – 294
We believe in God the Father – 296
Who can sound the depths of sorrow – 312

GOD'S CHURCH

Call to Worship
All people that on earth do dwell – 9
Be still, for the presence of the Lord – 26
Come and hear the joyful singing – 56
Come and sing the Christmas story – 60
Come let us join our cheerful songs – 62
Come let us worship Christ – 63
Come, light of the world – 64
Come, you thankful people – 65
God brings us comfort (Praise God today) – 92
Jesus come! for we invite you – 148
Jesus stand among us – 157
Let the people praise you – 169
Let us sing – 172
O worship the king – 230
O worship the Lord – 231
Praise him, praise him – 236
Praise, my soul – 237
Praise our God with shouts of joy – 238
Speak Lord, in the stillness – 260
Spirit divine, inspire our prayers – 261
To God be the glory – 293

Praise and Thanksgiving
All creation join to say – 4
All creatures of our God and king – 5
All glory, praise and honour – 6
All hail the power of Jesus' name – 7
All people that on earth do dwell – 9
Alleluia! Raise the anthem – 12
And can it be – 17

Angel voices ever singing – 18
At the name of Jesus – 22
Baptised in water – 25
Blow upon the trumpet – 31
Born in song – 32
Bring to the Lord a glad new song – 37
Christ is ascending – 42
Christ is going to the Father – 43
Christ is risen – 45
Christ is surely coming – 46
Christ is the king – 47
Christ triumphant, ever reigning – 50
Come let us join our cheerful songs – 62
Crown him with many crowns – 69
Fill now my life – 76
Fill your hearts with joy – 77
For the beauty of the earth – 79
From the sun's rising – 86
Glory in the highest – 89
God brings us comfort (Praise God today) – 92
God is love – 93
God of gods, we sound his praises – 98
God, whose almighty word – 100
Great is your faithfulness – 103
Hail to the Lord's anointed – 107
Heavenly hosts – 117
How good is the God we adore – 126
I love you, O Lord – 134
Immortal, invisible, God only wise – 137
Jesus is king – 151
Jesus shall reign where'er the sun – 156
Jesus! the name high over all – 159
King of glory, king of peace – 165
King of the universe – 166
Let the people praise you – 169
Let us love and sing – 171
Let us sing – 172
Lord, for the years – 176
Love divine, all loves excelling – 188
Mary sang a song – 194
Name of all majesty – 207
Not the grandeur of the mountains – 210
Now thank we all our God – 213
O for a thousand tongues to sing – 218
O Lord, the clouds are gathering – 224
O worship the king – 230
Praise God from whom all blessings flow – 235
Praise him, praise him – 236
Praise, my soul – 237
Praise the Lord of heaven – 239
Praise the Lord, you heavens – 240
Praise to the Lord, the almighty – 242
Rejoice, rejoice! Christ is in you – 244
Rejoice, the Lord is king – 245
See the feast our God prepares – 262
Sing of the Lord's goodness – 256
Sing praise to the Lord – 257
Songs of praise the angels sang – 259
Tell out my soul – 268
The trumpets sound – 282
The victory of our God is won – 283
This earth belongs to God – 290
This is the day the Lord has made – 291
To God be the glory – 293
We plough the fields and scatter – 302
When the king shall come again – 308
You holy angels bright – 313
You servants of God – 314
Yours be the glory – 316

Proclamation and Mission
All hail the power of Jesus' name – 7
And can it be – 17
Born in song – 32
Christ in majesty ascending – 40
Christ is risen – 45
Christ is the king – 47
Christ the Lord is risen again – 49
Church of God – 54
Darkness like a shroud – 70
Fill now my life – 76
For the bread – 80
From the sun's rising – 86
Go forth and tell – 90
God has spoken – 94
God of gods, we sound his praises – 98
God, whose almighty word – 100
How can we sing with joy – 124
How sweet the name – 129
I believe in God the Father – 131
I come with joy – 132
In heavenly armour – 140
Jesus Christ gives life – 145
Jesus shall reign where'er the sun – 156
Jesus! the name high over all – 159
Like a mighty river flowing – 179
Like the murmur of the dove's song – 173
Lord, I was blind – 177
Lord, your church on earth is seeking – 186
May the mind of Christ my saviour – 199
O Breath of life, come sweeping through us – 214
O for a thousand tongues to sing – 218
O Jesus, I have promised – 221
O Lord, the clouds are gathering – 224
O Lord, who came from realms above – 226
O Spirit of the living God – 228
O Trinity, O Trinity – 229
One thing I know – 233
Praise our God with shouts of joy – 238
Rejoice, rejoice! Christ is in you – 244
Rejoice, the Lord is king – 245
Restore, O Lord – 247
Revive your church O Lord – 248
Take my life and let it be – 266
Tell all the world of Jesus – 267
Tell out my soul – 268
The earth was dark – 270
The kingdom of God – 275
These are the facts – 287
To him we come – 294
We believe in God Almighty – 295
We believe in God the Father – 296
We have a gospel – 300
You servants of God – 314
Your hand, O God, has guided – 315

Confession and Repentance
  (see also 'Suffering and Dying')
A purple robe – 2
Almighty God, our heavenly Father – 14
Be still, for the presence of the Lord – 26
Bread of the world – 34
Broken for me – 38
Christ whose glory fills the skies – 51
Clothed in kingly majesty – 55
Come and see – 58
Come, O long-expected Jesus – 57
Creator of the earth and skies – 67
Dear Lord and Father – 71
Father God in heaven – 73

Forgive our sins as we forgive – 83
From deep despair to you I call – 81
Glory be to Jesus – 88
He lives in us – 111
He stood before the court – 112
Heal me, hands of Jesus – 113
Here, O my Lord – 120
How can we sing with joy – 124
How long O Lord – 128
How sweet the name – 129
I am trusting you, Lord Jesus – 130
I come with joy – 132
In awe and wonder, Lord our God – 138
Jesus, lover of my soul – 154
Jesus, the joy of loving hearts – 158
Judge eternal, throned in splendour – 162
Just as I am – 164
King of glory, king of peace – 165
King of the universe – 166
Lord be my vision – 175
Lord of the church, we pray for our renewing – 180
Lord, the light of your love – 182
May the grace – 196
My Lord, I did not choose you – 202
My Lord, what love is this – 205
My Lord you wore no royal crown – 204
No weight of gold or silver – 209
O Breath of life, come sweeping through us – 214
O for a heart to praise my God – 217
O Lord, the clouds are gathering – 224
O Lord, the refuge – 225
O love that will not let me go – 227
One thing I know – 233
Praise, my soul – 237
Praise to the holiest – 241
Remember, remember your mercy, Lord – 246
Restore, O Lord – 247
Revive your church O Lord – 248
Rock of ages, cleft for me – 250
Spirit divine, inspire our prayers – 261
Spirit of God most high – 264
Take my life and let it be – 266
The kingdom of God – 275
There is no moment of my life – 286
This earth belongs to God – 290
When all your mercies, O my God – 306
Who can sound the depths of sorrow – 312

Worship and Adoration
All my heart this night rejoices – 8
Angel voices ever singing – 18
As water to the thirsty – 20
At your feet we fall – 23
Be still, for the presence of the Lord – 26
Because the Lord is my shepherd – 27
Child in the manger – 39
Come and see – 58
Come let us join our cheerful songs – 62
Come let us worship Christ – 63
Crown him with many crowns – 69
Eternal light, shine in my heart – 72
Father in heaven – 74
For God so loved the world – 78
Forgive our sins as we forgive – 83
From heaven you came – 85
Glory be to Jesus – 88
God be in my head – 91
God of mercy, God of grace – 97
God whose love we cannot measure – 101
Hear me, O Lord – 116

Holy, holy, holy – 122
How good is the God we adore – 126
How sweet the name – 129
In awe and wonder, Lord our God – 138
In the cross of Christ I glory – 139
Jesus is king – 151
Jesus, lover of my soul – 154
Jesus stand among us – 157
Lord, as I wake – 174
Lord Jesus Christ – 178
Lord of the cross of shame – 181
Lord, you need no house – 183
Lord, you sometimes speak in wonders – 184
Lord, you were rich – 185
Love divine, all loves excelling – 188
Loved with everlasting love – 190
Meekness and majesty – 197
My God, how wonderful you are – 200
My Lord, I did not choose you – 202
My song is love unknown – 206
Not the grandeur of the mountains – 210
Now at last – 211
O come all ye faithful – 215
O God beyond all praising – 219
O worship the king – 230
O worship the Lord – 231
One thing I know – 233
Praise, my soul – 237
Spirit of faith, by faith be mine – 263
Such love – 265
There is a Redeemer – 285
There is no moment of my life – 286
We love the place, O God – 301
When all your mercies, O my God – 306
When I survey the wondrous cross – 307
When things began to happen – 309

Prayer
Alleluia, sing to Jesus – 13
Almighty God, our heavenly Father – 14
Father God in heaven – 73
God be in my head – 91
Hail the day that sees him rise – 106
Hear me, O Lord – 116
How long O Lord – 128
I know that my redeemer lives – 133
Jesus is king – 151
Jesus shall reign where'er the sun – 156
Like the murmur of the dove's song – 173
Lord be my vision – 175
Lord, you sometimes speak in wonders – 184
Make me a channel of your peace – 192
Praise our God with shouts of joy – 238
Spirit divine, inspire our prayers – 261
The Lord is king – 276
We give God thanks – 299
We love the place, O God – 301
What a friend we have in Jesus – 305
When you prayed beneath the trees – 310

Initiation and Dedication
Amazing grace – 16
And can it be – 17
Baptised in water – 25
Born of the water – 33
Come down, O Love divine – 61
Fight the good fight – 75
He lives in us – 111
Lord, for the years – 176
Lord, I was blind – 177

O for a heart to praise my God – 217
O Jesus, I have promised – 221
O love that will not let me go – 227
O Spirit of the living God – 228
Take my life and let it be – 266
We love the place, O God – 301
We worship God in harmony – 304
When I survey the wondrous cross – 307

Holy Communion
(see also 'Suffering and Dying', 'Risen and Victorious' and 'Confession and Repentance')

Almighty God, we thank you – 15
Because the Lord is my shepherd – 27
Bread of the world – 34
Broken for me – 38
Christ is risen – 45
Christ is surely coming – 46
Christ is the king – 47
Come let us worship Christ – 63
For the bread – 80
Guide me, O my great redeemer – 104
He gave his life – 109
He was pierced – 114
Here, O my Lord – 120
I am trusting you, Lord Jesus – 130
Jesus, the joy of loving hearts – 158
Lord Jesus Christ – 178
Love is his word – 189
O God beyond all praising – 219
Peace be with you all – 234
Put peace into each other's hands – 243
Revive your church O Lord – 248
See the feast our God prepares – 262
Sing of the Lord's goodness – 256
Such love – 265
The king of love my shepherd is – 274
The Lord my shepherd – 278
The Lord's my shepherd – 279
The Son of God proclaim – 280
The trumpets sound – 282
Through all the changing scenes – 292
We break this bread – 297
We come as guests invited – 298
We love the place, O God – 301
When I survey the wondrous cross – 307

Thirst for God
As water to the thirsty – 20
Blessed are the pure in heart – 30
Christ is surely coming – 46
Christ upon the mountain peak – 52
Christ whose glory fills the skies – 51
God brings us comfort (Praise God today) – 92
Here from all nations – 119
Jesus, the joy of loving hearts – 158
Just as a lost and thirsty deer – 163
Lord be my vision – 175
Love divine, all loves excelling – 188
My Lord, I did not choose you – 202
O for a heart to praise my God – 217
Revive your church O Lord – 248

Faith and Trust
Abide with me – 3
Alleluia, sing to Jesus – 13
And can it be – 17
At the name of Jesus – 22
Breathe on me, breath of God – 36

Bring to the Lord a glad new song – 37
Christ is made the sure foundation – 44
Come down, O Love divine – 61
Eternal light, shine in my heart – 72
Fight the good fight – 75
Fill now my life – 76
For God so loved the world – 78
He lives in us – 111
Here, O my Lord – 120
Holy Spirit, gracious guest – 123
How firm a foundation – 125
How good is the God we adore – 126
How sweet the name – 129
I am trusting you, Lord Jesus – 130
I believe in God the Father – 131
I know that my redeemer lives – 133
I love you, O Lord – 134
In heavenly love abiding – 141
Jesus come! for we invite you – 148
Jesus, lover of my soul – 154
Jesus! the name high over all – 159
Just as a lost and thirsty deer – 163
Just as I am – 164
King of glory, king of peace – 165
Lord be my vision – 175
Lord, for the years – 176
Lord, I was blind – 177
Love divine, all loves excelling – 188
My hope is built – 201
Name of all majesty – 207
No weight of gold or silver – 209
O for a thousand tongues to sing – 218
O God beyond all praising – 219
O Jesus, I have promised – 221
O worship the king – 230
Praise to the Lord, the almighty – 242
Rejoice, rejoice! Christ is in you – 244
Revive your church O Lord – 248
Rock of ages, cleft for me – 250
Safe in the shadow of the Lord – 251
Spirit of faith, by faith be mine – 263
Tell out my soul – 268
There is a green hill – 284
We trust in you – 303

Hope and confidence
And can it be – 17
At the name of Jesus – 22
Bring to the Lord a glad new song – 37
Christ is made the sure foundation – 44
Come let us worship Christ – 63
Come, light of the world – 64
Eternal light, shine in my heart – 72
From deep despair to you I call – 81
God is our fortress – 96
God is our strength and refuge – 95
Great is your faithfulness – 103
Hail to the Lord's anointed – 107
He lives in us – 111
Heal me, hands of Jesus – 113
Help us to help each other – 118
Here, O my Lord – 120
Holy Spirit, gracious guest – 123
How firm a foundation – 125
How good is the God we adore – 126
How sweet the name – 129
I know that my redeemer lives – 133
I love you, O Lord – 134
In heavenly love abiding – 141
Jesus Christ gives life – 145

Jesus come! for we invite you – 148
Jesus is king – 151
Jesus, lover of my soul – 154
Jesus! the name high over all – 159
Just as a lost and thirsty deer – 163
King of glory, king of peace – 165
Man of sorrows – 195
My hope is built – 201
O for a thousand tongues to sing – 218
O God, our help in ages past – 220
Praise to the Lord, the almighty – 242
Rejoice, rejoice! Christ is in you – 244
Rejoice, the Lord is king – 245
Soldiers of Christ, arise – 258
Tell out my soul – 268
Your hand, O God, has guided – 315

Love and devotion
As water to the thirsty – 20
Because the Lord is my shepherd – 27
Blessed are the pure in heart – 30
Breathe on me, breath of God – 36
Church of God – 54
Come down, O Love divine – 61
Dear Lord and Father – 71
Father in heaven – 74
Forgive our sins as we forgive – 83
From heaven you came – 85
From the sun's rising – 86
God is love – 93
He healed the darkness of my mind – 110
Hear me, O Lord – 116
Holy Spirit, gracious guest – 123
How can we sing with joy – 124
I love you, O Lord – 134
It is a thing most wonderful – 144
Jesus, Jesus, fill us with your love – 152
King of glory, king of peace – 165
Lord, as I wake – 174
Lord be my vision – 175
Lord of the cross of shame – 181
Lord, you need no house – 183
Love is his word – 189
Loved with everlasting love – 190
Make me a channel of your peace – 192
May the mind of Christ my saviour – 199
My God, how wonderful you are – 200
My Lord, I did not choose you – 202
New every morning is the love – 208
Now let us learn of Christ – 212
O for a heart to praise my God – 217
O God beyond all praising – 219
O Lord, who came from realms above – 226
O love that will not let me go – 227
One thing I know – 233
Speak Lord, in the stillness – 260
Such love – 265
Take my life and let it be – 266
The earth was dark – 270
The will of God to mark my way – 277
There is a green hill – 284
We come as guests invited – 298
We love the place, O God – 301

Unity and growth
Born in song – 32
Born of the water – 33
Christ is made the sure foundation – 44
Christ is the king – 47
Christ is the world's Light – 48

Church of God – 54
Come, light of the world – 64
Help us to help each other – 118
I come with joy – 132
Jesus, good above all other – 150
Jesus shall reign where'er the sun – 156
Jesus stand among us – 157
Like the murmur of the dove's song – 173
Lord of the church, we pray for our renewing – 180
Lord, your church on earth is seeking – 186
May the grace – 196
My Lord you wore no royal crown – 204
Now let us learn of Christ – 212
O Spirit of the living God – 228
Peace be with you all – 234
Spirit of God most high – 264
The day you gave us – 269
To him we come – 294
We break this bread – 297
We come as guests invited – 298
We worship God in harmony – 304
Your hand, O God, has guided – 315

Commitment and character
Almighty God, our heavenly Father – 14
Almighty God, we thank you – 15
Amazing grace – 16
At the name of Jesus – 22
Because the Lord is my shepherd – 27
Breathe on me, breath of God – 36
Church of God – 54
Come, light of the world – 64
Dear Lord and Father – 71
Father God in heaven – 73
Fight the good fight – 75
Fill now my life – 76
For the bread – 80
Freedom and life are ours – 84
Go forth and tell – 90
God be in my head – 91
Help us to help each other – 118
How sure the scriptures are – 127
I am trusting you, Lord Jesus – 130
I come with joy – 132
It is a thing most wonderful – 144
Jesus Christ gives life – 145
Jesus is king – 151
Just as I am – 164
Like a mighty river flowing – 179
Lord be my vision – 175
Lord, for the years – 176
Lord Jesus Christ – 178
Lord of the cross of shame – 181
Lord, the light of your love – 182
Lord, you need no house – 183
Lord, you sometimes speak in wonders – 184
Lord, you were rich – 185
Love is his word – 189
May the mind of Christ my saviour – 199
New every morning is the love – 208
Now let us learn of Christ – 212
O God, our help in ages past – 220
O Jesus, I have promised – 221
O Lord, the refuge – 225
O Lord, who came from realms above – 226
O love that will not let me go – 227
One thing I know – 233
Praise to the Lord, the almighty – 242
Put peace into each other's hands – 243
Rock of ages, cleft for me – 250

Spirit of God most high – 264
Take my life and let it be – 266
The earth was dark – 270
They who stand in awe of God – 288
To him we come – 294
We worship God in harmony – 304
When I survey the wondrous cross – 307
Who can sound the depths of sorrow – 312

Trials and temptation
  (see also 'Suffering')
Abide with me – 3
Amazing grace – 16
As water to the thirsty – 20
Because the Lord is my shepherd – 27
Before the heaven and earth – 29
Christ is alive – 41
Christ is ascending – 42
Father God in heaven – 73
Fight the good fight – 75
From deep despair to you I call – 81
God is our fortress – 96
God is our strength and refuge – 95
God whose love we cannot measure – 101
Guide me, O my great redeemer – 104
He lives in us – 111
How firm a foundation – 125
How long O Lord – 128
How sure the scriptures are – 127
How sweet the name – 129
I love you, O Lord – 134
In heavenly armour – 140
In heavenly love abiding – 141
It came upon the midnight clear – 143
Jesus, lover of my soul – 154
Just as a lost and thirsty deer – 163
Just as I am – 164
Lead us, heavenly Father – 167
Let us love and sing – 171
Lord, your word shall guide us – 187
My hope is built – 201
My Lord you wore no royal crown – 204
Now let us learn of Christ – 212
O Jesus, I have promised – 221
O Lord my God – 223
O Lord, the refuge – 225
Praise, my soul – 237
Praise our God with shouts of joy – 238
Rejoice, rejoice! Christ is in you – 244
Safe in the shadow of the Lord – 251
Soldiers of Christ, arise – 258
The king of love my shepherd is – 274
The Lord is king – 276
The Lord my shepherd – 278
The Lord's my shepherd – 279
The victory of our God is won – 283
Through all the changing scenes – 292
To him we come – 294
What a friend we have in Jesus – 305
Your hand, O God, has guided – 315
Yours be the glory – 316

Suffering
  (see also 'Trials and Temptation')
A purple robe – 2
All glory, praise and honour – 6
And can it be – 17
Before the heaven and earth – 29
Bread of the world – 34
Broken for me – 38

Child in the manger – 39
Christ is alive – 41
Christ is ascending – 42
Christ is going to the Father – 43
Christ is the world's Light – 48
Christ triumphant, ever reigning – 50
Come and see – 58
Come let us join our cheerful songs – 62
Crown him with many crowns – 69
Father in heaven – 74
For God so loved the world – 78
From heaven you came – 85
Glory be to Jesus – 88
Glory in the highest – 89
God brings us comfort (Praise God today) – 92
God of gods, we sound his praises – 98
Had he not loved us – 105
He gave his life – 109
He stood before the court – 112
He was pierced – 114
How sweet the name – 129
I believe in God the Father – 131
I cannot tell – 135
In silent pain the eternal Son – 142
In the cross of Christ I glory – 139
It is a thing most wonderful – 144
Jesus Christ gives life – 145
King of glory, king of peace – 165
Led like a lamb – 168
Let us love and sing – 171
Lord Jesus Christ – 178
Lord of the cross of shame – 181
Lord, you were rich – 185
Man of sorrows – 195
May the mind of Christ my saviour – 199
Meekness and majesty – 197
My Lord of light – 203
My Lord, what love is this – 205
My song is love unknown – 206
Name of all majesty – 207
No weight of gold or silver – 209
O love that will not let me go – 227
Praise to the holiest – 241
Ride on, ride on in majesty – 249
The hands of Christ – 272
The head that once was crowned – 273
There is a green hill – 284
There is a Redeemer – 285
These are the facts – 287
This is the day the Lord has made – 291
To God be the glory – 293
We believe in God Almighty – 295
We believe in God the Father – 296
We have a gospel – 300
When I survey the wondrous cross – 307
When you prayed beneath the trees – 310
Who can sound the depths of sorrow – 312

Spiritual warfare
All hail the power of Jesus' name – 7
At your feet we fall – 23
Blow upon the trumpet – 31
Christ is risen – 45
Crown him with many crowns – 69
Darkness like a shroud – 70
Fight the good fight – 75
Freedom and life are ours – 84
Glory be to Jesus – 88
God is our fortress – 96
God is our strength and refuge – 95

Guide me, O my great redeemer – 104
He lives in us – 111
How firm a foundation – 125
How sure the scriptures are – 127
In heavenly armour – 140
Jesus! the name high over all – 159
Lord be my vision – 175
Praise our God with shouts of joy – 238
Praise to the holiest – 241
Rejoice, rejoice! Christ is in you – 244
Safe in the shadow of the Lord – 251
Soldiers of Christ, arise – 258
Tell all the world of Jesus – 267
The strife is past – 281
To him we come – 294
We trust in you – 303
Your hand, O God, has guided – 315

Healing and personal renewal
At your feet we fall – 23
Be still, for the presence of the Lord – 26
Blessed are the pure in heart – 30
Breathe on me, breath of God – 36
Christ is alive – 41
Come down, O Love divine – 61
Come, light of the world – 64
Creator Spirit, come, inspire – 68
Fill your hearts with joy – 77
God, whose almighty word – 100
Guide me, O my great redeemer – 104
He gave his life – 109
He healed the darkness of my mind – 110
He who created light – 115
Heal me, hands of Jesus – 113
How sweet the name – 129
Jesus, lover of my soul – 154
Jesus! the name high over all – 159
Jesus the saviour comes – 160
Just as I am – 164
Let trumpets sound! (Hark, the glad sound) – 170
Lord, I was blind – 177
Lord of the church, we pray for our renewing – 180
Lord of the cross of shame – 181
Lord, you need no house – 183
My song is love unknown – 206
Now thank we all our God – 213
O Breath of life, come sweeping through us – 214
O for a heart to praise my God – 217
O for a thousand tongues to sing – 218
O Lord my God – 223
O love that will not let me go – 227
One thing I know – 233
Praise, my soul – 237
Praise to the Lord, the almighty – 242
Rejoice, rejoice! Christ is in you – 244
Restore, O Lord – 247
Revive your church O Lord – 248
Spirit of God most high – 264
The earth was dark – 270
Through all the changing scenes – 292
We believe in God Almighty – 295
We come as guests invited – 298
We give God thanks – 299
When all your mercies, O my God – 306
When the king shall come again – 308

Caring for others
Christ is ascending – 42
Christ is the world's Light – 48
Church of God – 54

For the fruits of his creation – 82
Forgive our sins as we forgive – 83
From heaven you came – 85
Go forth and tell – 90
Help us to help each other – 118
Jesus, Jesus, fill us with your love – 152
Judge eternal, throned in splendour – 162
Lord, for the years – 176
Make me a channel of your peace – 192
May the mind of Christ my saviour – 199
O Lord, the clouds are gathering – 224
Put peace into each other's hands – 243
The earth was dark – 270
They who stand in awe of God – 288
Through all the changing scenes – 292
We give God thanks – 299
We worship God in harmony – 304
Who can sound the depths of sorrow – 312

Guidance
Because the Lord is my shepherd – 27
Come down, O Love divine – 61
Creator Spirit, come, inspire – 68
Darkness like a shroud – 70
Fight the good fight – 75
Guide me, O my great redeemer – 104
Hear me, O Lord – 116
I am trusting you, Lord Jesus – 130
In heavenly love abiding – 141
Jesus come! for we invite you – 148
Jesus, good above all other – 150
Lead us, heavenly Father – 167
Let us sing – 172
May the mind of Christ my saviour – 199
Now thank we all our God – 213
O Jesus, I have promised – 221
O worship the Lord – 231
Remember, remember your mercy, Lord – 246
The will of God to mark my way – 277
Your hand, O God, has guided – 315

The Church triumphant: Heaven
Abide with me – 3
All hail the power of Jesus' name – 7
Amazing grace – 16
Because the Lord is my shepherd – 27
Born in song – 32
Born of the water – 33
Bring to the Lord a glad new song – 37
Christ in majesty ascending – 40
Christ is risen – 45
Christ is surely coming – 46
Come let us join our cheerful songs – 62
God of gods, we sound his praises – 98
Guide me, O my great redeemer – 104
Had he not loved us – 105
Hail the day that sees him rise – 106
Heavenly hosts – 117
Here from all nations – 119
Here, O my Lord – 120
Holy, holy, holy – 122
Jesus! the name high over all – 159
The king of love my shepherd is – 274
The Lord my shepherd – 278
The Lord's my shepherd – 279
The strife is past – 281
You holy angels bright – 313
You servants of God – 314

Tunes: Alphabetical

A purple robe – 2
Aberystwyth – 154i
Adeste Fideles – 215
All for Jesus – 139
All my heart – 8
All people – 9ii
All things bright and beautiful – 11
All through the night – 60, 82
All your mercies – 306
Almighty God, our heavenly Father – 14
Almighty God, we thank you – 15
Amazing grace – 16
Amazing love – 205
Angel voices – 18
Angelic spirits – 138
Ansdell – 295
Antioch – 161
Arise shine – 70
At your feet we fall – 23
Auld Lang Syne – 304
Austria – 240

Balmoral – 55
Baptised in water – 25
Barbara Allen – 203
Be still – 26
Beatrice – 272ii
Because the Lord – 27
Bergers – 185
Besselsleigh – 284ii
Blackdown – 209
Blaenwern – 117, 188
Bodmin – 177
Brammit – 92
Bridegroom – 173
Broken for me – 38
Bullinger – 130i
Bunessan – 39, 198

Calypso Carol – 253
Camberwell – 22
Carlisle – 248
Caswall – 88
Celeste – 126
Chatsworth – 32
Chelston – 234
Chereponi – 152
Christ arose – 191
Christ is alive – 41
Christ is risen – 45
Christ triumphant – 50
Church triumphant – 133, 276
Cleveland – 184
Come and see – 58

Come down – 61
Come together – 235i
Commitment – 170
Converse – 305
Cradle Song – 24
Created things – 28
Creator God – 251
Cresswell – 189
Crimond – 279
Cross of Jesus – 57, 80
Cross of shame – 181
Crüger – 107, 298
Cwm Rhondda – 104

Dambusters March – 95i
Dartmeet – 262
Darwall's 148th – 127, 313
Diademata – 69
Dim ond Jesu – 131, 190
Dix – 21, 79
Dominus regit me – 274
Duke Street – 75

Easter Hymn – 146
Easter Morning – 66
Easter Song – 5i
Ebenezer – 94, 196
Ein 'feste Burg – 96
Ellers – 105ii
Enmore – 222ii
Epiphany Hymn – 119
Eventide – 3
Everglade – 33

Faithful love – 210
Felicity – 229
Finlandia – 303
Forest Green – 222i
Forgiveness – 83
From strength to strength – 84, 258
From the sun's rising – 86
Fulda – 300

Gerontius – 241, 286
Gideon – 144
Give me joy – 172
Glory – 52
Go forth – 90, 268
God be in my head – 91
God of mercy – 97
God rest you merry – 99
Gopsal – 245
Gracias – 213i
Great is thy faithfulness – 103

Gwalchmai – 165

Hajej, nynej, Jezisku – 155
Halad – 74
Hanover – 230
Heaven and earth – 29
Heavenly love – 123
Helmsley – 149
Hereford – 226
Hickling – 98
Hoffman – 266
Hollingside – 154ii
Holy Child – 121
Horsley – 284i
How long O Lord – 128
Humility – 252
Hyfrydol – 13

I am the bread of life – 63
I am trusting you – 130ii
I heard the voice – 136
Ich rede – 309
Icom – 287
Immortal Praise – 67
In dulci jubilo – 102
In heavenly love – 141i
In silent pain – 142
Invocations – 64
Irby – 232
Iris – 19
Irstead – 211

Jane – 134
Jerusalem – 37
Jesus come – 148
Jesus is king – 151
Jubilant – 31

Kelvingrove – 310
King of the universe – 166
Kum ba yah – 73

Land of hope and glory – 46, 89
Lathbury – 35
Laudate Dominum – 257, 314
Launde – 208
Let the people praise you – 169
Let us love – 171
Liege – 47
Life and gladness – 145
Lights to the world – 270
Like a lamb – 114
Listen to my prayer – 157i
Little Cornard – 160, 264
Little Stanmore – 263
Littlemore – 5ii
Living Lord – 178, 294
Llanfair – 106

Lobe den Herren – 242
Londonderry Air – 78, 135, 180
Lord as I wake – 174
Lord of heaven – 239
Lord of the years – 176
Love unknown – 206
Lux Eoi – 54
Lydia – 159
Lyngham – 218

Maccabaeus – 42, 316
Majestas – 207
Man of sorrows – 195
Mannheim – 167
Marching through Georgia – 59
Martyrdom – 124
Mary sang a song – 194
Maryton – 158
Matthew – 132
Mendelssohn – 108
Miles Lane – 7
Moortown – 81
Morar Murphy – 233
Moscow – 100, 115
My God, how wonderful – 200

Nativity – 62
New City Fellowship – 250ii
Newinnton – 299
Nicaea – 122, 236
Nöel – 143
Noel nouvelet – 193
North Coates – 157ii
Nos Galan – 56
Nun Danket – 213ii

O Lord my God – 223
O Lord the clouds – 224
O Lord the refuge – 225
O Righteous Lord – 68
Oasis – 20
Ode to Joy – 186
Old 100th – 9i
Old Yeavering – 179

Pamela – 116
Parkstone – 212
Penlan – 141ii
Personent Hodie – 93
Petra – 250i
Pickering – 261
Pilgrim's Joy – 291
Praise my soul – 237
Praise our God – 238
Psalm 46 – 95ii
Puer nobis – 147
Pure in heart – 30, 280

Quam dilecta – 301
Quem pastores laudavere – 150, 254
Quietude – 260

Rachel – 129ii
Ratisbon – 51
Ravenshaw – 187
Regent Square – 40, 77
Rejoice rejoice – 244
Remember, remember – 246
Repton – 71
Restore, O Lord – 247
Rhuddlan – 162
Richmond – 76
Rockhaven – 87
Rockingham – 307
Roewen – 202
Roundhay – 105i
Royal crown – 204
Russian Air – 43

St Agnes – 120
St Albinus – 153
St Anne – 220
St Catherine – 201
St Clement – 269
St Columbia – 118, 243
St Denio – 125, 137
St Francis – 192
St George's, Windsor – 65
St John – 112
St Leonard's – 199
St Magnus – 273
St Margaret – 227
St Peter – 129i
St Theodulph – 6
Sagina – 17
Sawley – 217
Selfless love – 109
Seven Seas – 72
Shine Jesus shine – 182
Sing of the Lord's goodness – 256
Sitley – 272i
Slane – 175
Song 46 – 10
Song of thanks – 101
Spiritus vitae – 34, 214
Stille Nacht – 255
Such love – 265
Sutton Common – 113

Tallis' Canon – 235ii
Tempus Adest Floridum – 308
Thaxted – 219
The battle belongs to the Lord – 140
The Feast is ready – 282
The first nowell – 271
The kingdom of God – 275
The Lord my shepherd – 278
The Servant King – 85
There is a Redeemer – 285
They who stand – 288
Thirsting for God – 163
This Child – 289
This is you God – 197
Thornbury – 221, 267, 315
To God be the glory – 293
Trentham – 36
Trumpet Voluntary – 290
Truro – 156

Unless the Lord – 277
Unser Herrscher – 12

Veni Emmanuel – 216
Victory – 281
Vision – 110

Wareham – 228
Was lebet – 231
Waterside – 111, 283
Waxham – 183
We believe – 296
We break this bread – 297
We'll call him Jesus – 1
Westminster Abbey – 44
Wharfedale – 259
Who can sound – 312
Wiltshire – 292
Winchester New – 249
Winchester Old – 311
Wir pflügen – 302
Woodworth – 164
World's light – 48
Württemberg – 4, 49

Yorkshire – 53
You're alive – 168

Tunes: Metrical

3 9 3 6 9 9
Chatsworth – 32

4 5 5 7 7 7 9
Chereponi – 152

5 5 5 5 5 5 5 4
Halad – 74

5 5 7 D
Everglade – 33

5 5 8 D
Baptised in water – 25

5 6 6 4
Waxham – 183

6 4 6 4 D
Lathbury – 35

6 5 6 3 and refrain
Amazing love – 205

6 5 6 4 and refrain
Christ arose – 191

6 5 6 5
Caswall – 88
Listen to my prayer – 157i
North Coates – 157ii
Quietude – 260

6 5 6 5 D
Camberwell – 22
Lord of heaven – 239
Noel nouvelet – 193

6 6 11 D
Come down – 61
Cross of shame – 181

6 6 4 6 6 6 4
Moscow – 100, 115

6 6 5 5 6 6 6 4
Majestas – 207

6 6 6 6
Parkstone – 212
Quam dilecta – 301
Ravenshaw – 187

6 6 6 6 6 5 5 3 9
Personent Hodie – 93

6 6 6 6 8 8
Darwall's 148th – 127, 313
Gopsal – 245
Little Cornard – 160, 264
Love unknown – 206
St John – 112

6 6 7 7 7 8 5 5
In dulci jubilo – 102

6 6 8 6 (SM)
Carlisle – 248
Heaven and earth – 29
Pure in heart – 30, 280
Sutton Common – 113
Trentham – 36

6 6 8 6 D (DSM)
Diademata – 69
From strength to strength – 84, 258

6 7 6 7 6 6 6 6
Gracias – 213i
Nun Danket – 213ii

6 7 7 11
Easter Morning – 66

6 9 6 8 9 9 8 6
Trumpet Voluntary – 290

7 4 7 4 D
Gwalchmai – 165

7 5 5
Balmoral – 55

7 6 7 6 and refrain
All things bright and beautiful – 11
Let the people praise you – 169

7 6 7 6 6 6 4 4 6
Oasis – 20

7 6 7 6 D
Blackdown – 209
Crüger – 107, 298
Ich rede – 309
In heavenly love – 141i
Penlan – 141ii
Roewen – 202

St Theodulph – 6
Tempus Adest Floridum – 308
Thornbury – 221, 267, 315

7 6 7 6 D and refrain
Wir pflügen – 302

7 6 7 7
Puer nobis – 147

7 7 7 5
Heavenly love – 123

7 7 7 5 7 7 11
Dambusters March – 95i
Psalm 46 – 95i

7 7 7 6
Created things – 28

7 7 7 7
Chelston – 234
Dartmeet – 262
Hoffman – 266
Wharfedale – 259

7 7 7 7 and Alleluias
Easter Hymn – 146
Llanfair – 106

7 7 7 7 and refrain
Humility – 252

7 7 7 7 4
Württemberg – 4, 49
Dix – 21, 79
God of mercy – 97
New City Fellowship – 250ii
Petra – 250i
Ratisbon – 51

7 7 7 7 D
Aberystwyth – 154i
Dim Ond Jesu – 190
Hollingside – 154ii
Holy Child – 121
Praise our God – 238
St George's, Windsor – 65
They who stand – 288

7 7 7 7 D and refrain
Mendelssohn – 108

7 7 7 8
Man of sorrows – 195

7 8 7 8 and Alleluia
Glory – 52

St Albinus – 153

8 3 3 6 D
All my heart – 8

8 4 8 4 8 8 8 4
All through the night – 60, 82

8 5 8 3
Bullinger – 130i

8 5 8 3 D
I am trusting you – 130ii

8 5 8 5 7 9
Christ triumphant – 50

8 5 8 5 8 7
Angel voices – 18

8 6 8 6 (CM)
All your mercies – 306
Amazing grace – 16
Angelic spirits – 138
Antioch – 161
Besselsleigh – 284ii
Creator God – 251
Crimond – 279
Forgiveness – 83
Gerontius – 286
Gerontius – 241
Horsley – 284i
Martyrdom – 124
My God, how wonderful – 200
Nativity – 62
Pickering – 261
Pilgrim's Joy – 291
St Columba – 118
St Peter – 129i
St Anne – 220
St Magnus – 273
Sawley – 217
Unless the Lord – 277
Wiltshire – 292
Winchester Old – 311
Moortown – 81
Richmond – 76

8 6 8 6 (CM) extended
Lydia – 159
Lyngham – 218
Miles Lane – 007
Woodworth – 164

8 6 8 6 Triple
A purple robe – 2

8 6 8 6 6 5 5
  We'll call him Jesus – 1

8 6 8 6 7 7 8 8
  Felicity – 229

8 6 8 6 8 8 8 6
  In silent pain – 142

8 6 8 6 D (DCM)
  Auld Lang syne – 304
  Commitment – 170
  Enmore – 222ii
  Forest Green – 222i
  I heard the voice – 136
  Matthew – 132
  Nöel – 143
  Rachel – 129ii
  Selfless love – 109
  The Lord my shepherd – 278
  Waterside – 111, 283

8 6 8 8 6
  How long O Lord – 128

8 6 8 8 6 extended
  Repton – 71

8 7 8 5
  St Leonard's – 199

8 7 8 7
  All for Jesus – 139
  Barbara Allen – 203
  Cross of Jesus – 57, 80
  Dominus regit me – 274
  St Columba – 243

8 7 8 7 and refrain
  Iris – 19

8 7 8 7 10
  Cleveland – 184

8 7 8 7 4 7 extended
  Cwm Rhondda – 104
  Helmsley – 149

8 7 8 7 6
  Bridegroom – 173

8 7 8 7 6 6 6 6 7
  Ein 'feste Burg – 96

8 7 8 7 7 7
  Irby – 232
  Let us love – 171

8 7 8 7 8 7
  Ansdell – 295
  Jesus come – 148
  Life and gladness – 145
  Mannheim – 167
  Praise my soul – 237
  Regent Square – 40, 77
  Rhuddlan – 162
  Unser Herrscher – 12
  Westminster Abbey – 44

8 7 8 7 8 7 5 5 4
  Who can sound – 312

8 7 8 7 8 8 8 7
  Hickling – 98

8 7 8 7 D
  Austria – 240
  Blaenwern – 117, 188
  Converse – 305
  Dim Ond Jesu – 131
  Ebenezer – 94, 196
  Faithful love – 210
  Hyfrydol – 13
  Lux Eoi – 54
  Nos Galan – 56
  Ode to Joy – 186
  Russian Air – 043
  Song of thanks – 101

8 7 8 7 D and refrain
  We believe – 296

8 8 4 4 8 8 with Alleluias
  Easter Song – 5i
  Littlemore – 5ii

8 8 4 8 8 5 5 3
  O Lord my God – 223

8 8 8 4
  Liege – 47
  Victory – 281

8 8 8 5
  Kum ba yah – 73
  Such love – 265

8 8 8 6
  Little Stanmore – 263

8 8 8 7
  Quem pastores laudavere – 150, 254
  Old Yeavering – 179

8 8 8 8 (LM)
All people – 9ii
Bodmin – 177
Celeste – 126
Christ is alive – 41
Church triumphant – 133, 276
Come together – 235i
Duke Street – 75
Fulda – 300
Gideon – 144
Hereford – 226
Immortal Praise – 67
Launde – 208
Lord as I wake – 174
Maryton – 158
Newinnton – 299
O Righteous Lord – 68
Old 100th – 009i
Rockhaven – 87
Rockingham – 307
Royal crown – 204
Seven Seas – 72
Tallis' Canon – 235ii
Thirsting for God – 163
Truro – 156
Vision – 110
Wareham – 228
Winchester New – 249

8 8 8 8 and refrain
The Feast is ready – 282

8 8 8 8 4
Beatrice – 272ii
Sitley – 272i

8 8 8 8 6
St Margaret – 227

8 8 8 8 8 8
St Catherine – 201
Veni Emmanuel – 216

8 8 8 8 8 8 extended
Sagina – 17

8 8 8 8 D (DLM)
Jane – 134
Jerusalem – 37
Lights to the world – 270

8 8 9 7 10 7
Cresswell – 189

9 10 10 5 and refrain
This Child – 289

9 6 6 6 6 6 9 6
Be still – 26

9 8 8 8 8 3
Living Lord – 178, 294

9 8 9 8
Morar Murphy – 233
St Clement – 269
Spiritus vitae – 34, 214

9 8 9 8 9 8
Bergers – 185

9 9 9 9
Mary sang a song – 194

10 10
Song 46 – 10

10 10 and refrain
Brammit – 92

10 10 10 10
Eventide – 3
Go forth – 268, 90
Ellers – 105ii
Jesus is king – 151
Roundhay – 105i
St Agnes – 120
Slane – 175

10 10 10 10 10 10
Yorkshire – 53

10 10 11 10
Icom – 287

10 10 11 11
Hanover – 230
Laudate Dominum – 257, 314
The kingdom of God – 275

10 11 11 11 and refrain
Maccabaeus – 42, 316

10 11 11 6
World's light – 48

10 12 10 13
Restore, O Lord – 247

10 7 8 8 8 8
Hajej, Nynej, Jezisku – 155

10 8 10 8
Bunessan – 39
Pamela – 116

10 9 10 9
Bunessan – 198

10 9 6 6 10
Invocations – 64

11 10 11 10
Epiphany Hymn – 119
Lord of the years – 176
O Lord the refuge – 225

11 10 11 10 and refrain
Great is thy faithfulness – 103

11 10 11 10 D
Londonderry Air – 180

11 10 11 10 11 10
Finlandia – 303

11 10 11 10 11 10 11 12
Londonderry Air – 78, 135

11 10 12 10
King of the universe – 166

11 11 11 11
Cradle Song – 24
St Denio – 125, 137

11 11 11 11 and refrain
To God be the glory – 293

11 11 11 11 11
Land of hope and glory – 46, 89

11 12 12 10
Nicaea – 122

11 9
Irstead – 211

12 10 12 10
Was lebet – 231

12 11 12 11
Jubilant – 31

12 11 12 11 and refrain
This is you God – 197

12 13 12 10
Nicaea – 236

12 7 7 7 and refrain
Sing of the Lord's goodness – 256

13 11 13 11 and refrain
Come and see – 58

13 13 13 13 13 13
Thaxted – 219

13 13 13 8 10 10 13 8
Marching through Georgia – 59

13 13 14 13
Kelvingrove – 310

14 14 4 7 8
Lobe den Herren – 242

Irregular
Adeste Fideles – 215
Almighty God, our heavenly Father – 14
Almighty God, we thank you – 15
Arise shine – 70
At your feet we fall – 23
Because the Lord – 27
Broken for me – 38
Calypso Carol – 253
Christ is risen – 45
From the sun's rising – 86
Give me joy – 172
God be in my head – 91
God rest you merry – 99
I am the bread of life – 63
Like a lamb – 114
O Lord the clouds – 224
Rejoice rejoice – 244
Remember, remember – 246
St Francis – 192
Shine Jesus shine – 182
Stille Nacht – 255
The battle belongs to the Lord – 140
The first nowell – 271
The Servant King – 85
There is a Redeemer – 285
We break this bread – 297
You're alive – 168

Index of First Lines with Tunes

Italics indicate former first lines and other names by which the hymns are known

A child is born for us today   We'll call him Jesus – 1
A mighty fortress is our God – God is our fortress and our rock
   Ein 'feste Burg – 96
A purple robe   A purple robe – 2
A safe stronghold our God is still – God is our fortress and our rock
   Ein 'feste Burg – 96
Abide with me   Eventide – 3
All creation join to say   Württemberg – 4
All creatures of our God and king   1 Easter Song   2 Littlemore – 5
All glory, praise and honour   St Theodulph – 6
All hail the power of Jesus' name   Miles Lane – 7
All my heart this night rejoices   All my heart – 8
All people that on earth do dwell   1 Old 100th   2 All people – 9
All shall be well   Song 46 – 10
All things bright and beautiful   All things bright and beautiful – 11
All through the night – Come and sing the Christmas story
   All through the night – 60
All through the night – For the fruits of his creation   All through the night – 82
Alleluia! Raise the anthem   Unser Herrscher – 12
Alleluia, sing to Jesus   Hyfrydol – 13
Almighty God   Almighty God, our heavenly Father – 14
Almighty God, we thank you   Almighty God, we thank you – 15
Amazing grace   Amazing grace – 16
Amazing love – My Lord, what love is this?   Amazing love – 205
And can it be (revised and traditional versions)   Sagina – 17
Angel voices ever singing   Angel voices – 18
Angels from the realms of glory   Iris – 19
Arise, shine – Darkness like a shroud   Arise shine – 70
As water to the thirsty   Oasis – 20
As with gladness   Dix – 21
At the name of Jesus   Camberwell – 22
At your feet we fall   At your feet we fall – 23
Auld Lang Syne – We worship God in harmony   Auld Lang syne – 304
Away in a manger   Cradle Song – 24

Baptised in water   Baptised in water – 25
Be still, for the presence of the Lord   Be still – 26
Be thou my vision – Lord be my vision   Slane – 175
Because the Lord is my shepherd   Because the Lord – 27
Before the heaven and earth   Heaven and earth – 29
Bless the Lord   Created things – 28
Blessed are the pure in heart   Pure in heart – 30
Blow upon the trumpet   Jubilant – 31
Born in song   Chatsworth – 32
Born of the water   Everglade – 33
Bread of the world   Spiritus vitae – 34
Break now the bread of life   Lathbury – 35
Breathe on me, breath of God   Trentham – 36
Bring to the Lord a glad new song   Jerusalem – 37
Broken for me   Broken for me – 38

Calypso Carol – See him lying on a bed of straw   Calypso Carol – 253
Child in the manger   Bunessan – 39

Christ in majesty ascending   Regent Square – 40
Christ is alive   Christ is alive – 41
Christ is ascending   Maccabaeus – 42
Christ is going to the Father   Russian Air – 43
Christ is made the sure foundation   Westminster Abbey – 44
Christ is risen   Christ is risen – 45
Christ is surely coming   Land of hope and glory – 46
Christ is the king   Liege – 47
Christ is the world's Light   World's Light – 48
Christ the Lord is risen again – **All creation join to say**   Württemberg – 4
Christ the Lord is risen again   Württemberg – 49
Christ triumphant, ever reigning   Christ triumphant – 50
Christ upon the mountain peak   Glory – 52
Christ whose glory fills the skies   Ratisbon – 51
Christians, awake   Yorkshire – 53
Church of God   Lux Eoi – 54
Clothed in kingly majesty   Balmoral – 55
Come and hear the joyful singing   Nos Galan – 56
Come and see   Come and see – 58
Come and see the shining hope   Marching through Georgia – 59
Come and sing the Christmas story   All through the night – 60
Come down, O Love divine   Come down – 61
Come let us join our cheerful songs   Nativity – 62
Come, let us worship Christ   I am the bread of life – 63
Come, light of the world   Invocations – 64
Come, O long–expected Jesus   Cross of Jesus – 57
Come, thou long-expected Jesus – **Come, O long-expected Jesus**
   Cross of Jesus – 57
Come, ye faithful, raise the anthem – **Alleluia! Raise the anthem**
   Unser Herrscher – 12
Come, you thankful people   St George's, Windsor – 65
Comes Mary to the grave   Easter Morning – 66
Creator of the earth and skies   Immortal Praise – 67
Creator Spirit, come, inspire   O Righteous Lord – 68
Crown him with many crowns   Diademata – 69

Dambusters March – **God is our strength and refuge**   Dambusters March – 95i
Darkness like a shroud   Arise shine – 70
Dear Lord and Father   Repton – 71
Deck the hall with boughs of holly – **Come and hear the joyful singing**
   Nos Galan – 56

Eternal light, shine in my heart   Seven Seas – 72

Father God in heaven   Kum ba yah – 73
Father in heaven   Halad – 74
Fight the good fight   Duke Street – 75
Fill now my life   Richmond – 76
Fill thou my life – **Fill now my life**   Richmond – 76
Fill your hearts with joy   Regent Square – 77
For God so loved the world   Londonderry Air – 78
For the beauty of the earth   Dix – 79
For the bread   Cross of Jesus – 80
For the fruits of his creation   All through the night – 82
Forgive our sins as we forgive   Forgiveness – 83
Freedom and life are ours   From strength to strength – 84
From deep despair to you I call   Moortown – 81
From heaven you came   The Servant King – 85

From the sun's rising   From the sun's rising – **86**

Glad music fills the Christmas sky   Rockhaven – **87**
Glory be to Jesus   Caswall – **88**
Glory in the highest   Land of hope and glory – **89**
Go forth and tell   Go forth – **90**
God be in my head   God be in my head – **91**
God brings us comfort   Brammit – **92**
God has spoken   Ebenezer – **94**
God is love   Personent Hodie – **93**
God is our fortress   Ein 'feste Burg – **96**
God is our strength and refuge   1 Dambusters March   2 Psalm 46 – **95i**
God of gods, we sound his praises   Hickling – **98**
God of mercy, God of grace   God of mercy – **97**
God rest you merry, gentlemen   God rest you merry – **99**
God, whose almighty word   Moscow – **100**
God whose love we cannot measure   Song of thanks – **101**
Good Christians all, rejoice   In dulci jubilo – **102**
Gracious Spirit, Holy Ghost – **Holy Spirit, gracious guest**   Heavenly love – **123**
Great is your faithfulness   Great is thy faithfulness – **103**
Guide me, O my great redeemer   Cwm Rhondda – **104**

Had he not loved us   1 Roundhay   2 Ellers – **105**
Hail the day that sees him rise   Llanfair – **106**
Hail to the Lord's anointed   Crüger – **107**
Hark the glad sound – **Let trumpets sound**   Commitment – **170**
Hark! the herald angels sing   Mendelssohn – **108**
He gave his life   Selfless love – **109**
He healed the darkness of my mind   Vision – **110**
He lives in us   Waterside – **111**
He stood before the court   St John – **112**
He was pierced for our transgressions   Like a lamb – **114**
He who created light   Moscow – **115**
Heal me, hands of Jesus   Sutton Common – **113**
Hear me, O Lord   Pamela – **116**
Heavenly hosts   Blaenwern – **117**
Help us to help each other   St Columbia – **118**
Here from all nations   Epiphany Hymn – **119**
Here, O my Lord   St Agnes – **120**
Holy child, how still you lie   Holy Child – **121**
Holy, holy, holy (revised and traditional versions)   Nicaea – **122**
Holy Spirit, gracious guest   Heavenly love – **123**
How can we sing with joy   Martyrdom – **124**
How firm a foundation   St Denio – **125**
How good is the God we adore   Celeste – **126**
How long, O Lord   How long O Lord – **128**
How sure the Scriptures are   Darwall's 148th – **127**
How sweet the name of Jesus sounds   1 Rachel   2 St Peter – **129**

I am the bread of life – **Come let us worship Christ**   I am the bread of life – **63**
I am trusting you, Lord Jesus   1 Bullinger   2 I am trusting you – **130**
I believe in God the Father   Dim Ond Jesu – **131**
I cannot tell   Londonderry Air – **135**
I come with joy   Matthew – **132**
I know that my redeemer lives   Church Triumphant – **133**
I love you, O Lord   Jane – **134**
I vow to thee my country – **O God beyond all praising**   Thaxted – **219**
If Christ had not been raised   I heard the voice – **136**

Immortal, invisible, God only wise   St Denio – 137
In awe and wonder, Lord our God   Angelic spirits – 138
In dulci jubilo – **Good Christians all, rejoice**   In dulci jubilo – 102
In heavenly armour   The battle belongs to the Lord – 140
In heavenly love abiding   1 In heavenly love   2 Penlan – 141
In silent pain the eternal Son   In silent pain – 142
In the cross of Christ I glory   All for Jesus – 139
It came upon the midnight clear   Nöel – 143
It is a thing most wonderful   Gideon – 144

Jerusalem – **Bring to the Lord a glad new song**   Jerusalem – 37
Jesus Christ gives life   Life and gladness – 145
Jesus Christ is risen today   Easter Hymn – 146
Jesus Christ the Lord is born   Puer nobis – 147
Jesus come! for we invite you   Jesus come – 148
Jesus comes with clouds descending   Helmsley – 149
Jesus, good above all other   Quem pastores laudavere – 150
Jesus is king   Jesus is king – 151
Jesus, Jesus, fill us with your love   Chereponi – 152
Jesus lives! Your terrors now   St Albinus – 153
Jesus, lover of my soul   1 Aberystwyth   2 Hollingside – 154
Jesus, saviour, holy child   Hajej, nynej, Jezisku – 155
Jesus shall reign where'er the sun   Truro – 156
Jesus stand among us   1 Listen to my prayer   2 North Coates – 157
Jesus, the joy of loving hearts   Maryton – 158
Jesus! the name high over all   Lydia – 159
Jesus the saviour comes   Little Cornard – 160
Joy to the world – the Lord has come   Antioch – 161
Judge eternal, throned in splendour   Rhuddlan – 162
Just as a lost and thirsty deer   Thirsting for God – 163
Just as I am   Woodworth – 164

King of glory, king of peace   Gwalchmai – 165
King of the universe   King of the universe – 166

Land of hope and glory – **Christ is surely coming**   Land of hope and glory – 46
Land of hope and glory – **Glory in the highest**   Land of hope and glory – 89
Lead us, heavenly Father   Mannheim – 167
Led like a lamb   You're alive – 168
Let the people praise you O Lord   Let the people praise you – 169
Let trumpets sound (Hark the glad sound)   Commitment – 170
Let us love and sing   Let us love – 171
Let us sing   Give me joy – 172
Lights to the world – **The earth was dark**   Lights to the world – 270
Like a mighty river flowing   Old Yeavering – 179
Like the murmur of the dove's song   Bridegroom – 173
Lo, he comes with clouds descending – **Jesus comes with clouds descending**   Helmsley – 149
Lord, as I wake   Lord as I wake – 174
Lord be my vision   Slane – 175
Lord, for the years   Lord of the years – 176
Lord, I was blind   Bodmin – 177
Lord Jesus Christ, you have come to us   Living Lord – 178
Lord of the church   Londonderry Air – 180
Lord of the cross of shame   Cross of shame – 181
Lord, the light of your love   Shine Jesus shine – 182
Lord, thy word abideth – **Lord your word shall guide us**   Ravenshaw – 187
Lord, you need no house   Waxham – 183

Lord, you sometimes speak in wonders   Cleveland – 184
Lord, you were rich   Bergers – 185
Lord, your church on earth is seeking   Ode to Joy – 186
Lord, your word shall guide us   Ravenshaw – 187
Love divine, all loves excelling   Blaenwern – 188
Love is his word   Cresswell – 189
Loved with everlasting love   Dim Ond Jesu – 190
Love's redeeming work is done – All creation join to say   Württemberg – 4
Low in the grave he lay   Christ arose – 191

Make me a channel of your peace   St Francis – 192
Man of sorrows   Man of sorrows – 195
Marching through Georgia – Come and see the shining hope
   Marching through Georgia –   59
Mary came with meekness   Noel nouvelet – 193
Mary sang a song   Mary sang a song – 194
May the grace   Ebenezer – 196
May the mind of Christ my saviour   St Leonard's – 199
Meekness and majesty   This is you God – 197
Morning has broken   Bunessan – 198
My God, how wonderful you are   My God, how wonderful – 200
My hope is built   St Catherine – 201
My Lord, I did not choose you   Roewen – 202
My Lord of light   Barbara Allen – 203
My Lord, what love is this   Amazing love – 205
My Lord you wore no royal crown   Royal crown – 204
My song is love unknown   Love unknown – 206

Name of all majesty   Majestas – 207
New every morning is the love   Launde – 208
No weight of gold or silver   Blackdown – 209
Not the grandeur of the mountains   Faithful love – 210
Now at last   Irstead – 211
Now let us learn of Christ   Parkstone – 212
Now thank we all our God   1 Gracias   2 Nun Danket – 213

O Breath of life, come sweeping through us   Spiritus Vitae – 214
O come all ye faithful   Adeste Fideles – 215
O come, O come, Emmanuel   Veni Emmanuel – 216
O for a heart to praise my God   Sawley – 217
O for a thousand tongues to sing   Lyngham – 218
O God beyond all praising   Thaxted – 219
O God, our help in ages past   St Anne – 220
O Jesus, I have promised   Thornbury – 221
O little town of Bethlehem   1 Forest Green   2 Enmore – 222
O Lord my God   O Lord my God – 223
O Lord, the clouds are gathering   O Lord the clouds – 224
O Lord, the refuge   O Lord the refuge – 225
O Lord, who came from realms above   Hereford – 226
O love that will not let me go   St Margaret – 227
O praise ye the Lord – Sing praise to the Lord   Laudate Dominum – 257
O Spirit of the living God   Wareham – 228
O thou who camest from above – O Lord, who came from realms above
   Hereford – 226
O Trinity, O Trinity   Felicity – 229
O worship the king   Hanover – 230
O worship the Lord   Was lebet – 231
Ode to joy – Lord, your church on earth is seeking   Ode to Joy – 186

Once in royal David's city Irby – 232
One thing I know Morar Murphy – 233

Peace be with you all Chelston – 234
Praise God from whom all blessings flow
  1 Come together 2 Tallis' Canon – 235
Praise God today – **God brings us comfort** Brammit – 92
Praise him, praise him Nicaea – 236
Praise my soul Praise my soul – 237
Praise our God with shouts of joy Praise our God – 238
Praise the Lord of heaven Lord of heaven – 239
Praise the Lord, you heavens Austria – 240
Praise to the holiest Gerontius – 241
Praise to the Lord, the almighty Lobe den Herren – 242
Put peace into each other's hands St Columbia – 243

Rejoice, rejoice! Christ is in you Rejoice rejoice – 244
Rejoice, the Lord is king Gopsal – 245
Remember, remember your mercy, Lord Remember, remember – 246
Restore, O Lord Restore, O Lord – 247
Revive your church, O Lord Carlisle – 248
Ride on, ride on in majesty Winchester New – 249
Rock of ages, cleft for me 1 Petra 2 New City Fellowship – 250
Rocking Carol – **Jesus saviour, holy child** Hajej, nyneji, Jezisku – 155

Safe in the shadow of the Lord Creator God – 251
See amid the winter snow Humility – 252
See him lying on a bed of straw Calypso Carol – 253
See the feast our God prepares Dartmeet – 262
Shepherds came Quem pastores laudavere – 254
Shine, Jesus, shine – **Lord, the light of your love** Shine Jesus shine – 182
Silent night! holy night Stille Nacht – 255
Sing of the Lord's goodness Sing of the Lord's goodness – 256
Sing praise to the Lord Laudate Dominum – 257
Soldiers of Christ, arise From strength to strength – 258
Songs of praise the angels sang Wharfedale – 259
Speak Lord, in the stillness Quietude – 260
Spirit divine, inspire our prayers Pickering – 261
Spirit of faith, by faith be mine Little Stanmore – 263
Spirit of God most high Little Cornard – 264
Such love Such love – 265

Take my life and let it be Hoffman – 266
Tell all the world of Jesus Thornbury – 267
Tell out my soul Go forth – 268
The battle belongs to the Lord – **In heavenly armour**
  The battle belongs to the Lord – 140
The day you gave us St Clement – 269
The earth was dark Lights to the world – 270
The feast is ready – **The trumpets sound** The Feast is ready – 282
The first nowell The first nowell – 271
The hands of Christ 1 Sitley 2 Beatrice – 272
The head that once was crowned St Magnus – 273
The king of love my shepherd is Dominus regit me – 274
The kingdom of God The kingdom of God – 275
The Lord is king Church triumphant – 276
The Lord my shepherd The Lord my shepherd – 278
The Lord's my shepherd Crimond – 279

The Lord's Prayer – **Father God in heaven**   Kum ba yah – 73
The Servant King – **From heaven you came**   Servant King – 85
The Son of God proclaim   Pure in heart – 280
The strife is past   Victory – 281
The Trumpet Voluntary – **This earth belongs to God**   Trumpet Voluntary – 290
The trumpets sound   The Feast is ready – 282
The victory of our God is won   Waterside – 283
The will of God to mark my way   Unless the Lord – 277
There is a green hill   1 Horsley   2 Besselsleigh – 284
There is a Redeemer   There is a redeemer – 285
There is no moment of my life   Gerontius – 286
These are the facts   Icom – 287
They who stand in awe of God   They who stand – 288
Thine be the glory – **Yours be the glory**   Maccabaeus – 316
This Child   This Child – 289
This earth belongs to God   Trumpet Voluntary – 290
This is the day the Lord has made   Pilgrim's Joy – 291
Thou who wast rich – **Lord, you were rich**   Bergers – 185
Thou whose almighty word – **God whose almighty word**   Moscow – 100
Through all the changing scenes   Wiltshire – 292
Thy hand, O God, has guided – **Your hand, O God, has guided**
   Thornbury – 315
To God be the glory   To God be the glory – 293
To him we come   Living Lord – 294

Unto us a boy is born – **Jesus Christ the Lord is born**   Puer nobis – 147

We believe in God Almighty   Ansdell – 295
We believe in God the Father   We believe – 296
We break this bread   We break this bread – 297
We come as guests invited   Crüger – 298
We give God thanks   Newinnton – 299
We have a gospel   Fulda – 300
We love the place, O God   Quam dilecta – 301
We plough the fields and scatter   Wir pflügen – 302
We rest on thee, our shield and our defender – **We trust in you**
   Finlandia – 303
We trust in you   Finlandia – 303
We worship God in harmony   Auld Lang syne – 304
What a friend we have in Jesus   Converse – 305
When all your mercies   All your mercies – 306
When I survey the wondrous cross   Rockingham – 307
When the king shall come again   Tempus Adest Floridum – 308
When things began to happen   Ich rede – 309
When you prayed beneath the trees   Kelvingrove – 310
While shepherds watched   Winchester Old – 311
Who can sound the depths of sorrow   Who can sound – 312

You holy angels bright   Darwall's 148th – 313
You servants of God   Laudate Dominum – 314
Your hand, O God, has guided   Thornbury – 315
Yours be the glory   Maccabaeus – 316